The Investigative Journalist's

MORGUE

Edited by
Steve Weinberg and Jan Colbert

To the late Paul Williams,
whose dedication inspired IRE members
to name the resource center in his honor,

and

To John Ullmann,
whose energy and vision
made it all possible.

Acknowledgments

The stories and series in this book could not have been sorted, indexed and computerized without the dedication of many University of Missouri journalism students who did much of the work. They include Margaret Hunter, Pat Prince, Helene Feger, Michael O'Connell, Andy Scott, Craig Lincoln, Randye Hoder, Reagan Walker, Rima Janulevicius, Jill Goetz, Madeleine Smith and Virgil Tipton.

Acknowledgements

Introduction

Investigative Reporters and Editors, Inc. was established by journalists who were weary of starting at ground zero every time they began an investigation. The founders knew that sharing ideas and information was the cornerstone of IRE. They began compiling stories that had been done by investigative journalists around the country, and envisioned a resource center with easy access for all members.

The Paul Williams Memorial Resource Center, named for a Pulitzer Prize winner, IRE founder and professor at Ohio State University, has been available to members since 1979. Members can call with a topic; IRE researchers respond with copies of stories.

The center has been expanded three-fold in the last four years. With this book, readers will be able to see the holdings of the center. Because researchers add to the center every day, IRE will publish an update annually.

How to use this book

Stories and series in this book are available through Investigative Reporters and Editors. To get copies write or call IRE, P.O. Box 838, Columbia, MO 65205, phone (314) 882-2042. The cost is 10 cents per page plus postage and handling. There is an extra $10 research charge for those who are not members of IRE.

Please use a copy of the following form to order from the center.

Name _____

Affiliation _____

Address _____

City _____ State _____ Zip _____

Member — Yes or No   Membership Expiration Date _____

Number of the entries you want to order:

☐ Please send me information on IRE.

Mail to IRE, P.O. Box 838, Columbia, MO 65205

ABORTION
See also birth control

1-2858 *The Virginian-Pilot* (Norfolk) articles expose deceptive and illegal practices at an abortion clinic where a doctor was performing abortions on women who were not pregnant; reporter and colleagues submitted to exams at the clinic and were told they were pregnant when they weren't, July-September 1984.

1-3219 *WCBS-TV* (New York) sends reporter undercover to expose doctors who perform abortions on patients they know are not pregnant, 1979.

1-388 *Sun-Times* (Chicago) finds campaign files of the Kane County sheriff list two contributors linked to a Chicago abortion clinic scandal where phony doctors perform illegal abortions on women who weren't pregnant, November 1978.

ACQUIRED IMMUNE DEFICIENCY SYNDROME (AIDS)

1-2930 *The Wall Street Journal* reports on growing fear among businesses and insurance companies of the effects the AIDS epidemic might have in human and financial costs, Oct. 18, 1985.

1-2918 *Life* looks at AIDS among heterosexuals, July 1985.

1-726 *Mother Jones* articles say Reagan administration has dragged its feet on AIDS research; also discuss competition and duplication in the scientific community on AIDS research, April 1985.

1-310 *West (San Jose Mercury-News)* article describes the dangers of contracting AIDS through donated blood; tells what blood banks are doing and what they should be doing to test for AIDS in donors' blood, May 1984.

1-3097 *CBS News* reports cases of AIDS in the military are growing rapidly and that the services are under-reporting the extent of the problem, April 1984.

ADOPTION
See also child abuse

1-2036 *Roanoke (Va.) Times & World-News* discovers deception and misinformation by Roanoke welfare workers about the mental health backgrounds of two children up for adoption, May 1984.

1-2734 *Fort Worth Star-Telegram* series uncovers an adoption network operating between Mexico and the United States run by unlicensed groups with religious affiliations; reporters found couples paid for children they didn't get or got children with forged adoption papers, 1984.

ADVERTISING

1-2502 *Pensacola (Fla.) News-Journal* details false advertising and bait and switch tactics used by several bulk meat outlets in the Pensacola area, October 1983.

AFFIRMATIVE ACTION
See:
civil rights
discrimination
minorities

AGENT ORANGE
1-2250 *Marietta (Ohio) Times* runs series on five Vietnam veterans in the area who suffer from exposure to Agent Orange and the problems they suffered on return to the United States, 1982.
1-3206 *WBBM-TV* (Chicago) interviews Vietnam veterans exposed to the defoliant Agent Orange once and then a year later finds incidence of tumors, cancer, personality changes and birth defects in children increased during the period, 1979.

AGRICULTURE
See also:
chemicals
cooperatives
Farmers Home Administration
food
migrant labor
1-2920 *The Wall Street Journal* describes in detail the restructuring of U.S. agriculture now taking place, Nov. 9, 1985.
1-4038 *The Des Moines Register* publishes a series that describes the revolution in agricultural research and tells of the possible impacts on farmers and consumers, Sept. 8, 1985.
1-583 *The Des Moines Register* reports on the deteriorating quality of U.S. grain and its economic implications; finds the American grain industry is exporting cracked, dusty grain, some of it infested with insects, Sept. 8, 1985.
1-2233 *The Wall Street Journal* reports on severe financial problems at the Federal Farm Credit System, the nation's largest single holder of farm debt which is seeking federal support, Sept. 4, 1985.
1-589 *Minneapolis Star and Tribune* examines the cost to taxpayers and consumers of U.S. government aid to farmers and what would happen if support stopped, August 11, 12, 1985.
1-2827 *The Atlantic Monthly* takes a revisionist look at American farm policy, July 1985.
1-2926 *The Wall Street Journal* reports on the Sunkist corporation's monopoly of the fresh lemon industry and its opposition to a new storage process that could help other growers break its hold on the market, Jan. 24, 1985.
1-2372 *Reason* story on Garrison Diversion Unit, a $1.2 billion congressional irrigation project in North Dakota that after 20 years has yet to pump a drop of water; interesting coalition of groups may save project, January 1985.
1-2349 *Rochester (Minn.) Post-Bulletin* series looks at the growth of right-wing extremist sects in the Midwest whose members are often farmers; vigilante groups are also growing, November 1984.
1-2588 *Minneapolis Star and Tribune* reprint, titled "Toxic Harvest," reports on

2

the health dangers to workers and consumers of fumigants used to rid grain of insects, Sept. 2-4, 1984.

1-252 *The Des Moines Register* series details increasingly serious health and safety hazards to which farmers are routinely exposed, September 1984.

1-2042 *The Progressive* repobts organized labor turns its back on migrant farm workers, August 1984.

1-2826 *WSMV-TV* (Nashville) series finds high-ranking officials from a government controlled farm loan company, the Production Credit Association, a nation-wide network set up by the federal government to help finance farmers, deliberately misled farmers in connection with large loans, January 1984.

1-2489 *Gannett News Service* reprint finds Farmers Home Administration, chartered to aid small farmers, lending millions to the rich and politically well-connected; as a result, whole regional farm economies are nearing bankruptcy, December 1983.

1-2825 *Farm Futures* reports on how a new CEO created AGRI Industries out of a backwater farmer-owned cooperative and the financial and legal problems that followed, December 1983.

1-2 *The Atlantic Monthly* publishes article on milk farm subsidy program woes, October 1983.

1-562 *Daily Phoenix* (Muskogee, Okla.) articles say three organized bands of criminals have been stealing grain and farm chemicals for at least a decade, using burglary, manipulation and elevator scales fraud, October 1983.

1-3253 *WSB-TV* (Atlanta) looks at the acute economic troubles of black farmers in Georgia, Sept. 19, 1983.

1-2150 *The Progressive* looks at America's farm industry and finds poor farm policy, with farmers one season away from collapse; blames corporations; farmers profiting are those who ignored advice from the banks and government, September 1983.

1-2185 *The Des Moines Register* article indicates that under the Reagan administration, government and poultry industry cooperate, with industry increasingly allowed to conduct its own testing for harmful chemical residues and to decide when potential problems should be reported to the government, April 1983.

1-2298 *The Des Moines Register* shows farmer bankruptcies in Iowa on the rise; declining land values and crop prices, higher operating costs and interest rates, over-expansion and bad weather are all culprits, February 1983.

1-635 *The Farmer* runs article on a Jerusalem artichoke firm under investigation for running a pyramid scheme, February 1983.

1-2200 *The Courier-Journal* (Louisville) publishes series on the troubled farm credit system; examines reasons why farmers are debt-ridden; finds abuses in the Farm Credit Administration and the federally supervised Farm Credit System, August 1982.

1-2168 *The Kansas City Times* reprint titled "Grain: A Harvest of Danger" looks at hazards of working in a grain elevator and the failure of industry and the government to work for greater safety; industry can actually profit from elevator explosions, July 1982.

1-2459 *The Des Moines Register* publishes series on the vulnerability of crops to destruction by disease and pests because of increasingly similar genetic traits in plants, June 1982.

1-3185 *Rural Radio Network* (Indiana) investigates the Commodity Credit Corp.'s handling of the 1980 Soviet grain embargo; tax records indicate mismanagement led to a $471 million price cut for exporters and loss for farmers, 1982.

1-2101 *The Farmer* series exposes an advance fee fraud used against farmers seeking loans, September 1981.

1-605 *Wisconsin State Journal* (Madison) shows Wisconsin farmers paid big bucks to a Nebraska firm to help them find loans they never got, June 1981.

1-602 *Farm Journal* shows that new soil conditioners and inoculents flood the market despite hundreds of experiments showing they don't work, September 1980.

1-336 *Iowa Public Broadcasting Network* reports on grain elevator bankruptcies and the inadequacies of state and federal regulation of grain elevators, 1980.

1-622 *The Hanford (Calif.) Sentinel* looks into accusations of wrongdoing in Cotton Inc., the New York-based research and promotion arm of the cotton industry, August-December 1979.

1-668 *Mother Jones* article on the sale of domestically banned pesticides to developing nations discusses the health risks to native farmers and U.S. consumers of foreign crops, November 1979.

1-2186 *The Des Moines Register* series titled "Vanishing Acres" looks at the loss of prime crop lands through the encroachment of non-farmers into rural areas; the situation could affect food production, July 1979.

1-603 *Farm Journal* uses trial testimony to show how crooked cattle dealers falsify information about breeding, weight, place of origin and health of livestock, February 1979.

1-2460 *The Denver Post* series examines irrigation in the area of the Ogallala aquifer (High Plains region) and changes it is undergoing due to potential scarcity and the high cost of energy to pump it; water in the aquifer is dropping at an alarming rate, 1979.

1-2170 *The Des Moines Register* study of impact of agriculture on the environment indicates that ecological crisis may be brewing; one of the leading causes of water pollution, agriculture, is destroying much of U.S. soil, September 1978.

1-540 *Elgin (Ill.) Courier News* investigates a grain elevator operator who disappeared owing farmers more than a million dollars, then filed for bankruptcy and is being investigated for perjury, January 1978.

1-373 *The Daily Oklahoman* (Oklahoma City) looks into a grain export scandal that spans the Southwest, April-May 1975.

AIR FORCE
See also military

1-2001 *The Atlantic Monthly* article finds Air Force won't purchase a reliable and relatively cheap jet fighter only because Air Force didn't design it, August 1984.

1-1009 *Army Times* runs series on problems in the Air Force and Army system of testing personnel for drug use including mishandling of urine samples at testing lab, improper analysis of female personnel test results, problems with lab inspections, 1984.

1-3032 *WHA-TV* (Madison) investigates the A-10 fighter, a cheap and effective fighter that the Air Force says it doesn't want and is dumping on the Air National Guard, 1983.

1-2072 *Shreveport (La.) Journal* runs series on continuing contamination from the 1959 crash of Air Force cargo plane that contained three nuclear weapons; Air Force suppressed information about contamination, improperly disposed of debris, April 1982.

1-2229 *Atlanta Constitution* series, "The Health of Military Medicine," finds excessive surgical deaths in Air Force's showcase hospital because of one incompetent surgeon and an Air Force cover-up; also, a wider investigation finds inferior health care throughout the armed forces, December 1981.

1-2195 *The Kansas City Star* series looks into Whiteman Air Force Base; examines what is on base, charges that a critical error was made in 1979 in deployment of some Whiteman nuclear bombs, finds morale problems at the base, January 1981.

AIR POLLUTION
See also:
acid rain
chemicals
hazardous substances

1-2758 *The Reporter Dispatch* (White Plains, N.Y.) covers a controversy involving a Westchester county garbage-burning plant that initially exceeded federal emission limits; reporters look into the steps taken behind the scenes by county officials and the Environmental Protection Agency to raise the limits, November-December 1984.

1-2695 *Star-Gazette* Elmira, N.Y.) series looks at the effects of acid rain in the Northeast, particularly its implications for forests, bridges, crops, personal health and the economy, June 3-7, 1984.

1-24 *New Engineer* shows diesel fuel emissions hazardous to humans, 1977.

AIR-TRAFFIC CONTROLLERS
See also:
airlines
airports

1-2913 *The Wall Street Journal* examines whether airlines are neglecting maintenance in order to cut costs and be competitive, Nov. 6, 1985.

1-2707 *The Daily Herald* (Arlington Heights, Ill.) series exposes a large number of safety-threatening errors by air-traffic controllers occurring in Chicago due to inexperienced and overworked personnel; reporters made use of many public documents including Federal Aviation Administration reports and memos, July 8-9, 1984.

1-552 *The Tribune* (Oakland, Calif.) article uses Federal Aviation Administration documents to examine controller errors and violations of regulations that contributed to the death of four Bay area residents in a plane crash, August 1980.

AIRLINES

See also:
air-traffic controllers
airports

1-2537 *The Wall Street Journal* investigates the allegation that J. Lynn Helms (chief of Federal Aviation Administration in December 1983), while president of Piper Aircraft Corp., tried to keep the FAA from finding out about alleged safety defects in one of the company's planes, December 1983.

1-3033 *KAKE-TV* (Wichita) investigation finds airline preparation for inflight medical emergencies inadequate, 1983.

1-3035 *WOTV-TV* (Grand Rapids) airs series on the danger caused by the susceptibility of commercial airliners to catch fire, 1983.

1-2317 *Corporate Report* examines the quick demise of Northern Airlines, which flew from Minneapolis to several South Dakota cities; shoddy performance and management, the Civil Aeronautics Board, weather and economy and the airline's president Arthur Stock, can all be blamed. July 1982.

1-2363 *Texas Monthly* shows how former Braniff president Harding Lawrence, obsessed with converting Braniff from an obscure, regional airline into an international giant, destroyed the company, July 1982.

1-3309 *WKYC-TV* (Cleveland) airs in-depth series on widespread safety problems with commuter airlines, 1980.

1-577 *San Jose Mercury-News* publishes series on airline crew fatigue that jeopardizes the safety of passengers and has resulted in 350 close calls from 1973-1979; investigation uses internal Federal Aviation Administration letters, testimony of airline crews and employees, and scientific reports on fatigue, November 1979.

1-2130 *St. Paul Pioneer Press* article, "The plane that fell from the sky," gives minute-by-minute account of a TWA Boeing 727 flight that suddenly went out of control and fell 34,000 feet in 44 seconds; aftermath and investigation, April 1979.

AIRPORTS

See also:
air-traffic controllers
airlines
parking

1-2919 *The Chicago Reporter* finds some cab and limousine drivers at O'Hare Airport pay for special treatment from city and airport personnel in the competition for lucrative fares, August 1985.

1-3082 *KSDK-TV* (St. Louis) series raises questions about that city's Lambert Airport — its ability to handle flights without delays, safety of air traffic procedures and efforts to relieve effects of aircraft noise on surrounding neighborhoods, October 1984.

1-2732 *The New York Times* series finds that some of the nation's major airports were scheduling more peak-time takeoffs and landings than the airports were capable of handling, leading to major delay; July-October 1984.

1-2601 *Standard-Speaker* (Hazelton, Pa.) publishes series on contract arrangements between the city and its airport operator, December 1983.

1-2457 *Rocky Mountain News* series on parking fee losses at Denver's Stapleton

Airport reveals that millions of dollars were lost and that APCOA, the parking concessionaire, had ties to city officials, March 1982.
1-2509 *Fort Lauderdale News and Sun Sentinel* shows expansion of an overcrowded Fort Lauderdale airport became mired in tremendous cost overruns and political maneuvering, March 1982.
1-652 *The Honolulu Advertiser* publishes series on a privately-contracted airport security service that hired guards with felony records, planned to use excessive force in riot situations and monopolized contract bidding for services with the state, May-July 1979.

ALCOHOL

See:
drunk driving
liquor

ALIENS

See:
illegal aliens
immigration
migrant labor
refugees

AMBULANCES

See also:
emergency medical services
hospitals

1-2709 *The Capital* (Annapolis) article shows why area ambulance service is unreliable; sometimes there are no ambulance crews available to handle calls; also, crews sometimes refuse to take calls, Dec. 3, 1984.
1-2791 *The Record* (Hackensack, N.J.) investigates problems with volunteer ambulance squads in two New Jersey counties; reporters found some volunteers' inexperience could endanger the lives of patients and that no levels of government in New Jersey were willing to assert control over the volunteer corps, Oct. 14-17, 1984.
1-3026 *WCCO-TV* (Minneapolis) investigation of a private ambulance service finds the company puts profits ahead of patients — dispatching inferior ambulances and failing to call in another service when it is too busy to respond promptly, May 1983.
1-2144 *The Weekly News* (Johnson County, Iowa) article says lack of ambulance regulation in Iowa allows a Wisconsin operator whose license was revoked to set up shop, November 1981.
1-5 *Fort Lauderdale News and Sun-Sentinel* series shows high accident rate among ambulance drivers in city, September 1981.
1-604 *New Jersey Monthly* finds some New Jersey ambulance squads lack training, basic equipment, November 1979.
1-3199 *WABC-TV* (New York) reports on problems of emergency medical service delivery and finds that ambulances often arrive too late, 1979.
1-2131 *The Kansas City Star* series finds Kansas City suffers from a second-rate

ambulance system that does not respond quickly enough; finds needless deaths, failure of ambulances to respond, October 1978.

ANIMAL ABUSE
See also:
gambling
zoos

1-3086 *WJLA-TV* (Washington, D.C.) airs series on the supplying of animals to research laboratories by professional thieves and animal pounds, November 1984.

1-2333 *Atlanta* publishes articles on the underground dogfight industry, February 1982.

1-3166 *KMGH-TV* (Denver) series examines the illegal, lucrative and increasingly popular sport of dog fighting, October 1980.

1-3310 *KITV-TV* (Honolulu) airs series on cockfighting in Hawaii, Jan,. 28-Feb. 22, 1980.

1-324 *KMGH-TV* (Denver) documentary explores cattle and horse mutilations across the West and Canada; investigators have no idea who is doing the mutilating or why, 1980.

1-580 *Dayton Daily News* publishes series on illegal animal fight industry, May-June 1979.

1-35 *Federal Times* shows National Zoo critters in Washington, D.C. get poor care, March and April 1977.

ARAB INFLUENCE IN THE UNITED STATES
See:
Israel
lobbyists

ARCHAEOLOGY
1-3077 *KOAT-TV* (Albuquerque) series says two controversial New Mexico excavations that drew thousands of dollars in taxpayer funding were archaeological frauds, 1984.

ARMS
See:
nuclear weapons
weapons

ARMY
See also:
. military
weapons

1-443 *Regardie's* publishes in-depth article on the bidding process for the contract to supply sidearms to the U.S. Army; allegations that bidding and testing were rigged to favor an Italian firm as a quid pro quo for Italy; provides background on handgun industry, May 1985.

8

1-532 *Army Times* runs series on problems with the service's doctors — inadequacies in the Army's procedures for checking qualifications of doctors and failure to investigate them once employed, February 1985.

1-1009 *Army Times* runs series on problems in the Air Force and Army system of testing personnel for drug use, including mishandling of urine samples at testing lab, improper analysis of female personnel test results, and problems with lab inspections, 1984.

1-2346 *The Anniston (Ala.) Star* publishes article on three deaths at an Army hospital that resulted when argon, an inert gas often used for welding, was accidentally piped into the hospital's central oxygen system, December 1983.

1-687 *Army Times* runs series on problems with an Army hospital commander in Alaska and a white-washed investigation into a patient's death, 1983.

1-3289 *WCCO-TV* (Minneapolis) says young people trying to enlist in the U.S. Army were rejected by one psychiatrist at a 97 percent rate, Nov. 22-25, 1982.

1-2310 *Army Times* examines Army health care system; while rapidly improving with more doctors and more and newer equipment, it still has serious problems such as failure by doctors to detect early symptoms of serious illnesses, November 1982.

1-566 *The Denver Post* publishes article on recruiting violations by Army recruiters; complaints include concealing criminal records, falsifying birth and education records and forging parental permission papers, December 1981.

1-318 *Fort Worth Star-Telegram* publishes series on Army recruiters helping enlistees cheat on service qualifying exams, February 1979.

1-673 *The Daily Oklahoman* (Oklahoma City) series investigates Army's coverup of the Central Intelligence Agency's role in the My Lai massacre, May 1972.

ARMY CORPS OF ENGINEERS

1-244 *The Clarion-Ledger* (Jackson, Miss.) series, "The Hidden War: The Army Engineers vs. Rural America," looks at improprieties and unethical practices of the Army Corps of Engineers in north central Mississippi and southern Indiana, August 1981.

ARRESTS
See:
criminal justice
police brutality

ARSON
See also insurance

1-405 *The Philadelphia Inquirer* publishes in-depth article on the failure, despite many earlier fires, of Philadelphia officials to take action against a woman with pyromaniacal tendencies who eventually burned down a building, killing five people, January 1985.

1-20 *The News-Sentinel* (Fort Wayne, Ind.) reports on a police investigation of a botched arson case, November 1981.

1-3311 *ABC News 20/20* and the Better Government Association investigate a tightly knit Chicago arson-for-profit ring that buys up cheap buildings, trades them among themselves to inflate their values, heavily insures the buildings and then burns them down, Feb. 7, 1980.

1-747 *The News* (Paterson, N.J.) article details patterns of arson in Arab-owned businesses that cost insurance companies millions and how those businesses are suspected of having ties with the Palestine Liberation Organization, December 1979.

1-212 *The News* (Paterson, N.J.) investigation shows local cops make bucks by buying tenements, inflating prices by selling them to each other and collecting insurance settlements following suspicious fires, March 1979.

1-3191 *KMOX-TV* (St. Louis) series on arson for profit ring focuses on Missouri's arson problem and how MFA Insurance used questionable practices to prove policyholders set fire to their houses, 1979.

ART

See also museums

1-2829 *ARTnews* reports Austria's handling of the return of works of art stolen by the Nazis has been marked by neglect, ineptitude and questionable legal maneuvers; thousands of officially heirless paintings and other objects are still hidden and off limits to everyone except Austrian officials, December 1984.

1-312 *ARTnews* traces how a 27-year-old art dealer succeeded in bilking clients out of millions of dollars through art fraud, October 1980.

1-84 *ARTnews* examines the profitable manipulation of the reputation of painter Hans Hofmann by the movers and shakers in the art world; looks at the interplay of influence, patronage, exposure, politics, etc., that combine to propel an artist to the front rank, Summer 1980.

ASBESTOS

See also hazardous substances

1-2931 *The Pittsburgh Press* looks at the problem of asbestos in Pennsylvania schools and at the quality and safety of the asbestos-removal work, Sept. 22-23, 1985.

1-2706 *Education Week* articles look into the problem of asbestos in schools; the coverage examines the nature of the asbestos problem and what school officials should do after they discover asbestos in their schools, Sept. 26, 1984.

1-2660 *Federal Times* runs series on asbestos dangers in building materials in Veterans Administration hospitals, also deals with government workers unions and what they are doing to insure their members' safety while working at the hospitals affected, May 7-21, 1984.

1-3083 *WRTV-TV* (Indianapolis) airs series on the failure of the city's public school system to comply with Environmental Protection Agency asbestos identification and notification regulations, despite knowledge of dangerous conditions, 1984.

1-2550 *The Daily Freeman* (Kingston, N.Y.) shows exposure of major asbestos leak in a high-traffic area of the local high school led to discovery that students were in a potentially hazardous situation in all district buildings, November-December 1983.

1-3024 *WCAU-TV* (Philadelphia) follows up the problem of asbestos in public school system; finds city has failed to alleviate the problem despite a program designed to do just that, Sept. 19, 1983.

1-3283 *WCAU-TV* (Philadelphia) follows up the U.S. Consumer Product Safety Commission's efforts to get dangerous asbestos paper off the shelves, finds Commission has done nothing about the problem, Sept. 8, 1982.

1-102 *Arizona Republic* publishes reprint of investigative series on asbestos poisoning controversy and the failure of OSHA to act; also includes follow-up stories, September 1982.

1-739 *The Clarion-Ledger* (Jackson, Miss.) examines the asbestos industry in Mississippi and the threat it poses to workers, particularly those in Gulf Coast shipyards, November 1980.

1-3147 *WBZ-TV* (Boston) looks at the risk of exposure to cancer-producing asbestos in the town of Hudson, N.H., where Johns-Manville Co. dumped asbestos waste as free landfill for residents some 30 years ago, August 1980.

1-157 *Press-Telegram* (Long Beach, Calif.) shows workers in Long Beach naval shipyard run an extraordinary risk of developing cancer or other diseases because of exposure to asbestos, 1978.

ASSASSINATION
See murder

ASSESSMENTS
See:
county government
property taxes
real estate
taxes

ATHLETES
See:
college athletics
drugs
sports

ATOMIC ENERGY
See:
nuclear energy
nuclear weapons

ATTORNEYS
See lawyers

AUDITS
See also:
banks
income tax
taxes

1-2533 *The Wall Street Journal* discusses how Ernst & Whinney's unqualified audit of United American Bank of Knoxville, Tenn., missed the boat, with UAB collapsing just weeks after the report was issued, March 1983.

AUTOMOBILES

See also:
environment
insurance
towing
transportation

1-2160 *Consumer Reports* reports on the failure of Ford Motor Co. to recall or repair Ford models with a transmission design flaw; Ford has refused a recall despite several deaths when transmissions slipped into reverse because of the flaw, September 1985.

1-3106 *WPVI-TV* (Philadelphia) reports on able-bodied people using license plates intended for the handicapped to get free parking and special parking places; no doctor certification is needed to obtain the plate in Pennsylvania, October 1984.

1-3066 *KPNX-TV* (Phoenix) finds Arizona Motor Vehicle Department standards of licensing, documentation of age and physical description severely lacking; department issues licenses to people whose licenses from other states have been revoked, 1984.

1-3078 *WJZ-TV* (Baltimore) reports on the use of license plates intended for the handicapped by people who are not handicapped as a means of parking free and of avoiding crowded streets, 1984.

1-2642 *The Times* (Hammond, Ind.) takes in-depth look at a major regional car theft center; organized crime control, lack of police enforcement, December 1983.

1-2438 *United Features Syndicate* distributes series on government failure to act on problems in General Motors autos that were costing consumers millions of dollars, July-August, October 1983.

1-2612 *Detroit Free Press* series says General Motors built X-cars despite knowledge of problems with their brakes; federal government was lenient with automakers despite serious questions about auto safety, May 1983.

1-3012 *WISH-TV* (Indianapolis) investigates Indiana's motor vehicle license plate system, which is legally set up so the political party of the governor operates branches and keeps some of the profits; charges county party leaders skim thousands off public money, 1983.

1-2388 *The Journal-Bulletin* (Providence) series examines the multi-million dollar underworld of automobile theft and the agencies charged with fighting it; Rhode Island, which has the second highest car theft rate in the country, exacerbates problem through regulatory failure, May 1982.

1-3297 *WPIX-TV* (New York) reports on alleged rip-offs by a company that promises to lend you money to buy a car, 1982.

1-3312 *WLS-TV* (Chicago) series on pay-offs and corruption in the Illinois Motor Vehicles Department that allows people to get valid drivers licenses illegally; driving schools that can get anybody a license as long as they have $200, 1981.

1-779 *The Times* (Hammond, Ind.) series explores car theft and its impact on insurance costs, April-August 1980.

1-530 *Mother Jones* does expose on Fords that jump from park into reverse, causing thousands of accidents nationwide, June 1980.

1-3149 *KGO-TV* (San Francisco) investigates improper sales of Firestone 500 tires that were recalled in 1978; tires are sold by such firms as Montgomery Ward under their own label, February 1980.

1-596 *The Indianapolis Star* series examines problems in insurance programs sold by auto dealers, February 1980.

1-672 *Sun-Times* (Chicago) runs series on a $3 billion-a-year auto accident swindle business; reporters go undercover to examine the elaborate racket involving ambulance chasers, crooked lawyers, doctors and clinics who conspire to collect huge insurance sums, thereby raising car insurance rates by as much as one-third, February 1980.

1-3205 *WMAQ-TV* (Chicago) investigates an international auto theft ring that has ripped off more than $1.5 million in foreign cars with impunity because auto thieves are rarely arrested, October 1979.

1-226 *The Daily Journal* (Los Angeles) reports that thousands of stolen cars are apparently being used by Mexican law enforcement and other officials; organized crime, drug trade may be involved, November 1978.

1-174 *Mother Jones* runs classic expose of Ford Motor Company's production of the Pinto — a car the company knew was a firetrap, September/October 1977.

1-260 *Columbia (Mo.) Daily Tribune* publishes series on crime in Missouri, from-cocaine to auto theft; problems with law enforcement, judicial system, September 1977.

BAIL BONDSMEN

1-803 *The Times* (Shreveport, La.) articles find a parish sheriff failing to collect bail bond forfeitures, favoring bondsmen who should have had to pay up, May-November 1984.

1-2018 *The Tulsa (Okla.) Tribune* publishes reprint on abuses by bail bondsmen in Oklahoma, December 1982.

BANKRUPTCY
See also:
agriculture
courts
judges
loans

1-2021 *Roanoke (Va.) Times & World-News* publishes article on mismanagement of a private furniture plant that led to bankruptcy, June 1984.

1-3090 *WJZ-TV* (Baltimore) finds contractor who went bankrupt filtered much of money taken from people he contracted with into a still solvent company he owned, May 1984.

1-2063 *The Tennessean* special report finds U.S. bankruptcy system in chaos because its judges are seeking status equal to federal district judges who, in turn, don't want bankruptcy judges as equals, August 1983.

1-2248 *The Cleveland Press* series finds pattern of personal favoritism, illegal conduct and improper manipulation of the law by judges in U.S. Bankruptcy Court in Cleveland, April 1982.

1-3183 *WJR-Radio* (Detroit) investigates corruption and irregularities in Detroit U.S. Bankruptcy Court, including favoritism among judges, lawyers and bankruptcy trustees, February and June 1981.

1-315 *Pottsville (Pa.) Republican* publishes thorough investigation of the bankruptcy of the Blue Coal Company; liquidation of company was planned from beginning by company that purchased it as a way of manufacturing a coal shortage and driving up prices; Blue Coal dumped employee black lung disease claims on state, June 1978.

1-2526 *Philadelphia Magazine* does expose on Philadelphia bankruptcy courts, which reek of cronyism and favoritism, unethical and illegal business practices, November 1977.

1-311 *The Record* (Hackensack, N.J.) investigation of a small railroad finds its owner's dealings brought him a hefty profit while bankrupting the railroad, June 1977.

BANKS

See also:
business
credit unions
Federal Reserve Board
loans
money laundering
mortgage
redlining
savings and loans

1-2914 *Los Angeles Times* looks into a trend among banks toward risky, off-balance-sheet investments that are largely exempt from regulation and not backed by capital assets, Oct. 27, 1985.

1-428 *The Wall Street Journal* article shows how state bank regulatory agencies, charged with overseeing the nation's state-chartered financial institutions, are ill-equipped for the job because of underfunding, understaffing and undertrained staff, July 16, 1985.

1-474 *The New Yorker* in-depth series details the demise of Oklahoma's Penn Square Bank, April 1985.

1-2378 *The Tulsa Tribune* series looks at the financial collapse of Tulsa banker Wesley R. McKinney's undercapitalized, papier-mache empire, which jeopardized $72 million in uninsured deposits, December 1984.

1-2267 *American Banker* series looks at dangers of linked financing (making loans conditional on the receipt of brokered deposits); looks into abuses of the financing method, which have resulted in numerous bank failures, November 1984.

1-2094 *The Wall Street Journal* article, "Anatomy of a Failure, Continental Illinois," says bank deregulation wasn't the core of the bank's problems; also problems of pride, ego, fallibility of human judgment and fragility of public confidence, August 1984.

1-2024 *The Kansas City Times* shows bank vice president sold millions of dollars in stock options in the bank's name in a scheme that defrauded Shearson/ American Express, May 1984.

1-3125 *CTV* (Toronto) airs story on phony banks with foreign charters, March 1984.

1-2015 *The Denver Post* finds three leading executives at Continental Illinois Bank acquired interests in oil wells from a Denver oil man whose enterprises received hundreds of millions of dollars in credit from the bank, February 1984.

1-284 *Kansas City Business Journal* series follows disintegration of Indian Springs Bank of Kansas City following takeover attempt by Hawaiian investors, 1983-1984.

1-2062 *The Tennessean/The Knoxville Journal* runs 27-part series, "Borrowed Money, Borrowed Time, The Fall of the House of Butcher," on Jake and C.H. Butcher, who mixed banking, business, politics and reckless investing policies to the detriment of Tennesseans, October and November 1983.

1-63 *New York* article shows how mob in New York City launders money through legitimate banks, October 1983.

1-693 *The Washington Monthly* does article on the failure of regulatory agencies to monitor banking activities, September 1983.

1-141 *American Banker* examines a "house of cards" insurance organization that forced the failure of two banks and near-failure of a third in Wyoming, South Dakota and Montana, August 1983.

1-67 *The Oregonian* (Portland) series explains how a local bank failed, July 1983.

1-2427 *Seattle Post-Intelligencer* investigates the management policies and personalities that helped bring down Seattle-First National Bank; the bank made $1.2 billion in oil and gas loans, one-third of it through the failed Penn Square Bank, losing so much money it had to be rescued by Bank of America, July 1983.

1-2533 *The Wall Street Journal* discusses how Ernst & Whinney's unqualified audit of United American Bank of Knoxville, Tenn., missed the boat, with UAB collapsing just weeks after the report was issued, March 1983.

1-2464 *The Indianapolis Star* portrays the rise and fall of Larry J. Hannah, former president of American Fletcher Corp., Indiana's largest bank company; deals with shady Florida land deals, allegations of thievery and conflicts of interests, February 1983.

1-3296 *WBRZ-TV* (Baton Rouge) tells how Louisiana's largest bank made transactions with a fraudulent developer who used his political power for personal gain; the association led to grand jury probe and the loss of life savings for many bank customers, Nov. 2, 1982.

1-2321 *The Free Lance-Star* (Fredericksburg, Va.) describes the rise and fall of

Aquia Bank & Trust Co., the first Virginia bank to fold in 18 years; series documents how bank overextended itself with land loans and shows improper and illegal actions, May 1982.

1-2251 *Arizona Daily Star* investigation, "The Death of a Bank," looks at Southwestern Bank, which was racked by mismanagement and was in overwhelming disarray when regulators closed it, February 1982.

1-75 *American Banker* series explains the demise of Oklahoma's Penn Square Bank, 1982.

1-2223 *The Tulsa Tribune* articles on the collapse of Penn Square Bank find federal scrutiny of bank missed fact that portfolio was filled with under-collateralized loans, insider loans and outright fraud; major players in fiasco were linked to three earlier financial scandals, 1982.

1-544 *Albany Times-Union* runs series on embezzlement schemes at the State Bank of Albany in which bank executives paid out portions of loans and pyramided the balances in fraudulent loans, July 1980.

1-824 *The Clarion-Ledger* (Jackson, Miss.) publishes series, "Fidelity Bank: Anatomy of a Failure," on the chronic mismanagement and self-dealing of the bank's president which led to the bank's collapse, May 1980.

1-518 *Orlando Sentinel Star* series reconstructs the final 18 months of a small Florida bank that failed, March 1980.

1-759 *Harper's* uses a wide range of public documents to detail "The Bert Lance Affair;" piece illustrates the extent to which modern banking has become the work of silicon chips in high-speed computers, in which fictitious money can become the possession of the shrewdest programmer, September 1979.

1-317 *Santa Monica Evening Outlook* does series on an "off-shore" (foreign) bank operation; bank appears to be phony, April 1979.

1-2115 *Kansas City Star* article says Central Bank of Kansas City has helped finance an unusually high number of loans to mob associates, July 1979.

1-60 *Boston* looks at organized crime in Boston area banks, August 1978.

1-309 *The Record* (Hackensack, N.J.) publishes article on fraud scheme that won large loans from two New Jersey banks by using certificates of deposit from a front bank chartered in St. Vincent, February 1978.

1-362 *Omaha Sun Newspapers* reports on growing number of uninsured and unregulated industrial loan and investment companies, December 1977.

1-114 *Los Angeles* shows how illegal bank practices can lead to real estate speculation and redlining in poor neighborhoods, November 1976.

1-169 *San Antonio Express-News* series on Texas banks describes sweetheart deals between banks and politicians and how holding companies have gobbled up the Texas banking industry, October 1975.

BEER INDUSTRY

1-290 *The Record* (Hackensack, N.J.) profiles the business tactics, crime ties and legal problems of beer king William H. Pflaumer, January 1978.

1-269 *Pottsville (Pa.) Republican* series examines financial trail of a brewery that went bankrupt due to mismanagement and the illegal activities of its owner; a look at wheeling and dealing in the state's small brewery industry, September 1977.

BETTING
See gambling

BIDS, BID RIGGING
1-2970 *The Wall Street Journal* reports that the Justice Department's investigation of electrical contractors has uncovered rampant bid-rigging and resulted in a flurry of prosecutions, Nov. 29, 1985.

1-443 *Regardie's* publishes in-depth article on the bidding process for the contract to supply sidearms to U.S. Army; allegations that bidding and testing were rigged to favor an Italian firm as a quid pro quo for Italy; provides background on the handgun industry, May 1985.

1-2915 *Syracuse Herald-Journal* shows that competitive bidding for heavy equipment contracts in Onondaga County was manipulated by officials that tailored bids to favor certain contractors, Feb. 3-4, 1985.

1-2798 *Newsday* (Long Island) article is part of a long-term series on corruption in the bidding and awarding of public contracts on Long Island, Nov. 18, 1984.

1-2294 *The Daily Oklahoman* (Oklahoma City) shows how Oklahoma lost about $28 million a year on highway construction because of bid rigging, the lack of competition among contractors and the failure of transportation officials to get the best deal for their money, June 1983.

1-756 *Fairbanks (Alaska) Daily News-Miner* series investigates that city's school bus bids and traces bidding improprieties to the state Department of Education — prompting statewide reform of bidding system, January-December 1979.

1-820 *Delaware County (Pa.) Daily Times* articles find a county redevelopment authority contract was awarded to a fraudulent surety bonded bid by a contractor, 1979.

BINGO
See:
charities
gambling

BIRTH CONTROL
See also abortion
1-2972 *The San Francisco Bay Guardian* reveals that nearly a third of San Francisco gynecologists may be prescribing Depro-Provera as a contraceptive to patients even though the Food and Drug Administration has not approved it for that use; article examines the dangers of this contraceptive, Oct. 9, 1985.

1-2927 *Minneapolis Star and Tribune* reports on the Dalkon Shield, how it was developed, and how it injured thousands of users and destroyed the company that manufactured it, Sept. 15, 1985.

1-2578 *The Washington Post* runs article on how the A.H. Robins Co. marketed the Dalkon Shield after inadequate testing and continued to sell it as reports came in that the shield was ineffective and dangerous to women and their babies, May 1985.

1-2178 *Mother Jones* article says millions of women in developing countries are being injected with Depro-Provera, a contraceptive, under U.S.-sponsored programs, despite its being linked to tumors in animals and the FDA's refusal to approve it for domestic use, November 1981.

1-684 *New West* article examines the health risks resulting from the use of intrauterine devices (IUDs), including infection and infertility; also, how health care providers failed to warn women of those risks, May 1980.

1-175 *Mother Jones* looks at the marketing of the untested, unsafe, unregulated Dalkon Shield Intrauterine Device, November 1976.

BOARDING HOMES
See nursing homes

BOMBS
See nuclear weapons

BONDS
See also securities

1-512 *Kansas City Star* examination of the Jackson County Sports Complex Authority's handling of bond issues finds politics plays a large role; the authority dropped its long-time bank and invested in another without seeking proposals, May 1985.

1-2932 *Columbia (Mo.) Daily Tribune* looks at the pros and cons of using tax-free industrial development bonds to finance private projects, Feb. 10, 1985.

1-563 Series examines City of Jacksonville's bond practices; finds former city attorney was hired as bond counsel at three times the going rate; looks at the role of politics in the selling of municipal bonds, February 1985.

1-2835 *The Houston Post* reports on a Fort Worth man said to have passed 150 fake security bonds providing coverage to governmental entities and private sources across Texas, 1984-1985.

1-2471 *Reason* article reports use of tax-free Industrial Development Bonds by private businesses, which often amounts to government subsidies to business; focuses on abuses in the state of Texas, December 1984.

1-2644 *The Bond Buyer* series goes into detail on the Washington Public Power Supply System's default on $2.25 billion in bonds that were sold to build two nuclear plants in the Pacific Northwest, January 1984.

1-2532 *The Philadelphia Inquirer* shows how investors lost millions on tax-free bonds used to finance the development of a retirement facility; the bonds defaulted, raising questions about the nation's municipal bond market and how such deals are packaged and sold in that market, September 1983.

1-840 *The Pittsburgh Press* series, "Bonddoggle," tells how bond attorneys and brokers made a killing by slipping publicly owned securities through an obscure loophole in federal tax laws; in three months, the scheme was worked in 175 municipalities, 1980.

1-104 *Christian Science Monitor* identifies church-run institutions that raised money through bond sales and ran into deep trouble, Dec. 5, 1977.

BOOKIES
See gambling

BOY SCOUTS

1-3017 *WLOS-TV* (Greenville, N.C.) series investigates the padding of Boy Scout troop enrollment to win greater funding from contributors, 1983.

BRIBERY

See also:
city government
conflicts of interests
county government
state government

1-190 *San Diego Daily Transcript* investigation of $24 million county contract for microwave telecommunications system leads to federal investigation into charges that county official solicited bribes from contractors, 1983.

1-2074 *The Indianapolis Star* series, titled "Chemscam," finds chemical industry has used cash and gifts to bribe dozens of government, school and hospital administrators to buy more than $10 million in unneeded stocks of chemicals, August 1982.

1-768 *The San Diego Union* probes crime and corruption links between San Diego and Tijuana, including car theft, bribery and kickbacks, February-May 1979.

1-236 *Sun-Times* (Chicago) runs update on the Mirage Bar — one year after the operation, some abuses have been corrected, January 1979.

1-78 *Anaheim (Calif.) Bulletin* reports kickbacks by towing firms to tow cars at sports stadium, October 1978.

1-365 *Nevada Appeal* (Carson City) finds a brothel owner offered to pay the salary of a sheriff's deputy and assured him he would be promoted to sergeant, July 1978.

1-31 *Sun-Times* (Chicago) describes its "Mirage Bar" operation, January 1978.

1-150 *Charleston (W. Va.) Gazette* does bizarre, complicated story of the alleged attempt of a law partner of former West Virginia governor W.W. Baron to bribe a jury member while being tried on charges of bribery himself, February 1971.

BRIDGES

1-2812 *The Hartford Courant* runs special section on bridge inspections in Connecticut a year after a fatal bridge collapse; probe finds the state's revamped bridge inspection program marred by falsified records, wasted time, inconsistent performance and poor supervision; a model surveillance effort, June 24, 1984.

1-2450 *Detroit News* publishes articles on the poor design and construction that led to the near collapse of the world's largest concrete segmental bridge and the largest cost overrun in the history of Michigan roadbuilding, January and November 1983.

1-3128 *WPXI-TV* (Pittsburgh) airs series on poor safety conditions iron workers faced during a bridge reconstruction project; they were exposed to dangerous amounts of lead paint fumes for over a year; the contractor knew of exposure but did nothing for months, and when the company did act, it used a questionable form of treatment, 1983.

BRUTALITY
See police brutality

BURGLARY
See theft

BUSES
See also transportation

1-2928 *Arkansas Democrat* (Little Rock) investigates accidents involving old school buses; finds pre-1977 buses, which fail to meet current safety standards, are not regulated and are widely used by churches and other organizations nationwide that buy them for little money, Oct. 20, 1985.

1-756 *Fairbanks (Alaska) Daily News-Miner* series investigates that city's school bus bids and traces bidding improprieties all the way to the state Department of Education — prompting statewide reform of bidding system, January-December 1979.

BUSINESS
See also:
banks
bonds
economy
insurance
media
oil
organized crime
securities
Small Business Administration
sports

1-2934 *Business Week* explores the role of U.S. business in South Africa and the choices it is facing between leaving and staying as apartheid and civil unrest continue, Sept. 23, 1985.

1-877 *The Wall Street Journal* does in-depth article on how Allen-Bradley Co., thought to be a "safe" private company, was acquired despite an elaborate trust arrangement to safeguard the company; the pressures that scare private concerns into selling out, May 1985.

1-459 *Kansas City Business Journal* publishes series on shady business practices and stock trading by Billings Corp., a Missouri computer manufacturing and mineral development company, March 12-Dec. 30, 1984.

1-2699 *The Bradenton (Fla.) Herald* runs series about Siemens-Allis, a Milwaukee manufacturing company that moved its operations to Manatee County, Fla.; reporter looks at what the company does, its reputation in Milwaukee and what the new plant will mean economically and environmentally to the Florida community, Dec. 16-23, 1984.

1-2265 *Milwaukee Magazine* shows about 40 percent of America's biggest corporations are using psychologists to help hire executives through various forms of psychological tests, evaluations and assessments called "managerial mind probes," October 1984.

1-2703 *The Georgia Gazette* (Savannah) article shows how Gulfstream Aerospace Corporation avoided paying more than $2 million a year in local taxes by claiming unfinished corporate jets under construction were worth no more than scrap metal, and were then taxed as such, August 16, 1984.

1-177 *St. Louis Business Journal* looks at business transactions between "inside directors" and the St. Louis firms they serve, July 1984.

1-2021 *Roanoke (Va.) Times & World-News* publishes article on mismanagement of a private furniture plant that led to bankruptcy, June 1984.

1-2935 *Advertising Age* publishes a profile of Jeffrey Gluck whose business is reviving failing publications, and asks if his methods really work, May 3, 1984.

1-2654 *The Times-News* (Twin Falls, Idaho) series on the business practices of a fish farm began with a report that fish were being starved, series developed into detailed analysis of bad management, January-February 1984.

1-2052 *Tallahassee Democrat* runs investigative series on the power of the city's business elite, January 1984.

1-2531 *The Washington Post* discusses the issue of financial relationships between prominent economists and private corporations that pay large sums for the economists' testimony, December 1983.

1-2545 *San Jose Business Journal* reveals numerous problems surfaced when five California publishers hired an independent publisher with a dubious track record; problems included charges of false advertising; evidence points to mismanagement and deception by the publisher, June-December 1983.

1-2062 *The Tennessean/The Knoxville Journal* 27-part series, titled "Borrowed Money, Borrowed Time, The Fall of the House of Butcher," reports on Jake and C.H. Butcher, who mixed banking, business, politics and reckless investing policies to the detriment of Tennesseans, October and November 1983.

1-2037 *Fortune* article shows H. Ross Perot is banking on federal contracts to make Electronic Data Systems Inc. the leader in computer services industry, October 1983.

1-2551 *West County Times* (Pinole, Calif.) discovers that a condominium developer milked his project for millions in loans to sustain another business — this, in spite of the fact that the risky site for the condos required costly soils engineering, August-September 1983.

1-2929 *The Orlando Sentinel* publishes a series on the effects of a decision by Westinghouse Corp. to move one of its manufacturing facilities from Pennsylvania to the Sun Belt, June 12-16, 1983.

1-2421 *Dayton Daily News* runs articles on how Dayco Corp., a Fortune 500 company, was swindled by a foreign trade agent who placed about $120 million in phony Soviet orders for goods; also details scams the agent ran on other companies, April 1983.

1-245 *Los Angeles Times* overview of Warner Communications and chairman Steven J. Ross uses basic documents and peripheral sources to write story despite lack of cooperation from Ross, March 1983.

1-2535 *St. Louis Business Journal* articles discuss the $900 million economic link between Sears and St. Louis, which contains many companies that supply Sears, January 1983.

1-2299 *Akron Beacon Journal* describes how Arthur Modell, controlling force behind the Cleveland Browns football team, has his public image as general good guy altered by three lawsuits filed by a stockholder, January 1983.

1-2623 *The San Francisco Bay Guardian* investigation says since the end of World War II the city's business and political leaders have orchestrated a careful plan to turn the city into the financial capital of the West, 1983.

1-2297 *Forbes* lists the richest 400 people in America ("The Forbes Four Hundred"); includes reseach methods for determining who they were, September 1982.

1-253 *The Kansas City Times* uses documents, wide range of sources in article linking Chicago's Pritzker family (Hyatt Corp.) to organized crime, March 1982.

1-2122 *Grand Forks (N.D.) Herald* runs well-documented investigation of a local businessman who, despite his failures and bankruptcy, continues to get loans for new ventures, December 1981.

1-2536 *The Washington Post* runs comprehensive profile of the Mars company, one of the most private of private concerns, December 1981.

1-2327 *Los Angeles Herald Examiner* series, "Ripoff: The Story of Fraud in California's Garment Industry," looks at widespread unemployment insurance fraud scam run by the industry that has cost the state millions of dollars, October 1981.

1-2191 *The Hartford Courant* series profiles William Chipman, founder of a Major Indoor Soccer League team and a master manipulator of the limited partnership; Chipman gave investors false information, mismanaged and undercapitalized the venture and dipped into other investments in effort to save the team, August 1981.

1-2340 *Akron Beacon Journal* publishes reprint on that city's Coliseum, finds it a financial flop that has cost owners and banks millions while its builder escaped unscathed, June 1981.

1-2326 *Los Angeles Herald Examiner* series examines the use of illegal aliens in California's garment industry and the labor and health code violations they face, January 1981.

1-3177 *WMTV* (Madison) investigates the Iowa Beef Co., which engages in bait and switch tactics with customers; reveals firm's ties to organized crime figures, 1981.

1-454 *Boston Magazine* article investigates a company that buys gold and silver jewelry and antiques from the general public through motel room storefronts; finds company giving people half of what jewelry is worth, November 1980.

1-489 *The Kansas City Star* profiles Frank S. Morgan and his Kansas City business empire, which extends to shopping malls, apartment buildings, and real estate, August 1980.

1-708 *Atlanta Journal and Constitution* runs series on independent telephone companies in Georgia that charge high rates for poor service and in turn use those funds for personal gain; series also examines improprieties on the part of watchdog agencies that conducted shoddy, incomplete audits of the firms, July 1980.

1-2175 *WMAQ-Radio* (Chicago) investigates International Sporting and Leisure Club, the largest travel club in the country; finds club deliberately deceived public, May 1979.

1-665 *Center for Investigative Reporting* article looks into the wheelchair industry and how one California company has monopolized the business — the result of which is the lowering of quality standards, higher prices and little innovation in the industry, March 1979.

1-383 *Mesa (Ariz.) Tribune* runs article on a police investigation of a construction firm accused of refusing to pay outstanding material bills and to finish a home remodeling contract, January 1979.

1-3190 *KMOX-TV* (St. Louis) investigates abuses of 15 million consumers by the hearing aid industry; abuses include high-pressure selling, product misrepresentation, 1979.

1-173 *Mother Jones* researches shady international dealings on the Bechtel Corporation, September/October 1978.

1-224 *The Wall Street Journal* does Pulitzer Prize-winning article on conflicts of interests involving corporate executives who make "inside" profits by doing outside business with their own corporations, August 1960.

CABLE TELEVISION

1-2138 *Tucson Citizen* looks at the difficulties cities around the country have faced from cable operators as it looks at the promises cable companies are making in competition for the rights to Tucson, August 1981.

1-574 *Rocky Mountain Business Journal* article says cable company vying for Denver's cable franchise is "renting citizens" — offering influential Denverites shares in the company to help acquire the franchise, July 1981.

1-2134 *The Day* (New London, Conn.) series finds that valuable cable franchises in Connecticut were handed out as political gifts; of 21 franchises, 14 went to companies with political ties, December 1980.

1-2133 *Texas Monthly* article says Houston handed cable franchises over to political and business insiders; who got franchises had nothing to do with quality of service, March 1980.

CAMBODIA
See refugees

CAMPAIGN FINANCES
See also:
elections
politicians

1-2921 *Indianapolis News* reviews campaign spending records and finds Indiana State Supt. of Public Instruction used campaign funds for personal expenses, January-May, 1985.

1-550 *Common Cause* article shows how Chicago's commodity traders get their way on Capitol Hill through heavy political contributions; why hasn't Commodity Futures Trading Commission investigated an illegal campaign contributions scheme? January/February 1985.

1-2859 *Los Angeles Times* runs articles on a California businessman who made illegal campaign contributions to state politicians, April 1984-January 1985.

1-2617 *Richmond Times-Dispatch* reprint, "Money and Votes," uses computer to determine relationship between campaign contributions and subsequent votes by state legislators, December 1984.

1-2684 *Anchorage Daily News* publishes coverage of an Alaskan oilfield service company that raised money for Republican state senators through a payroll deduction plan that allowed the company to make large contributions without going over the $1,000 limit stipulated by Alaska law, August-December 1984.

1-2677 *The North Carolina Independent* article is an in-depth look at the financing of the most expensive congressional race in history — the 1984 Hunt-Helms Senate race; gives a detailed look at the people and special interests that put up the money for campaigns, Oct. 26, 1984.

1-2646 *The Journal-Gazette* (Fort Wayne, Ind.) runs stories concerning the Fort Wayne mayor under indictment for violating Indiana's campaign finance laws, June-October, 1984.

1-2678 *The North Carolina Independent* article looks at how campaign contributors influence North Carolina politics, focusing on state lieutenant governor's race; finds that disclosure laws do not always reveal the special interests behind the names and money, Sept. 18, 1984.

1-2653 *The Times-News* (Twin Falls, Idaho) runs series on the questionable finances of Idaho Congressman George Hansen; article exposes Hansen's connections with Rev. Sun Myung Moon's Unification Church, May-September 1984.

1-286 *The Washington Monthly* article shows what happens to leftover campaign funds; congressmen raise twice the funds necessary on average; many are free to spend the excess as they want, September 1984.

1-707 *The Philadelphia Inquirer* series investigates personal and campaign finances and Mafia ties of Geraldine Ferraro and John Zaccaro, 1984.

1-2801 *The Wall Street Journal* articles show how politicians, aided by political action committees, avoid campaign finance restrictions and accept a flood of contributions from business and the rich, 1984.

1-2240 *The Sun* (Baltimore) runs series on campaign fundraising illegalities of a right-wing Congressional candidate; thousands of dollars were raised by organizations not allowed to solicit political donations or diverted from magazine (published by Lyndon LaRouche) subscription fees, December 1982.

1-2534 *The Miami News* publishes special report on business political action committees in Florida; includes a listing of PAC contributions, a look at how they influence elections and some of the PAC activity in the 1982 elections, October 1982.

1-196 *Common Cause* articles illustrate how political action committee dollars are rapidly becoming more powerful than your vote, August 1982.

1-2356 *The New Republic* documents spending abuses by U.S. House incumbents of their campaign funds; uses include trips abroad, wardrobes, family moving expenses, silver flatware, August 1982.

1-767 *The Journal-Gazette* (Fort Wayne, Ind.) uses campaign finance reports and court records to expose misuse of campaign funds by Allen County prosecutor, December 1979-January 1980.

1-295 *The Record* (Hackensack, N.J.) investigates the campaign financing of a congressional candidate when it finds records indicate low-income people had made $1,000 contributions, November 1978.

1-298 *The Record* (Hackensack, N.J.) article says Rep. Mathew J. Rinaldo, R-N.J., illegally received about $7,000 in campaign contributions from part-time congressional employees; also, Rinaldo juggled payroll to beat congressional spending limits, September 1976.

CANADA

1-326 *CBC* airs two-part investigation of organized crime in Canada and United States, June 1977-June 1980.

1-3228 *CBC-Pacific Report* investigates kickbacks and questionable cash transactions of British Columbia's Minister of Highways, Phil Gaglardi, March, September 1979.

1-3189 *CBC* investigates Toronto's organized crime connections in developing Atlantic City casinos, 1979.

1-411 *WCAX-TV* (Burlington, Vt.) details how a Canadian firm with ties to organized crime figure Joe Bonnano tried to get industrial development bonds from Vermont, July 1978.

1-27 *Macleans* shows secret agreement involving Canadian government (plus Australia, New Zealand and United Kingdom) and Central Intelligence Agency, July 1974.

CANCER

See also:
carcinogens
nuclear energy

1-3099 *CBS News* reports internal studies done for the Department of Energy show an excess of deaths from cancer among nuclear defense workers exposed to uranium dust and radiation at numerous plants — which contradicts what the government says, October 1984.

1-2608 *The Brownsville (Texas) Herald* runs articles on a fraudulent cancer clinic operating in Mexico, December 1983.

1-2227 *The Washington Post* investigation of the war on cancer finds experimental anti-cancer drugs have led to deaths of hundreds of cancer patients; many times experimental drugs were given after studies showed they didn't work, October 1981.

1-527 *The Kansas City Star* publishes results of an Environmental Protection Agency medical study that names cancer hot spots in Kansas, Missouri, Iowa and Nebraska, March 1981.

1-197 *The Philadelphia Inquirer* medical reporter follows 18-year-old cancer patient through experimental drug treatment, medical bureaucracy and death, December 1980.

1-785 *The Boston Globe* documents repeated falsification of cancer research data and abuses of patient rights by a nationally-recognized cancer team, June-July 1980.

1-761 *The Record* (Hackensack, N.J.) traces the less-than-sterling records of two physicians, who bounced from hospital to hospital getting rich by performing unnecessary surgery on Medicaid patients and dispensing ineffective experimental cancer cures, June 1980.

1-456 *Penthouse* series, "The Politics of Cancer," argues that the cancer care establishment has failed in many instances due to its own folly, 1980.

1-2112 *The News World* (New York) does article on conflicts of interests in the National Cancer Institute, which gives away millions of dollars for cancer research; members of NCI board often award millions to their own institutions, October 1979.

1-66 *Sun Newspapers* describes problems with Omaha's Eppley Institute for Research in Cancer, June 1978.

1-561 *The Arizona Daily Star* articles examine one company's involvement in establishing Arizona's state standards for the cancer drug, laetrile, a product it manufactures in Vermont, April 1978.

CANDIDATES
See elections

CARCINOGENS
See also:
asbestos
cancer
chemicals
environment
hazardous substances
occupational safety and health
toxic wastes

1-2936 *The Montgomery County (Md.) Sentinel* reveals that children in public school art classes are exposed daily to poisonous and cancer-causing products, Sept. 19, 1985.

1-2414 *The Register* (Orange County, Calif.) runs investigation, "Deadly Smoke," on how cancer rates among firefighters is rising dramatically because of burgeoning use of synthetic materials in buildings; also, danger to firefighters of toxic chemical spills, December 1983.

1-103 *The Morning Call* (Allentown, Pa.) shows Pennsylvania company that manufactures carcinogen-laced food pellets for cancer research poses health hazard, November 1982.

1-2210 *The Times* (Hammond, Ind.) series, "Cancer Cluster," looks into a cluster around Lake Dale with a cancer rate 2.5 times the national norm, and a Hodgkin's Disease rate 25 times the norm; inefficient septic systems and government disinterest blamed, May 1982.

1-2358 *The Cleveland Press* investigates the agricultural chemical picloram, also known as Agent White, as a possible carcinogen; evidence includes one in four people in Cherokee County, N.C. died from cancer and the area has 97,000 acres of its 290,000 total acres dumped on each year, April 1982.

1-206 *Mother Jones* documents breakdown of regulatory system for testing drugs and consumer products including phony inadequate testing, altered data, shredded reports and results in sales of carcinogenic household products to public, 1982.

1-709 *The Courier-Journal* (Louisville) publishes series on the effects of workers' exposure to vinyl chloride at the B.F. Goodrich factory in Louisville; the death of a worker from a rare liver cancer raised questions about the monitoring systems and workplace precautions taken regarding this known carcinogen, August 1980.

1-3165 *ABC-TV News Closeup* entitled "The Unranium Factor" reports that the mining, milling and control of uranium poses severe health risks not only to workers, but also to residents of areas where it is processed, April 1980.

1-2142 *The Philadelphia Inquirer* publishes reprint, "Poison at our Doorsteps," on the dumping of toxic chemicals, September 1979.

1-87 *Congressional Quarterly* shows Occupational Safety and Health Act attempts to standardize definition of carcinogens, an effort that illustrates problems in controlling toxic substances, 1978.

CARS
See automobiles

CASINOS
See gambling

CENTRAL INTELIGENCE AGENCY (CIA)
See also:
espionage
military

1-501 *The Progressive* article investigates role of CIA and Pentagon in Salvadoran "Death Squad" activity beginning with Kennedy administration, May 1984.

1-3101 *CBS News* series investigates allegations that Ronald Rewald, whose investment firm bilked people of millions, was a CIA agent and his company a CIA front; and CIA abandoned him when his case got too much publicity, May 1984.

1-185 *St. Louis Post-Dispatch* and Center for Investigative Reporting look at America's spy network, 150,000 strong and fastest-growing part of the U.S. budget, March 1984.

1-2830 *Newsweek* reports the CIA is back in business on a scale unmatched since the agency's heyday 20 years ago and traces the extent of CIA involvement worldwide, Oct. 10, 1983.

1-3025 *KITV-TV* (Honolulu) airs series on Ron Rewald's connection to the CIA as the "housekeeper" of three CIA cover operations; how he operated, his fall from grace and problems with the agency's conduct, October 1983.

1-422 *The Washington Post* article explains how the CIA sets up front companies — airlines, insurance firms, etc. — to hide covert operations behind a mantle of private enterprise, July 1976.

1-27 *Macleans* shows secret agreement involving Canadian government (plus Australia, New Zealand and United Kingdom) and CIA, July 1974.

1-673 *The Daily Oklahoman* (Oklahoma City) series investigates the Army's co-verup of the CIA's role in the My Lai massacre, May 1972.

CETA
See job training

CHARITIES
See also:
gambling
nonprofit organizations
organized crime
religion

1-412 *The Tulsa Tribune* publishes series on the bingo industry in Oklahoma, a state with lax bingo regulation; how promoters rig the odds and cheat both players and the charities they represent; "stacking" and other methods of avoiding limitations; Indian bingo operates outside any regulation, allowing professionals to run their operations, May 1985.

1-633 *St. Paul Pioneer Press-Dispatch* article says charities saw little of the money raised by Minnesota Viking Celebrity (golf) Tournament for Charities — charities actually lost much of their investments, March 1985.

1-3065 *KNXT-TV* (Los Angeles) series investigates a private soup kitchen supposed to help the poor; it was actually selling privately donated and government surplus food for profit to restaurants, fencing stolen food stamps, trafficking drugs, February 1985.

1-3117 *KGW-TV* (Portland) finds Citizens Against Child Abuse is a sham organization, soliciting money without a city permit and not giving it to organizations it says it will, 1984.

1-3062 *Channel 8* (Dallas) investigates charity bingo promoters creating questionable charities to make money, offering charity money to use their licenses, siphoning off money from charities, October 1984.

1-147 *Channel 9* (Los Angeles) airs series on assorted wrongdoings at the Ecumenical Coalition of Concerned Americans, a million dollar non-profit corporation that sells food to the poor at a discount; inflated discount claims, thousands of dollars worth of food "walks" away, corporation officers dipping into corporate funds, misrepresentations, October-November 1983.

1-2406 *The Oregonian* (Portland) runs series on how professional gamblers posed as ministers and charitable operators to take advantage of Oregon's social gambling laws, March 1983.

1-2404 *The Buffalo News* series investigation of the Ron Jaworski Scholarship Fund, a celebrity fund-raising charity that raised thousands of dollars, finds only a paltry sum went to the target cause, November 1983.

1-53 *The Kansas City Times* gives People-to-People, headquartered in Kansas City, heavy fire for activities, September 1983.

1-3039 *WBTV* (Charlotte) investigation finds only a small fraction of bingo proceeds in Mecklenburg County goes to charity; most is diverted to professional bingo operators, 1983.

1-3069 *WOWT-TV* (Omaha) investigation of local charity bingo and pickle operations finds not all money is going to charity; they are paying outrageously high rents for halls and are illegally paying workers, 1983.

1-204 *The Plain Dealer* (Cleveland) investigation of private relief agencies in U.S. finds unethical practices galore, November 1982.

1-2128 *The Charleston (W.Va.) Gazette-Mail* series, entitled "Charity Begins in the Boardroom," finds charities as big business, with highly paid executives, are proliferating, November 1982.

1-198 *The Philadelphia Inquirer* series looks at how international relief effort has distorted the economy of Somalia, has led to theft and corruption and, in the end, is hurting those it seeks to help, September 1981.

1-2189 *The Investigator* article finds the Red Cross, America's largest charity, is concealing income and wealth through incomplete and confusing accounting practices, September 1981.

1-3178 *WKBU-TV* (New York) investigates the Salvation Army and finds food collection and gas distribution are abused by staffers, April 1981.

1-515 *The Herald* (Everett, Wash.) series, titled "Where Did The Money Go?" investigates the Evangelical Scripture Mission in Monroe, Wash., after two people sponsoring different impoverished children in the Third World receive identical letters from the children, June 1980.

1-3187 *ABC News 20/20* investigation finds the International Children's Appeal, fundraiser for the International Year of the Child, is a money laundering front for drug and weapons merchants, 1979.

1-2249 *The Cleveland Press* series, titled "Money and the Mob," investigates Mafia controlled loan company and finds it has money invested in it from three Cleveland charities, 1978.

1-425 *Minneapolis Tribune* series investigates the city's United Way operation; its financing, management and effectiveness in serving the needy, December 1977.

1-107 *Sunday Gazette-Mail* (Charleston, W.Va.) examines United Way in piece titled "United Way — Uneven Way?" August 1977.

1-108 *The Charleston (W.Va.) Gazette* series finds fund-raising for charity is big, tax-free industry, open to abuse; reforms needed in both national and local charities, March 1977.

1-2831 *Newsday* (Long Island) article looks at organized crime's involvement in charity gambling in New York City and Long Island, Sept. 27, 1976.

1-36 *Newsday* (Long Island) finds charity gambling spreading on Long Island and the mob becoming involved, September 1976.

1-154 *Delaware Today* finds a couple suffering from arthritis set up a charitable foundation but were put out of business by state regulators, September 1974.

CHEMICALS
See also:
agriculture
air pollution
carcinogens
environment
hazardous substances
toxic wastes
water
water pollution
worker safety

1-2916 *The Wall Street Journal* takes a look at American Cyanamid Company, where worker training and maintenance and inspection procedures are being improved after a series of chemical mishaps, Nov. 11, 1985.

1-2802 *Baton Rouge Morning Advocate* publishes reprint, titled "Louisiana's Chemical Legacy," on a variety of the effects of chemical dumping, pesticides, hazardous waste sites and transporting toxic substances in the state — including cancer and air and water pollution, April 25, 1985.

1-3109 *WOKR-TV* (Rochester, N.Y.) investigates a chemical distributorship scam that promises people the opportunity to make thousands of dollars delivering chemicals to area customers, October 1984.

1-2474 *The Daily Herald* (Arlington Heights, Ill.) explores the situation in which five Chicago Magnet Wire Corp. executives were indicted on various charges for recklessly exposing employees to toxic chemicals, September 1984.

1-2716 *Not Man Apart* runs articles on controversial Environmental Protection Agency plans for incinerating chemical wastes off the coast of California — the first time such a program had been approved for an area upwind of a major population center, April, September 1984.

1-2013 *Science Digest* reports Paraquat, the world's most effective herbicide, is so effective hundreds of people have died from its misuse; bad data the reason for EPA approval of Paraquat, 1983.

1-3046 *WXYZ-TV* (Detroit) series finds Detroit Edison Co. is spilling large amounts of PCBs in dozens of residential neighborhoods and not cleaning them up despite claims that it is, 1983.

1-3248 *KMOX Radio* (St. Louis) does three-part investigation of dioxin; who is responsible for contamination, how dangerous the substance really is and the best methods of cleaning it up, 1983.

1-2394 *St. Louis Post-Dispatch* investigates Missouri's dioxin waste sites; includes account of the toxic trail of dioxin through Missouri and reports on dioxin's health effects, November-December 1982.

1-2216 *The New York Times* articles find a Connecticut company intentionally and secretly deposited vast amounts of dangerous chemicals over a period of years into Waterbury's water and soil, October 1982.

1-2074 *The Indianapolis Star* series, titled "Chemscam," finds chemical industry has used cash and gifts to bribe dozens of government, school and hospital administrators to buy more than $10 million in unneeded stocks of chemicals, August 1982.

1-2269 *Tampa Tribune* looks at problems caused by Temik, a highly potent pesticide, in Florida and other parts of the nation; also questions federal efforts at controlling the pesticide, August 1982.

1-2188 *Pacific News Service* reports Environmental Protection Agency considering ban of toxaphene, once the nation's most heavily used insecticide; significant amounts of the dangerous chemical found in the Great Lakes, far from its chief point of use on southern crops, June 1982.

1-2077 *The Courier-Journal* (Louisville) runs series on the failure of the city's Metropolitan Sewer District to prevent industry from pouring waste water containing toxic metals at levels far greater than its regulations allow into sewers, August 1981.

1-2145 *Reason* article argues that the City of Niagara Falls, not Hooker Chemical Co., was responsible for Love Canal, February 1981.

1-2273 *The Ledger* (Lakeland, Fla.) publishes series on Polk County pollution, more than half of which comes from phosphate chemical fertilizer complexes; EPA says much of the pollutants are hazardous to health — so do people living near some of the industrial plants while industry denies any hazard, June 1980.

1-597 *New Jersey Home News* series examines problem of chemical contamination from dumping, February 1980.

1-485 *The Dallas Morning News* series on the chemical pentachlorophenal reveals alarming levels of contamination in a food study and death and illness among workers at manufacturing plants in three states, September 1980.

1-593 *Willamette Week* (Portland) publishes series on aerial spraying of herbicides and its effects, December 1979.

1-2182 *Connecticut Telegram* runs articles on potentially hazardous chemicals buried in Fairfield County, Conn., November 1979.

1-668 *Mother Jones* article examines the dumping of dangerous U.S.-manufactured pesticides in Central and South America for use in banana and pineapple plantations; it isn't just the pests that are killed as a result, November 1979.

1-664 *The Village Voice* article looks at the lack of hard data and research done on the health effects of paraquat prior to the government's spraying the herbicide on opium and marijuana crops, March 1979.

1-3212 *KOIN-TV* (Portland) reports on leakage of nerve gas from a munitions storage facility at an Army depot in Eastern Oregon, 1979.

1-599 *The News* (Snyder, Texas) runs articles on how Browning-Ferris Industries disposed of lethal doses of cyanide by mixing the chemical into road oil, 1979.

1-571 *Columbia (Mo.) Daily Tribune* takes an in-depth look at a chemical spill in Sturgeon, Mo. and its effects on the health of members of the community and their farms, as well as the failure of federal and local authorities to protect citizens from such spills; the article examines the overall problem of hazardous waste spills on the regional and national level as well, July 1979.

1-3211 *KOCE-TV* (Huntington Beach, Calif.) examines the effects of a local chemical spill and how public health considerations were ignored by state and local agencies, 1979.

1-522 *The Lake County (Ohio) News-Herald* series reveals that urea formaldehyde, an inexpensive foam insulation used in houses, is injurious and possibly lethal to humans, April 1979.

1-344 *The Tribune* (Lewiston, Idaho) runs article on the mishandling of a highly toxic liquid chemical used in sewer construction by the municipal shop in Garden City, Idaho, February 1979.

1-413 *Chemical Week* article outlines problems of chemical waste disposal with emphasis on who are the "midnight dumpers" and where they operate, March 1978.

CHILD ABUSE
See also juveniles

1-772 *The Progressive* reports on problems in America's war against child abuse, a war that often assumes the guilt of parents charged with abuse from anonymous callers, and uses laws with low standards of proof, September 1985.

1-2567 *Minneapolis Star and Tribune* reprint series of child sexual abuse allegations in Jordan, Minn., a quiet, suburban community that was shook by charges of a large number of abuse cases, Oct. 21, 1984; Follow-up takes look behind the scenes of the case and how charges grew and then disintegrated, May 26, 1985.

1-2803 *The Plain Dealer* (Cleveland) reprint details how one young girl was sexually abused by her father and how her mother learned of it; problems with the justice system in child sex abuse cases, child sex abuse warning signs, March 13-17, 1985.

1-2675 *The Journal* (Lorain, Ohio) runs series on a child adopted by a couple who physically abused him, resulting in severe injuries and brain damage; series questions functioning of adoption process and government checks on child abuse, October-December 1984.

1-2650 *The News Chief* (Winter Haven, Fla.) series about checks on backgrounds of applicants for teaching positions in Florida public schools finds that since it is not policy to make the checks, child molesters get hired, March-December, 1984.

1-2642 *The Cullman (Ala.) Times* conducts continuous eight-month coverage of child abuse at home for children, March-November, 1984.

1-228 *The Charlotte Observer* series on child sexual abuse includes interviews with victims, profiles of offenders, what's being done about it, September 1984.

1-181 *Buffalo News* series shows that sexually abused children are also abused by the legal system; abusers rarely charged with crime, May 20-27, 1984.

1-2017 *Champaign-Urbana (Ill.) News-Gazette* says reports of child sexual abuse grow as awareness increases, June 1984.

1-3107 *KXLY-TV* (Spokane, Wash.) series examines Fatima Crusade, a conservative offshoot of the Roman Catholic Church known for rigid discipline; exposes child abuse and sexual abuse, April 1984.

1-3243 *KMOX Radio* (St. Louis) does 10-part series on child abuse and what is being done about the problem; findings include excessive numbers of cases assigned to small numbers of social workers and inadequate amounts of funding; moral and fiscal responsibility are explored, May and November 1983.

1-2628 *The Anchorage Times* runs series on sexual abuse of children in Alaska, March 1983.

1-2308 *The El Paso Times* series examines sexual abuse of children in terms of the long-term trauma of victims, the shame of offenders, the cycle that links both and frequently turns victim into offender, and how victim and offender try to put their lives back together, May 1982.

1-3290 *WCCO-TV* (Minneapolis) series looks at sexual abuse of children — who does it and why, Feb. 8-12, 1982.

1-2116 *Gannett News Service* reprint finds institutionalized children in Oklahoma were beaten, sexually abused and assaulted over a period of years with the knowledge of high-ranking state officials, 1982.

1-3313 *WOR-TV* (New York) report on pedophiles, how they operate and the growth of "call-boy" services, Dec. 13, 1980.

1-3146 *WMAQ-TV* (Chicago) 10-part series investigates the sexual abuse of girls by a group of adults who use drugs and force to involve them in child prostitution and pornography, November 1980.

1-828 *Burlington County (N.J.) Times-Advertiser* articles investigate financial misconduct and child sex-abuse by a teacher and township committeeman, 1979.

1-3217 *WAST-TV* (Albany) investigates child abuse in publicly funded child care agencies, 1979.

1-306 *The Record* (Hackensack, N.J.) examines the suicide of a child who was abused by her parents, November 1978.

1-274 *Rochester Times-Union* publishes series on child abuse and the roadblocks to protecting victims, November 1977.

CHILD LABOR
See juveniles

CHILD SUPPORT
1-2746 *Call-Chronicle* (Allentown, Pa.) looks at local enforcement of child support awards; finds system delays seeking justice on uncollected support payments, defers decisions to bureaucrats and discourages defendants from exercising their rights, April 22, May 1, 1984.

CHILDREN
See:
adoption
child abuse
day care centers
juveniles

CHIROPRACTORS
1-3064 *WQAD-TV* (Moline, Ill.) airs series on chiropractors using "No Out of Pocket Expense" plans — the acceptance of whatever insurance companies pay as full payment (with no deductible from the patient); bills are, however, four times higher than the area norm, 1984.

CHURCH CORRUPTION
See religion

CIGARETTES
1-3188 *The Wall Street Journal* reports the tobacco industry in the wake of declining U.S. consumption is avidly courting consumers in the Third World (with success), July 5, 1985.

1-302 *The Washington Monthly* article tells how cigarette companies, with help from Congress and the media, get around the inconvenience of the TV ban to advertise their products and misrepresent the dangers of smoking to consumers, April 1984.

1-656 *Mother Jones* publishes article on home fires caused by cigarettes that are long-burning and why Congress and federal government agencies are reluctant to legislate for self-extinguishing cigarettes — a move that could cost the tobacco industry its profits, July 1979.

1-2166 *The Philadelphia Inquirer* series says racketeers and government officials have combined forces to build cigarette smuggling into organized crime's second

biggest moneymaker; who was involved, how they did it, May 1979.
1-37 *Newsday* (Long Island, N.Y.) shows New York mob steals millions of cigarettes, causing loss of millions of dollars, February 1975.

CITY GOVERNMENT
See also:
cable television
conflicts of interests
county government
fire departments
inspections
lawyers
nonprofit organizations
politicians
politics
power structure
special districts
state government
toxic wastes
urban renewal
water
zoning

1-2917 *The Philadelphia Inquirer* investigates why city officials ignored violations of city codes by members of the MOVE organization when they built a bunker on the roof of their row house, and how that inaction may have contributed to the eventual confrontation between MOVE and police in which 11 people died, Oct. 27, 1985.

1-2619 *Columbia (Mo.) Daily Tribune* series details the failure of the city's mayor and city manager to report unauthorized foreign stays charged to taxpayers; other improprieties include allegations both men routinely charged lodging and meals for their wives to the city in violation of policy, January 1985.

1-430 *The Miami Herald* investigates zoning in Hialeah; among the findings: city officials rezone for personal profit, the City Council solicits and offers bribes for zoning charges, January 1985.

1-2736 *Sun-Times* (Chicago) series shows how Chicago aldermen spend city money to maintain personal staffs that often include family members and friends, Dec. 19-20, 1984.

1-2832 *WGST Radio* (Atlanta) reports on how Atlanta's city council president failed to disclose that he was registered as a minority subcontractor on a highway construction project his council vote saved, December 1984.

1-2704 *The Georgia Gazette* (Savannah) runs series on corruption in the office of Savannah's mayor and his political machine; reporters used many kinds of public documents to implicate the mayor and his cronies in activities from selling appointments to public boards to a sex extortion scheme, November-December 1984.

1-2778 *The Plain Dealer* (Cleveland) examines the finances and managment of two Cleveland civic events; found the promoters were systematically bilking the city and participants by giving themselves a variety of service and supply contracts, sometimes with the help of city officials, July-December 1984.

1-2971 *The Ledger-Star* (Norfolk, Va.) investigates Chesapeake's economic development director's failure to account for $180,000 in his budget and his methods to lure business; leads to state investigation, September 1984.

1-2714 *The San Francisco Bay Guardian* article looks into the results of a 1969 San Francisco Redevelopment Agency project that was to provide 2,400 new jobs to residents of a low-income neighborhood; so far only 55 jobs have gone to those residents, the rest going to commuting workers; in addition, the community has lost millions in property tax revenues, Sept. 26, 1984.

1-3250 *WGST Radio* (Atlanta) learns a collection agency hired by city has close ties to the city council president and his part-time aide works as a bookkeeper for the firm, August 3-16, 1984.

1-2651 *The Anniston (Ala.) Star* article exposes local government's tampering with city growth projections to convince voters of need for bond issue for water system expansion, July 27, 1984.

1-3089 *WKBW-TV* (Buffalo) series finds that city's Municipal Softball Association, a quasi-public agency, is run by political cronies of the mayor who use its revenues as a private slush fund — paying for expensive dinners, political contributions and unvouchered expense accounts, July 1984.

1-2649 *Durham (N.C.) Morning Herald* article is the result of research into events that led to hiring of developer to build civic center for the city of Durham; investigation found there was no competition nor much inquiry into the development firms' background, March 11, 1984.

1-2860 *The Evening Sun* (Baltimore) series investigates a city agency formed to help poor people; reporters found gross mismanagement resulted in millions of dollars in unspent funds while the agency was putting on fundraisers in the poor communities it was supposed to serve, March 9-16, 1984.

1-2031 *St. Petersburg Times* reports chairman of that city's housing authority had a business arrangement with firm that got money from agency; handful of interrelated real estate speculators who own large apartment complexes receive most of the money from the federal program intended to fund renovation of deteriorated, primarily single-family rental buildings, January-February 1984.

1-2901 *WTVT-TV* (Tampa) reports on the wrongdoings of a six-term mayor who is the political boss of Bradenton Beach, a Florida resort town; allegations include the use of police to harass political enemies and improper use of city workers and equipment, 1984.

1-819 *The Virginian-Pilot* (Norfolk) and *The Ledger-Star* articles investigate expense payments city official received; official could not substantiate nearly $180,000 in spending, used funds illegally, 1984.

1-2601 *Standard-Speaker* (Hazelton, Pa.) publishes series on contract arrangements between the city and the operator of its airport, December 1983.

1-2443 *The Post-Standard* (Syracuse, N.Y.) series finds that for political and financial reasons the city of Syracuse has, for years, overtaxed downtown business properties and forced owners to go to court for tax refunds, December 1983.

1-2417 *Sun-Times* (Chicago) articles examine waste, inefficiency, nepotism and insider deals in Chicago's patronage ridden park system, which make it the most expensive system per acre in the U.S., May, September-December, 1983.

1-2538 *Chicago Tribune* investigates allegations that the Chicago Park District superintendent received a retainer from a firm awarded contracts for construction, December 1983.

1-2412 *The Miami Herald* article finds mayoral candidate had cozy relationship with officials of a Venezuelan government-owned bank that led to one of Miami's largest real estate failures, the near collapse of the bank and the disappearance of $9 million, September 1983.

1-2610 *The Daily Press* (Newport News, Va.) and *Times Herald* investigation finds misconduct — including embezzlement and improper record keeping — in the operation of city garage, July-August, 1983.

1-2516 *Erie (Pa.) Daily Times* studies a city employees' pension fund and finds that officials overstated the market value of the holdings and that the investments were handled imprudently, July 1983.

1-2483 *Newport News Daily Press* and *Times-Herald* does articles on a city councilwoman who used her position to postpone the donation of two lots of land to the city and then bought them herself, March 1983.

1-2499 *Hot Springs (Ark.) Sentinel-Record* runs articles on spending illegalities and conflicts of interests by the city's advertising commission, which publicizes the city's tourist attractions, 1983.

1-2433 *Fort Lauderdate News* and *Sun-Sentinel* articles on abuses in Fort Lauderdale's public works department find employees used department equipment to do private jobs for which they were paid while on city time, 1983.

1-2435 *The Sun* (Baltimore) series investigates Baltimore's $300 million plan to burn its sludge at an incinerator owned by a prominent supporter of the mayor through a no-bid "sweetheart" deal; also investigates city's decision to sell the same incinerator two years earlier, 1983.

1-2445 *The Post-Standard* (Syracuse, N.Y.) runs articles on the administration of the City of Syracuse's attempt to pull off a sweetheart real estate deal, using friends of the mayor as intermediaries, 1983.

1-2632 *Sun-Times* (Chicago) investigation finds Mayor Jane Byrne politicized to an unprecendented degree the awarding of city contracts and handed out financial favors to political supporters, 1983.

1-2258 *Albany Times-Union* series examines the way the City of Albany spends public money to reward its politicians' friends; city doesn't bid contracts, is charged exorbitant fees for services, December 1982, with 1983 update.

1-3275 *WNEV-TV* (Boston) investigates allegations of conflicts of interests and of election law violations undertaken by the state ethics committee and the county district attorney, August 18, 1982.

1-257 *San Diego Reader* shows that city records of public land transactions are a mess, July 1982.

1-3315 *WCBS-TV* (New York) airs series on that city's unique and controversial system of "City Marshals," who are appointed to enforce actions of the civil courts on a freelance basis, working for commissions; the system is rife with abuse, Nov. 18-21, 1981.

1-2077 *The Courier-Journal* (Louisville) runs series on the failure of the city's Metropolitan Sewer District to prevent industry from pouring waste water containing toxic metals at levels far greater than its regulations allow into sewers, August 1981.

1-2090 *Chicago Tribune* series, "Chicago: City on the Brink," examines the effects of financial crises and dwindling resources on the city, May 1981.

1-3314 *WQAD-TV* (Quad Cities) airs series on abuse and padding of travel expense reports by city officials in East Moline and Rockford, Illinois and Davenport, Iowa, 1981.

1-3153 *KTVI-TV* (St. Louis) exmaines that city's license collector office and finds a pattern of laxity and gold-bricking at the expense of the taxpayer, September 1980.

1-551 *Pittsburgh Post-Gazette* article details how members of the City Council hire friends and relatives for well-paying make-work jobs, August 1980.

1-199 *The Sun* (Baltimore) explores the city's "shadow government," the unelected officials who run the city from behind the scenes, July 1980.

1-541 *Albany Capital Newspapers Group* finds that the city clerk was receiving money for a person he put on the city payroll and whom he paid — in cash — for occasional jobs, May 1980.

1-3237 *WDHN-TV* (Dothan, Ala.) reports on widespread irregularities in that city's government from misuse of public funds by city clerk to the illegal issuance of arrest warrants by the mayor, 1980.

1-645 *The Eunice (La.) Gazette* investigates illegal voting activities in St. Landry Parish, October-December 1979.

1-818 *Anderson (Ind.) Daily Bulletin* series on corruption finds conflicts of interests and ties to organized crime of mayor, former city attorney, police chief and police officials, February 1979.

1-346 *Tucson Citizen* runs articles on city councilman who used his position to approach businessmen, seeking employment, September 1978.

1-417 *KSL-TV* (Salt Lake City) shows how that city's taxi service violates safety regulations with official sanction, August 1978.

1-345 *The News* (Waukegan, Ill.) probes irregularities in city's sewer contracting procedures, 1977-1978.

1-273 *Rochester (N.Y.) Times-Union* articles indicate city insurance commissions were paid out as patronage to political friends and contributors, March 1977.

1-297 *The Record* (Hackensack, N.J.) does articles on how city officials padded expense accounts and double billed a publicly financed trip, 1976.

1-117 *The Kansas City Star* finds fraud of city officials in connection with company supplying crushed rock for highway construction, 1975.

1-293 *The Record* (Hackensack, N.J.) series, "Closeup on Paramus," examines wrongdoings by officials in the community's municipal government, September 1973.

1-764 *The News* (Paterson, N.J.) investigates a disco-lounge of dubious character and finds that an interlocking network of friendships with influential people in city, county and state government protects owner from crackdown, June-November 1971.

1-131 *Charleston (W.Va.) Gazette* shows street commissioner resigns after employees on city payroll found working on private home, 1970.

CIVIL DEFENSE

1-2114 *Columbia (Mo.) Daily Tribune* article finds Missouri's emergency plans to help residents during a nuclear attack are worthless and dangerous, September 1984.

1-2245 *The Willimantic (Conn.) Chronicle* article says state officials admit Connecticut's evacuation plans were done backwards; say federal government wouldn't let them do it right, September 1982.

1-2194 *Press-Enterprise* (Bloomsburg, Pa.) series examines plans for evacuation in a nuclear attack; finds planning not workable, January 1982.

1-3316 *KBGL-TV* (Pocatello, Idaho) reports on the poor state of readiness for a disaster in Idaho Falls, Dec. 12, 1980.

CIVIL RIGHTS
See also:
discrimination
minorities

1-2573 *Chicago-Tribune* looks at Operation PUSH, a social change/civil rights organization started by the Rev. Jesse Jackson in 1971 on $10,000; today it operates on a minimum of $167 million and keeps a very low profile financially, November 1983.

CLINICS
See also hospitals

1-2587 *Miami News* series investigates unlicensed and unregulated prepaid health clinics that serve thousands of Dade County Cubans, October 1983.

1-3262 *WDIV-TV* (Detroit) examines medical fraud in Detroit, including phony laboratories and tangled insurance billings, Feb. 4, 5, 8 and August 2, 11982.

1-3281 *ABC News 20/20* looks at clinic in Mexico that promises to cure arthritis, an incurable disease; drugs administered have devastating effects on patients, March 25, 1982.

1-2039 *New West* charges Feminist Women's Health Centers lack of conventional medical personnel, reliance upon lay health workers and self-examination means member clinics are practicing medicine without a license, May 1981.

1-558 *WFAA-TV* (Dallas) investigates thriving blood donor clinics in El Paso that feed off of Mexican illegals and jeopardize their health, August 1980.

COAL
See also energy

1-2643 *The Charleston (W. Va.) Gazette* series investigates the failure of state and federal agencies to enforce environmental regulations governing coal mines in West Virginia; reporter uses records of U.S. Office of Surface Mining, October-December 1984.

1-2007 *The Oregonian* (Portland) details Port of Portland's bungled $43 million coal export terminal; port chose to award project to a shadowy company headed by a man with theft and securities crimes convictions over a multi-billion dollar company with impressive credentials in international coal trade, March 1984.

1-2833 *Coal Age* reports why a device, the Thin Seam Miner (TSM), that was supposed to revolutionize coal mining in Appalachia never got off the ground; the Dutch firm that produced the system was taken by con man James D. Stacy, November 1983.

1-219 *The Courier-Journal* (Louisville) investigation shows that, despite attempts at reform, the coal industry remains an outlaw industry, rife with illegal practices and unsafe conditions that kill employees in appalling numbers, January 1983.

1-59 *The Courier-Journal* (Louisville) runs article about hazardous Kentucky mining industry, May 1982.

1-2357 *Roanoke (Va.) Times & World News* provides a detailed look at the past, present and future of Virginia coalfields, the changes that are bringing new economic stability to the region, and the people who live and work in the coal counties, June-July 1981.

1-142 *The Washington Monthly* shows the "energy" crisis is really an oil pricing crisis; examines coal and oil industries, October 1980.

1-742 *The Kentucky Post* (Covington) series investigates the murder of an international coal company president with ties to organized crime figures; the series details his illicit campaign contributions to Reagan's presidential race in 1976 and also examines his firm's history of swindles and scams; 20-month investigation relied on FBI, Securities and Exchange Commission and Bureau of Prisons documents, 1980.

1-2362 *The Pottsville (Pa.) Republican* runs series on the problems of pensioned coal miners; death benefits dropped without notice, long legal delays in court suits, inability to collect money the miners say is owed to them, October 1979.

1-315 *The Pottsville (Pa.) Republican* publishes reprint of investigation of the bankruptcy of the Blue Coal Company; liquidation of Blue Coal was planned from the beginning by the company that purchased it as a way of manufacturing a coal shortage and of greatly driving up coal's price; Blue Coal dumped employee black lung disease claims on the state, June 1978.

1-2466 *The Pottsville (Pa.) Republican* outlines impact of the mine safety laws of 1969 on coal mines, especially independents; crackdown has resulted in 90 of 202 mines being closed, January 1973.

COAST GUARD
1-2295 *Newsday* (Long Island, N.Y.) takes a look at the Coast Guard — how it was "saved" from being transformed into a civilian agency — and the politics that support it.

COCAINE
See drugs

COLLEGE ATHLETICS
See also sports

1-1010 *The Wall Street Journal* reports on payments to Southern Methodist University football players made by boosters, Dec. 27, 1985.

1-2794 *Lexington Herald-Leader* publishes articles on widespread booster payoffs to University of Kentucky basketball players and illegal recruiting methods used by a number of universities, Oct. 27-28, 1985.

1-2834 *The Commercial Appeal* (Memphis) reports on the existence of an illegal booster club fund used to provide Memphis State University football recruits with cars and cash, August 4 and 6, 1985.

1-4055 *USA Today* article examines graduation rate of Memphis State University scholarship basketball players, June 5, 1985.

1-2933 *The Chronicle of Higher Education* runs a collection of articles on proposals to reform college sports programs, May 15, 1985.

1-2370 *St. Petersburg Times* runs account of how the University of Florida and its athletic system became corrupt which resulted in one of the stiffest penalties by the National Collegiate Athletic Association in college football history, December 1984.

1-2690 *Phoenix* (San Francisco State University) series on athletic eligibility violations at San Francisco State ran despite intimidation and threats of legal action from concerned parties to show that a basketball player was academically ineligible to play according to National Collegiate Athletic Association standards, October-November 1984.

1-263 *Columbia (Mo.) Daily Tribune* investigation finds National Collegiate Athletic Association recruiting rules violated by University of Missouri booster, September 1983.
1-2254 *The Denver Post* and *The Miami Herald* publish articles on the highest paid college football coaches and where their money comes from, May 1982.
1-642 *The Dallas Morning News* series reports on illegal college football recruiting methods, including universities sending hired agents after high school stars; National Collegiate Athletic Association's enforcement problems, March 8-11, 1981.
1-453 *Sports Illustrated* runs article, "The Student-Athlete Hoax," on academic abuses in college athletics, May 1980.
1-2302 *The (Tucson) Arizona Daily Star* stories report numerous findings of corruption in the University of Arizona athletic department in the area of football recruiting, paying players for jobs never done and reimbursing staff for flights to nowhere, January-April 1980.

COLLEGES
See also universities
1-2262 *Sun-Times* (Chicago) runs series on patronage at Triton College, a publicly supported school; elected board chairman of the school awarded extensive business contracts to political allies, family members and syndicate connected-firms; patronage was rampant and chairman tried to dictate academic appointments, November 1984.
1-3094 *WXYZ-TV* (Detroit) investigation of Wayne County Community College finds many of its instructors don't have college degrees and have no coursework in subjects they are teaching; many have advanced degrees (which mean big raises) from diploma mills, March 1984.
1-677 *Jacksonville (Fla.) Times-Union and Journal* investigation of a community college reveals many spending irregularities by administrators in entertainment, international education program and travel expenditures, 1984.
1-2547 *The News Journal* (Mansfield, Ohio) reports personnel from a local business college and the corporation that owns the college were turning huge profits through state and federal funds generated by the recruiting of poor minority students — at the expense of quality education, December 1983.

COMMODITIES
See also securities
1-2993 *The Wall Street Journal* investigates possible conflicts of interests within the National Futures Association, Sept. 17, 1985.
1-2922 *Des Moines Register* looks into the failure of a Des Moines commodity brokerage firm and the effect it may have on many Iowans, July 16, 1985.
1-550 *Common Cause* article shows how Chicago's commodities traders get their way on Capitol Hill through heavy political contributions; why hasn't the Commodity Futures Trading Commission investigated an illegal campaign contributions scheme? January/February 1985.
1-962 *The Wall Street Journal* runs article on the emergence of the Soviet Union as a very big, very clever trader in commodities; Soviets use size and secrecy to drive hard bargains, January 1985.
1-3119 *WBBM-TV* (Chicago) reports on "churn and burn" trading tactics, often for expensive commissions, not only by fly-by-night commodities trading companies but some established companies; the failure of the Commodity Futures

C

Trading Commission to adequately regulate the industry, November 1984.

1-2093 *The Wall Street Journal* article says there are close ties between Commodity Futures Trading Commission and the commodities industry — which it is supposed to regulate under the Reagan administration; supposed watchdog is more like a puppy, August 1984.

1-2045 *The Wall Street Journal* runs article on the questionable tactics of Thomas Dittmer, one of the country's biggest futures brokers; he exceeds speculative limits, tricks brokers, August 1984.

1-611 *Fort Lauderdale News and Sun-Sentinel* runs investigation of the enforcement gap that turned South Florida into a haven for precious metals fraud; details a boiler room firm that bilked investors of millions, 1984.

1-2548 *News Journal* (Mansfield, Ohio) investigation of a commodity brokerage firm reveals trade practices that resulted in huge broker commissions but giant client losss, May 1983.

1-774 *Gannett News Service* special project explores the multi-faceted story behind the Hunts' raid on the silver market; findings include evidence that the spectacular silver buy-up was orchestrated with the help of radical right-wing groups; details of Hunts' scheme to control international silver market, May-December 1980.

1-3317 *ABC News 20/20* reports on fraudulent firms selling gold and silver options and futures, March 6, 1980.

1-291 *The Record* (Hackensack, N.J.) article details how con men are moving from land fraud into selling London commodity options at great markups, October 1977.

COMPANIES
See business

COMPREHENSIVE EMPLOYMENT AND TRAINING ACT (CETA)
See job training

COMPUTERS
1-2924 *The Wall Street Journal* reports the results of a study conducted to test the vulnerability of computers to electronic spying, Oct. 18, 1985.

1-2907 *The Wall Street Journal* publishes special section on the applications and implications of new technology in the workplace; "the current state and future course of this 'unfinished revolution,'" Sept. 16, 1985.

1-2648 *The Journal-Gazette* (Fort Wayne, Ind.) does story on how that city spent money to attract a computer firm in financial trouble; uncovered fact that city lacked policy for determining which companies should get public money in this way, Feb. 23, 1984.

1-703 *The New York Times* series examines how major bureaucracies — FBI, IRS, etc. — are using computers in revolutionary ways that affect the privacy of Americans, 1984.

1-2037 *Fortune* article shows H. Ross Perot is banking on federal contracts to make Electronics Data Systems Inc. the leader in computer services industry, October 1983.

1-2198 *San Jose Mercury-News* series, "Silicon Valley: Secrets For Sale," finds security and business ethics so low in the region that important computer secrets

41

are for sale to the highest bidder; also, well organized networks of thieves make parts stealing rampant, May 1982.

1-250 *The New York Times, Newsday* and *Business and Society Review* — three articles by Hesh Wiener show how U.S. computers are an essential element of police control and repression in Latin America, South Africa and other totalitarian states, Februray 1977-November 1978.

1-21 *The Times-Picayune* (New Orleans) discovers the state of Louisiana over-buying and under-utilizing computers by $30 million annually, 1978.

CONFLICTS OF INTERESTS

See also:
bribery
business
city government
Congress
county government
courts
food
hospitals
housing
minorities
nursing homes
politicians
politics
special districts
state government

1-2925 *Sun-Times* (Chicago) looks into loans made by a banker and hotel owner to director of a Chicago hotel complex apparently in exchange for his help in securing favorable board decisions, Sept. 11, 1985.

1-2577 *The Wall Street Journal* publishes article on the possibility Deputy U.S. Budget Director Joseph R. Wright Jr. held up price-fixing complaint against his father's oil company with a phone call to the Department of Energy, May 1985.

1-2736 *Sun-Times* (Chicago) series hows how Chicago aldermen spend city money to maintain personal staffs that often include family members and friends; finds nearly one-third of the city's 50 aldermen had at least one other family member on the City Council's payroll, Dec. 19-20, 1984.

1-2773 *The Atlanta Journal and Constitution* articles on the improprieties of an Atlanta city councilman who worked as a zoning consultant to a real estate developer while promoting his zoning proposal before the City Council, June-December 1984.

1-2766 *The Daily Free Press* (Boston University) discloses the Massachusetts Attorney General was investigating the presidents of Boston University and Brandeis University and the Archibishop of Boston's Catholic Archdiocese because of alleged conflicts of interests regarding allocation of grant money, Oct. 9 and 17, 1984.

1-2786 *The Charlotte Observer* investigates a Charlotte computer wizard who designed a traffic light control system for the city while directing the Transportation Department's equipment purchases to a close business associate, June 10 and Oct. 5, 1984.

1-2795 *Providence (R.I.) Journal-Bulletin* investigates the abuse of power by Providence Mayor Vincent A. "Buddy" Cianci in the hiring of political cronies, awarding contracts without bids and political favoritism, March-October 1984.

1-2645 *The Journal-Gazette* (Fort Wayne, Ind.) does series concerning conflicts of interests between a city official and a contract ambulance firm; newspaper sued the City of Fort Wayne for some documents and won, Sept. 9-13, 1984.

1-2694 *Watertown (N.Y.) Daily Times* article exposes New York State Fair director's practice of awarding lucrative concessionaire contracts and leases to friends and members of his family, July 5, 1984.

1-2708 *The San Francisco Bay Guardian* investigates the possible conflicts of interests faced by Willie L. Brown Jr., a representative for San Francisco in the State Assembly who also represents clients through his law practice; reporters found Brown introduced and voted on legislation that would benefit one of his private clients — Southern Pacific Corporation, March-May 1984.

1-2702 *The Times Union* (Albany) series studies patronage appointments on the Temporary State Commission on Real Property Tax; appointees got paid for little or no work and commission's work had never been audited by an outside agency, April 1984.

1-110 *The Kansas City Star* finds Occupational Safety and Health Administration director helped drop $12,000 worth of penalties against a local company whose parent firm had named him president, March 11, 1984.

1-712 *The Plain Dealer* (Cleveland) series on rampant conflicts of interests and questionable dealings of Arnold Pinkney, the Port of Cleveland's chief financial officer and national campaign manager for Jesse Jackson, 1984.

1-2531 *The Washington Post* discusses the issue of financial relationships between prominent economists and private corporations who pay large sums for the economists' testimony, December 1983.

1-3038 *WJLA-TV* (Washington, D.C.) reports on conflicts of interests on the board of trustees at Southeastern University and the awarding of a number of diplomas to people who hadn't earned them, including a member of the board; also, sweetheart contracts awarded to friends and partners of the university's business manager, one of them a convicted con artist, 1983.

1-3295 *WTAJ-TV* (Altoona, Pa.) shows conflicts of interests mar flood recovery program of that devastated community; five members of city's redevelopment authority are suspended for misappropriation of funds and three later resigned, May 1982.

1-2387 *St. Louis Post-Dispatch* investigation of St. Charles Fire District finds lax safety standards, conflicts of interests and nepotism in the district's financial dealings, 1982.

1-475 *Tallahassee Democrat* runs article on private consultants, hired by the Florida Department of Transportation, making decisions that benefit themselves, December 1980.

1-553 *The Times-Union* (Albany) series examines nepotism in county Democratic organization as well as the city and county governments, including the benefits to recipient and the cost to taxpayers, November 1980.

1-2112 *The News World* (New York) does article on conflicts of interests in the National Cancer Institute, which gives away millions of dollars for cancer research; members of NCI board often award millions to their own institutions, October 1979.

1-678 *The Herald Citizen* (Cookeville, Tenn.) series looks at conflicts of interests in the running of the Upper Cumberland Development District, January 1979.

1-390 *Boston Herald American* investigation reveals that dozens of former State Department of Mental Health employees have been awarded no-bid consulting contracts, December 1978.

1-356 *Tri-City (Wash.) Herald* does article on conflicts of interests between an agency that assists low-income Mexican-Americans with federal funds and three United Farm Workers organizers, December 1978.

1-264 *The Knickerbocker News* (Albany) describes how nepotism pervades rental arrangements, hiring practices of Elmira claims court, March 1977, February 1978, July 1978.

1-115 *The Washington Post* shows a lawyer using a public position on a federal commission to study gambling laws to launch a lobbying career for Nevada casinos, February 1976.

1-16 *Detroit Free Press* shows Detroit county officials hire friends and relatives for summer employment, November 1973.

CONGRESS
See also:
campaign finances
politicians

1-2177 *UPI* and *Better Government Association* does 10-part series, "American Royalty," on government officials and agents living high on the hog at taxpayer expense; topics include Congressional overseas travel abuses, unauthorized use of military transport and the Pentagon supplying free travel and expensive entertainment to its congressional watchdogs, February 1982.

1-626 *The Evening Sun* (Baltimore) uses data from legislators' expense accounts, financial disclosure forms, General Accounting Office audits and vouchers to conclude that it costs taxpayers an average of $1 million per Congressman and Senator just to keep each one paid and comfortable, September-October 1979.

CONSERVATION
See environment

CONSTRUCTION
See also:
bids, bid rigging
bridges
contractors
roads

1-2658 *Northeaster* (Minneapolis) series on faulty trusses, installed in a Minneapolis public school gymnasium; reporter goes through construction inspection records as well as weather statistics for period construction took place to determine the cause of the trusses' failure, January-February 1984.

1-2084 *The Wall Street Journal* article reports on brittleness of "high strength steel" — a key structural underpinning of modern life — which is causing it to fail, causing accidents; U.S. Steel's efforts to reassure worried customers, January 1984.

1-3249 *KSYR Radio* (Syracuse, N.Y.) looks at major construction project originally envisioned as a jewel of that city's urban renewal program; development delayed by lags in financing and land acquisition; the same contractor for this project is the one responsible for $50 million project in Florida that is also marred by serious construction delays, Nov. 28-Dec. 1, 1983.

1-2630 *The Anchorage Times* series exposes a financial empire and massive debt; Arctic government's quest to complete a $1.7 billion construction deal resulted not in modernization for Eskimos but in a blow to their economy, April and July 1983.

1-2204 *The Kansas City Star and Times* investigation, "The Hyatt Papers: Documentation of a Disaster," examines documents surrounding construction of the Hyatt Regency; indicates trouble signals were missed, contractor faced bankruptcy, skywalks were never inspected, October 1982.

1-3258 *KTVI-TV* (St. Louis) series examines the Harry S Truman Dam in the Missouri Ozarks that has mechanical failures, has killed tons of fish and has posed a threat to nearby town, July 17-22, 1982.

1-2214 *The New York Times* series finds New York's construction industry is plagued by corrupt and collusive practices that affect virtually every building, road and tunnel built, April 1982.

1-2247 *The Kansas City Times* examination of Hyatt Regency disaster finds earlier construction accidents, skywalk design changes, wiring problems; also looks at city's inspections of construction, July 1981.

1-2283 *Cocoa (Fla.) Today* examines the cause of the collapse of a condominium complex, and the shortcomings in condominium construction and building regulations statewide, April 1981.

1-383 *Mesa (Ariz.) Tribune* publishes article on police investigation of a construction firm accused of refusing to pay outstanding material bills and fulfilling a home remodeling contract, January 1979.

1-126 *Space City* magazine in Houston tells story of Brown and Root, second largest building contractor in the world, and the irregularities of the empire, 1971.

CONTRACEPTIVES
See:
birth control
Food and Drug Administration

CONTRACTORS
See also:
construction
minorities

1-404 *The Charlotte Observer* in-depth article examines the tactics of a plumbing contractor in deceiving clients and charging outrageous fees as well as the regulatory gap that allows him to continue doing it, March 1985.

1-2723 *Daily Press* (Newport News, Va.) publishes stories on unscrupulous contractors preying on unsophisticated homeowners resulting in home foreclosures; series found loan companies had contractors co-sign loan notes when the families appeared to be poor risks, April-September 1984.

1-2836 *KPRC-TV* (Houston) reports on three unscrupulous contractors who prey on the poor and uneducated by getting them to sign inflated home remodeling contracts, provide shoddy services and then foreclose when the people can't pay, 1984.

1-3318 *WCCO-TV* (Minneapolis) airs series on Central States Waterproofing, a company that uses phony inspections and false claims to convince people that the basements of their homes need expensive waterproofing and then applies a phony treatment at ridiculously expensive prices, Nov. 9-13, 1981.
1-3319 *WDTN-TV* (Dayton) airs series on shady and illegal sales pitches and financing arrangements of an aluminum siding contractor, 1981.

CONTRACTS
See also:
defense contracts
military
1-2037 *Fortune* shows H. Ross Perot is banking on federal government mega-contracts to make his Electronic Data Systems Inc. the leader in computer services industry, October 1983.

COOPERATIVES
See agriculture

CORONERS
See medical examiners

CORPORATIONS
See business

CORRECTIONAL INSTITUTIONS
See prisons

CORRUPTION
See:
bribery
city government
conflicts of interests
county government
embezzlement
favoritism
fraud
politics, politicians
scams
state government

COUNTERFEITING
1-2500 *Pensacola (Fla.) News-Journal* articles outline the history of a con man, William Glascock, indicted in a $6 million counterfeiting ring, October 1983.

C

COUNTY GOVERNMENT
See also:
bribery
city government
conflicts of interests
inspections
lawyers
politics, politicians
property taxes
state government
zoning

1-2835 *The Houston Post* article shows how the Harrison County engineer's office approved phony bonds, which were supposed to guarantee county construction projects, leading to reports of widespread corruption in the engineer's office, 1984-1985.

1-2724 *Asbury Park (N.J.) Press* story on patronage in county government identifies officeholders, relatives and party workers whose political connections helped them get on the Monmouth County payroll, Oct. 25, 1984.

1-2693 *Press-Enterprise* (Bloomsburg, Pa.) series studies abuses of a government-funded county weatherization program; lists addresses and names of all people whose properties were weatherized under the program, not all of whom qualified, August 1984.

1-2686 *The Times* (Hammond, Ind.) series investigates controversial Indiana township trustee for the way he manages his district's business, from parks management to low-income relief programs, August 1984.

1-2006 *Fort Lauderdale News and Sun-Sentinel* finds funds from a county tax aimed at increasing area tourism have been spent inefficiently and tourism has actually declined, April 1984.

1-2667 *The Clarion-Ledger* (Jackson, Miss.) series uncovers dishonest dealings of a county comptroller who handled the investment of county money; reporters discovered that he borrowed $1 million for personal use from the same banks with which he was investing county money at or below normal interest rates, March 1984.

1-2710 *The Capital* (Annapolis, Md.) article uses county government documents to show that county workers are abusing sick leave privileges, taking twice the sick leave of the average U.S,. worker, Feb. 20, 1984.

1-2774 *Greenboro (N.C.) News & Record* series puts together the story of the FBI's Abscam-style investigation of county officials that resulted in indictments for various kinds of corruption; reporters use FBI memorandums and court records, Jan. 22-26, 1984.

1-2558 *The Jersey Journal* (Jersey City) publishes roundup of all the elected officials in Hudson County who held other jobs in the public sector, September 1983.

1-2559 *The Star-Herald* (Belton, Mo.) shows possible political motives of the newly elected county prosecutor, who had dropped, reduced or failed to prosecute an unusually high proportion of serious felony cases; retribution against political enemies appeared to be motivation, August 1983.

1-3011 *WTSP-TV* (St. Petersburg) finds conflicts of interests among public officials in Hernando County makes them money and pollutes the political process as the county develops, 1983.

1-190 *San Diego Daily Transcript* investigation of $24 million county contract for microwave telecommunications system leads to federal investigation into charges that county official solicited bribes from contractors, 1983.

1-2615 *Delaware (Pa.) Daily Times* investigation uncovers evidence that powerful county Republican leaders rigged a Democratic primary election, paid off candidates and then tried to cover it up, 1983.

1-2173 *Fort Myers News-Press* articles on corruption in Lee County, Fla., show county inspectors and commissioners were being bribed by contractors they are supposed to regulate, December 1982.

1-323 *The Pottsville (Pa.) Republican* issues reprint of thorough investigation into the fiscal chaos, mismanagement, manipulation and theft that allowed Schuylkill County to run up a tremendous debt in the 1970s and early 1980s, September 1982.

1-28 *The Towson Times* (Baltimore) shows Baltimore County planning and zoning officials accept bribes, August 1982.

1-2260 *The Daily Transcript* (Little Falls, Minn.) runs article on use of per diem and expense money by members of a county board; some see costs as extravagant, July 1982.

1-2399 *The Clarion-Ledger* (Jackson, Miss.) investigates a county supervisor who was using county funds and county workers for his personal benefit, 1982.

1-564 *The Daily Oklahoman* (Oklahoma City) and *Tulsa Tribune* run series on corruption within county governments in Oklahoma, in which county commissioners defrauded taxpayers and received sizable kickbacks from materials suppliers for county contracts, May-August 1981.

1-719 *Beaver County (Pa.) Times* series examines a sweetheart deal for a public tenant program that handsomely rewarded the private operator of a sports facility; after searching through shoeboxes full of records in the basement of the county building, the reporter showed that the private operator skimmed 90 percent of the program's income, November 1980.

1-847 *Chicago Tribune* series details how former Cook County assessor became a millionaire through real estate deals with property developers for whom he cut taxes while heading the assessor's office, May 1980.

1-782 *Citizen-Journal* (Columbus, Ohio) finds officials of the Franklin County Mental Health and Retardation Board ran amuck and spent county funds on themselves and on their friends, January-April 1980.

1-607 *KGW-TV* (Portland) looks into the wrongdoings of the Marion County district attorney who spent thousands of county dollars, ostensibly for investigations but, in fact, he pocketed it, March 1980.

1-618 *The Bakersfield Californian* does overview of the Kern County assessor's office and finds improprieties include illegal tax rollbacks before elections, November 1979.

1-523 *Chronicle Tribune* (Marion, Ind.) documents that the Grant County clerk was playing with public money by delaying — often by as much as a year — county bank deposits, April 1979.

1-676 *Willamette Valley Observer* (Eugene, Ore.) does series on county chief executive's government land swaps that benefitted his private real estate development firm, March 1979.

1-644 *The Montgomery County Daily Courier* (Conroe, Texas) uses county auditor's documents to discover that the county has been losing money by depositing its funds in non-interest-bearing checking accounts, February 1979.

1-300 *The Record* (Hackensack, N.J.) investigation of a county real estate appraiser finds he was copying the work of other appraisers (county law requires two or more appraisers make independent audits), September 1978.

1-764 *The News* (Paterson, N.J.) investigates a disco-lounge of dubious character and finds that an interlocking network of friendships with influential people in city, county and state government protects owner from crackdown, June-November 1977.

1-268 *The Times-News* (Lehighton, Pa.) runs articles on county commissioners' failure to bid contracts as legally required, resulting in overpayment for county goods, September-November 1977.

1-361 *The Register-Guard* (Eugene, Ore.) investigation discovers that the county district attorney may have improperly used county funds to traverse the country speaking on marijuana reform, November 1975.

1-292 *The Record* (Hackensack, N.J.) investigation finds contractors shortchanging Bergen County on soil deliveries to its garbage dump, April 1975.

1-16 *Detroit Free Press* shows Detroit county officials hire friends and relatives for summer employment, November 1973.

1-399 *The Pottsville (Pa.) Republican* documents failure of county commissioners' plan to save money by replacing private assessing firm with staff assessors, August 1973.

COURTS
See also:
bail bondsmen
bankruptcy
child abuse
conflicts of interests
criminal justice
judges
juries
lawyers
probate

1-2580 *Cleveland* article explains cronyism and patronage in the Cuyahoga County Court system and how one politically connected judge used the criminal justice system to ruin the lawyer who ran for his seat on the bench, May 1984.

1-817 *The Plain Dealer* (Cleveland) publishes series on increasingly powerful chief justice of the Ohio Supreme Court and his complete politicization of the court and the administrative functions attendant to it; political considerations play a large role in the court's decisions, April 1984.

1-2381 *The Philadelphia Inquirer* issues reprint of investigation of the Pennsylvania Supreme Court that found the court awash in politics, patronage, misconduct and nepotism, May 1983.

1-4001 *Fayetteville (N.C.) Times* series examines the Cumberland County District Court system; topics include ticket-fixing, judges changing verdicts after trials, higher percentage of blacks convicted than whites, etc., March 1983.

1-584 *The Plain Dealer* (Cleveland) reprinted series investigates criminal courts in

Cuyahoga County; uses computer to analyze and evaluate 28,000 felony cases, December 1979.

1-264 *The Knickerbocker News* (Albany) finds nepotism pervades rental agreements, hiring practices of Elmira, N.Y. claims court, March 1977, February 1978, July 1978.

1-162 *The Philadelphia Inquirer* issues reprint of 11 editorials lambasting the Pennsylvania Supreme Court for being "a dismal swamp of self-protective secrecy, a chaos of indifference to the needs of private citizens and the legal community alike;" among the worst abuses: huge backlog and unaudited slush fund, February-March 1978.

1-348 *Quad-City Times* (Davenport, Iowa) runs series on how Scott County Associate District Court is encouraging people with more serious violations — many of which don't involve driving — to plead guilty to phony loud muffler citations, January 1978.

1-2261 *Courier-Post* (Cherry Hill, N.J.) reports on the municipal courts in southern New Jersey; rates judges and the system of justice, October 1977.

1-746 *The Philadelphia Inquirer* series describes the plea-bargaining system in Philadelphia in which defendants shop for judges and get reduced sentences on murder charges.

CREDIT UNIONS

1-625 *Jacksonville (Fla.) Times-Union and Journal* investigates a loan of $500,000 by a Postal Credit Union to a contract mail hauler who declared bankruptcy shortly after receiving the loan, February 1979.

CRIMINAL JUSTICE

See also:
courts
judges
juries
lawyers
murder
parole
witness protection program

1-4026 *Esquire* publishes article on the 70-year-old murder conviction and subsequent lynching of a man whose only crime was being a stranger in the Old South, September 1985.

1-2938 *The Wall Street Journal* tries to untangle the confusion surrounding procedures for making legal searches and arrests, Aug. 9, 1985.

1-2903 *The Milwaukee Journal* publishes series on widespread injustices to the accused, particularly the indigent accused, in that city's municipal legal system, April 21-28, 1985.

1-49 *Jacksonville (Fla.) Times-Union* reports on the mishandling of a kidnapping and rape case by Jacksonville police; a convicted child molester and wanted fugitive in a stolen car was released when the girl he kidnapped didn't press charges, Oct. 4 and Dec. 4, 1984.

1-2902 *People* reports on the political reasons behind the refusal to release a Colorado man convicted of murder, despite another man's confession to the murder, Nov. 5, 1984.

1-2685 *News/Voice* (Highland Park, Ill.) runs editorial series on growing abuse of a provision in the 1970 Omnibus Crime Bill that allowed authorized testimony by immunized witnesses without corroboration; series found this led zealous prosecutors to grant immunity to unscrupulous witnesses for testimony against government targets — in effect, buying testimony, May-September 1984.

1-2663 *Fort Myers (Fla.) News-Press* series investigates the plea bargaining and sentencing in a triple-murder case involving an organized crime drug smuggling operation; reporters got access to transcripts of confidential tapes and court documents, July 29-31, 1984.

1-192 *The New Yorker* publishes overview of history, controversy surrounding insanity plea, July 1984.

1-2020 *The Washington Post* article reveals an innocent man who resembles a confessed robber is serving a 25-year sentence, June 1984.

1-2700 *The Courier-News* (Bridgewater, N.J.) article details the crime and trial of a young New Jersey man who committed suicide after being sentenced to 30 days for possession of stolen cans of tuna fish; the state of New Jersey subsequently criticized the judge for his handling of the trial, March 2, 1984.

1-2059 *Rolling Stone* article, "The Mysterious Death of Mrs. Jerry Lee Lewis," questions the determination that she wasn't murdered by her husband, singer Jerry Lee Lewis; official cover-up suspected, March 1984.

1-2775 *Philadelphia Daily News* runs article about a 20-year-old black college student arrested for arson because of a psychological profile of the likely arson suspect prepared by the FBI based on wrong information; police later dropped charges against her and arrested a white suspect, Jan. 27, 1984.

1-3073 *WBRZ-TV* (Baton Rouge) documentary and series investigate the pressures the U.S. government can use when it targets a criminal for prosecution, including breaking the rules of the justice system; problems of insider witnesses and what happens when one jurisdiction wants to prosecute another's witness; abuses by overzealous prosecutors and drug agents, 1984.

1-804 *Akron Beacon Journal* runs articles on how an innocent man was convicted of raping and murdering a child; articles blame eager cops and a politically ambitious prosecutor, 1984.

1-2539 *The High Point (N.C.) Enterprise* details the plight of a man serving a prison sentence for a robbery that evidence indicates he may not have committed; evidence also points to the possibility that the prosecutor may have taken unethical action in the case to protect himself and his conviction record, January-December 1983.

1-2937 *Newsweek* examines the death penalty debate in its special report concerning condemned killer J.D. Autry, Oct. 17, 1983.

1-2440 *Seattle Times* article chronicles arrest and trials of man tried for series of rapes and sodomies and suggests he is the victim of mistaken identity; also, suggests overzealous prosecutors don't want to admit they have been prosecuting the wrong man, October 1983.

1-2613 *Dallas Times Herald* runs articles on conviction of the wrong man for a series of fast-food holdups; unwillingness of prosecution to concede mistakes may have put wrong man behind bars despite convincing evidence, 1983.

1-230 St. Petersburg Times series on mass murderer Gerald Stano includes interviews with victims' families, in-depth profile of Stano, discussion of legal system that often allows most heinous criminals to plea bargain while others are executed, December 1982.

1-2386 *Sacramento Union* runs series, "Odd Partners in Crime," on how government confidentiality laws about welfare and public aid recipients prevent the capture of thousands of criminals, November 1982.

1-3266 *KMTV-TV* (Omaha) investigates inability of law enforcement officials to handle inmates out on the streets in furlough or work release programs; one man arrested for sexual assault is learned to have been a former furlough escapee, May 4-6, 1982.

1-2176 *Columbus Dispatch* articles find Ohio law makes it difficult to hold a mentally-deficient criminal suspect, even when there is evidence that the suspect continues to be a danger to society; mentally ill found incompetent to stand trial for homicide allowed to walk streets, May 1982.

1-2160 *The Arizona Republic* article finds prosecution in the murder of Don Bolles was "prosecution gone awry;" case at a standstill, February 1982.

1-2390 *Arkansas Democrat* (Little Rock) investigation finds an innocent man was convicted of murder and rape; articles led to his release, 1982.

1-3293 *KPLC-TV* (Lake Charles, La.) does five-part series examining four criminal cases in that city, with special attention to adequacy of the plea bargaining system, November 1981.

1-2451 *The Daily Olympian* (Olympia, Wash.) determines the extent of the injustice to a man who had been wrongly sent to military prison; investigation led to the man's freedom, September 1981.

1-2454 *Philadelphia Magazine* article shows how and why soft sentences are meted out in Philadelphia's criminal list rooms; the backlog of cases is expanding by the thousands; conclusion: if judges get tougher, more attorneys will demand jury trials and the whole criminal justice system will be damaged by backlog, September 1981.

1-2104 *Seattle Times* issues reprint of the Pulitzer Prize-winning stories about an innocent man who was found guilty of rape; reporter's investigation led to man's release, May/June 1981.

1-826 *The Denver Post* articles indicate the U.S. government betrayed undercover informants to avoid bringing fugitive Robert Vesco back the the United States, April 1981.

1-3320 *WTEN-TV* (Albany) reports that because of defects in the law, the Criminal Insanity Defense Act of 1980, which was designed to make it difficult for criminals with mental handicaps to repeat their crimes, was having the opposite effect, Feb. 9, 1981.

1-557 *The Detroit News* does series on Michigan's public defender system in which indigents are often defended by incompetent and corrupt attorneys, January 1981.

1-5456 *The Times-Union* (Albany) runs series on wrongdoing in $10 million civil suit in which the plaintiff's attorney withheld evidence and made a secret agreement with the judge not to disclose pertinent information in the case, December 1980.

1-3236 *WNED-TV* (Buffalo) investigates the case of an Attica inmate serving time for murder and questions the evidence brought against him, 1980.

1-3233 *WCVB-TV* (Boston) investigates the use of paid witnesses and informants in criminal trials and illustrates the risks of perjury that result from excessive use of rewards and inducements to get witnesses to talk, 1980.

1-813 *Saginaw (Mich.) News* reprint of investigation of Saginaw County Circuit

Court uses computer analysis to show disparities in sentencing by the five justices, mistakes of judges and prosecutors, etc., November 1979.

CULTS
See also:
Ku Klux Klan
religion

1-503 *Columbia Journalism Review* examines the difficuties reporters face when trying to cover religious sects, November/December 1985.

1-2838 *The Oregonian* (Portland) 20-part series examines the worldwide religious movement directed by Bhagwan Shree Rajneesh and his followers in central Oregon, June 30-July 19, 1985.

1-2939 *Jacksonville (Fla.) Times-Union* reports that the Yahwehs, an all-black sect, seems to be preaching revolt against white rule, July 14, 1985.

1-455 *Fort Worth Star-Telegram* and *The Dallas Morning News* publish articles on the Synergetic Civilization, a small "cult of intellectual elitists," who are preparing to forge a new civilization; the group is heavily funded by Edward Bass, one of the four Bass brothers, whose money is used to fund ranches, an art gallery, scientific expeditions, March 1985.

1-784 *New England Monthly* does article on the Northeast Kingdom Community Church, a cult in rural Vermont founded in 1971 by a carnival barker and now known for brutalizing the children of its members, December 1984.

1-2743 *St. Paul Pioneer Press and Dispatch* series goes into the background of a controversial religious commune located in St. Paul; besides practicing severe forms of physical discipline and regimented lifestyle, group also has substantial property and financial holdings, July 8-11, 1984.

1-3088 *WJLA-TV* (Washington, D.C.) series on the Rajneeshee religious cult, which buses thousands of the homeless poor to rural Oregon, where it is setting up a city and seeking control of the local government, 1984.

1-3052 *ABC News 20/20* investigates Eternal Flame, a Scottsdale, Ariz., cult that tells its members they can live forever, and steals thousands of dollars from them, November 1983.

1-3040 *WTHR-TV* (Indianapolis) documentary investigates the high number of deaths in the Faith Assembly, which teaches that doctors and medical science are inspired by Satan, 1983.

1-3031 *KPNX-TV* (Scottsdale, Ariz.) series investigates Eternal Flame Foundation, a religious cult that promises members they can live forever, brainwashes them and bilks them out of thousands of dollars, 1983.

1-3001 *KMOX-TV* (St. Louis) series looks at The Covenant, The Sword and the Arm of the Lord, a right-wing religious survivalist paramilitary cult on the Arkansas-Missouri border, 1983.

1-220 *The News-Sun* (Waukegan, Ill.) runs series on Christian Fellowship, Inc., an ultra-conservative Christian cult with centers at Navy bases with nuclear or other technical training schools in the U.S. and Europe; cult leader indicted for having homosexual relations with young members, February-December 1982.

1-535 *News World* (New York) reveals ties between the American Family Foundation — a non-profit, anti-cult organization opposed to certain new religions — and big business and politics, July 1981.

1-621 *The Register* (Orange County, Calif.) series investigates Santa Ana-based

Madeley Trinity Methodist Church (no affiliation with any organized Methodist group) — a secretive group which requires members to physically abuse each other to exorcise "evil demons;" members may have relocated in Springfield, Mo., April 1980.

1-3201 *WKYC-TV* (Cleveland) reports on The Way, an international cult that claims to be a biblical research and study group; it has millions of dollars in holdings and an armed protection squad; includes reports of violence and harassment by the patrol, 1979.

1-341 *WISN-TV* (Milwaukee) series investigates an ultra-conservative shrine in Necedah, Wis., and the backgrounds of several controversial clergymen connected with the Roman Catholic splinter group involved with the shrine, 1979.

DANCE STUDIOS

1-2665 *The Clarion-Ledger* (Jackson, Miss.) series investigates the deceptive, high-pressure tactics by dance schools to convince students — often elderly people — to sign up for expensive dance lessons; series led to state legislation to regulate dance schools, July 1984.

1-831 *The Tulsa Tribune* article investigates local Fred Astaire Dance Studio that took advantage of elderly clients, stealing thousands of dollars from them, August 1980.

DAY CARE CENTERS

See also juveniles

1-2124 *Des Moines Register* series on problems in Iowa's day care centers and baby sitting operations and the failure of state regulation, Sept. 22-25, 1985.

1-414 *The Tulsa Tribune* series offers some background on day care and the inadequacy of state regulation and health inspections, May 1985.

1-2303 *Honolulu Star-Bulletin* examines Hawaii's day care regulatory apparatus and finds too few regulations and too few inspectors to enforce them, March 7-Sept. 10, 1984.

1-2428 *Dallas Morning News* series on the quality of child day care in Texas; focuses on shortcomings in the state's attempts to inspect and regulate the homes, where there have been incidents of sexual abuse, beatings, and deaths of children, September-December 1983.

1-2270 *Buffalo Evening News* takes a comprehensive look at the issue of day care in the 1980s in western New York state; findings include conditions that were unsanitary, little attention from regulatory agencies and many centers barely making ends meet, January 1983.

1-752 *The Clarion-Ledger* (Jackson, Miss.) series on federally funded day care centers uses FOI requests to overcome official roadblocks, and finds waste, inefficiency and improper practices have turned a community service into a fun-and-profit farce, September 1979.

1-140 *Fort Lauderdale News and Sun Sentinel* series shows non-compliance with health department and state law, loopholes in county inspection system with case histories, an insider's view of a day care center (written after reporter got job in one), suggested reforms, lots more, July-August, September 1979.

1-132 *Soho Weekly News* article reports on New York City's day care programs, which are built on a controversial "direct-lease" program, and how insurance companies and banks reap profits on day care; also discusses the criticisms from the state senator who had fostered it in 1969, June 1976.

DEATHS
See also:
hospitals
murder
suicide

1-2556 *Journal-Review* (Crawfordsville, Ind.) deals with the improper use of the term "Dead on Arrival" (DOA) on death certificates; its incorrect use had no effect on insurance, December 1983.

DEFENSE
See also:
Air Force
Army
Coast Guard
defense contracts
military
National Guard
Navy

1-4027 *The Washington Post's* "Defense Inc.," examines the hidden cost to America's economy and industrial might of sustained, heavy defense spending, Dec. 1, 1985.

1-4028 *The New Yorker* article on several problem areas in America's plans to ward off a nuclear attack, including communications problems with "the button," the system that would launch an American counter attack, and with the transportation system that is supposed to move the American government out of Washington, April 1, 1985.

1-2584 *Iron Age* reports the decline of the U.S. manufacturing base has seriously cripped manufacturing capacity in the event of a sustained, conventional war, October 1984.

1-296 *The Washington Monthly* article describes how the Pentagon's penchant for glamor and expense in weaponry results in better and less expensive alternatives getting overlooked; article compares "drone" aircraft projects by U.S. Army and Israeli company; Army project still on the drawing board and will cost over a billion dollars — Israeli project is cheap, it works and is already deployed, July-August 1984.

1-2599 *National Journal* article discloses an internal review of deficiencies in military readiness that was provided to Defense Secretary Caspar Weinberger; it mentions far more serious problems than Weinberger said existed, June 1984.

DEFENSE CONTRACTS
See also military

1-4029 *St. Louis Post-Dispatch* examines the widespread flaws in the military procurement system that allow spending scandals to occur, Dec. 15, 1985.

1-2942 *The Wall Street Journal* examines the problems of subcontractor payoffs to executives of military contractors, Nov. 14, 1985.

1-2941 *The Wall Street Journal* reports the Defense Department commonly gets defective or substandard products among the tons of spare parts it purchases daily, July 8, 1985.

1-560 *The Washington Monthly* runs article on semi-conductor companies taking shortcuts — from minor infractions to full-scale cheating on critical heat tests — in production of conductors for Defense Department contracts, February 1985.

1-2943 *Chicago Tribune* series examines the relationship between the defense industry and the government, focusing on problems of contract fraud, overcharges, kickbacks, and tax evasion among contractors, 1985.

1-2839 *St. Louis Post-Dispatch* reports on widespread wrongdoings and illegalities in the handling of defense contracts by General Dynamics Corp., 1984-1985.

1-2780 *United Press International* series details the controversy surrounding the General Dynamics Corp. and allegations of fraud on nuclear submarine contracts; reporters made extensive use of company and government documents, Dec. 17-21, 1984.

1-2862 *The Day* (New London, Conn.) articles cover the unfolding drama at General Dynamics submarine yard involving the company's attempts to defraud the Navy and questionable gifts made to Navy officers, July-December 1984.

1-2863 *Boston Magazine* publishes article on the Patriot Missile system built by the Raytheon Corp.; the missile cost the Army $6 billion and probably doesn't work; article uses government documents to show how inadequate testing, among other things, resulted in wasted money and inadequate defense, May 1984.

1-2061 *Common Cause* article says taxpayers are paying millions of dollars for defense contractors' public relations efforts, March/April 1984.

1-2137 *Common Cause* article, "Whistleblower," says Rockwell International fired the employee who reported the company illegally mischarged costs from the B-1 bomber to company contracts for the space shuttle; government and private industry interdependence questioned, March/April 1984.

1-2804 *Fort Worth Star-Telegram* issues reprint on inaction by both the government and Bell Helicopter in correcting design flaws in an Army helicopter, despite nearly 250 deaths because of the flaw, March 25-29, 1984.

1-2586 *National Journal* article details how the aerospace industry enlisted the support of top Pentagon officials to protect the existing, lucrative compensation packages for industry executives when the Air Force tried to clamp down on high executive salaries and fringe benefits, March 1984.

1-3076 *CBS News* series reports on disclosures of kickbacks, cost overruns, etc., at General Dynamics released by former executive Takis Veliotis, 1984.

1-2405 *The Arizona Daily Star* (Tucson) runs series on Hughes Aircraft Co.'s handling of Air Force contracts for the Maverick missile; construction takes 17 times as long as it is supposed to; Hughes has a "revolving door" policy of hiring retired officers who approved cost increases on the missile while in the military;

Hughes bills employees' idle hours to military weapons contracts, October-December, 1983.

1-2606 *The Daily Southeast News* (Los Angeles) runs series on million-dollar mischarges by Rockwell International to contracts for the space shuttle, October 1983.

1-2080 *Common Cause* article says government foots bill of defense contractors' lobbying because Department of Defense has no definition of lobbying, and therefore, no regulation that prevents lobbying costs from being included in government contracts, August 1981.

DENTISTS

1-3075 *WBRZ-TV* (Baton Rouge) airs investigation of Denta-Care, a prepaid dental plan, which operates outside of any regulation; its dentists have checkered pasts, there is evidence of insurance fraud, quality of care is poor and the plan is in financial difficulty, 1984.

1-3068 *KMGH-TV* (Denver) investigates silver amalgam controversy; allegation that common silver tooth filling might cause a host of serious diseases, some deadly, 1984.

1-3051 *ABC News 20/20* investigates the danger to children of an anesthetic drug, Nisentil, approved by the Food and Drug Administration and widely used in pediatric dentistry; the manufacturer, Hoffman-La Roche, promoted it despite knowledge it can paralyze, 1983.

DESEGREGATION
See:
discrimination
minorities

DEVELOPING NATIONS

1-4030 *The Christian Science Monitor* publishes series "The Neglected Resource: Women in the Developing World," on the condition of women in developing countries, Dec. 17-19, 1985.

DIOXIN
See chemicals

DIPLOMA MILLS
See also universities

1-73 *Arizona Republic* runs series in which investigative team created the phony but legitimate "University of the Republic," in order to test one academician's assumption that diploma mills are a "festering sore on the academic landscape," March 1983.

1-3221 *KAET-TV* (Tempe, Ariz.) reports on the Arizona College of Naturopathic Medicine, a school based on the philosophy of natural healing and where students don't have to attend classes, advertised courses are never taught and transcripts are routinely forged; the school is licensed by the state of Arizona, April 18 and 25, 1980.

1-203 *The Kansas City Times* shows Missouri and three other states have no laws regulating degree mills, and have become havens for these mail-order businesses, April 1977.

DISABILITY AND RETIREMENT PLANS
See pensions

DISCRIMINATION
See also:
minorities
redlining

1-728 *Dallas Morning News* in-depth series, "Separate and Unequal," finds illegal segregation pervades the nation's subsidized housing with blacks getting lower quality housing than whites, February 1985.

1-2725 *Asbury Park (N.J.) Press* runs story by two teams of reporters — one white and one black — posing as apartment hunters; found outright discrimination against the blacks despite painstaking efforts to eliminate differences between the teams other than race, Dec. 30, 1984.

1-2730 *The Miami Herald* articles make use of a computerized study of Dade Circuit Court's jury system and find that, contrary to charges of being unfair and discriminatory against blacks, the system is actually racially balanced, July 15, 1984.

1-2754 *Philadelphia Daily News* series concerns systematic discrimination by Atlantic City casinos against blacks; series finds that casino-bound buses are allowed to make few stops in most black neighborhoods in Philadelphia and other Eastern cities, April 25-26, 1984.

1-354 *The Cbhicago Reporter* does article on the history of a west Chicago suburb that has gerrymandered and enlarged schools to stay segregated, despite a growing black population, April 1984.

1-2840 *The Miami Herald* reprints series explaining reasons for the isolation of the black community in Dade County; placement of a new interstate highway, rental discrimination, education system discrimination, etc., Nov. 27-Dec. 3, 1983.

1-2087 *Detroit News* article finds that though blacks wield greater power than at any time in American history, some black leaders fear certain white power groups skew the system in favor of whites; some fear racial persecution and criticism aimed at black leaders, July 1983.

1-2620 *The San Francisco Bay Guardian* article says that city's fire department's strength and agility exam inherently discriminates against women, March 1983.

1-3251 *WSB Radio* (Atlanta) looks at integration in the nation's cities; finds segregation has actually increased in some areas and concludes that, for many major cities such as Atlanta, school desegregation is not a reality, March 7, 1983.

1-2287 *The Record* (Hackensack, N.J.) finds racial discrimination exists in funeral arrangements, especially in burial sites, July 1981.

1-514 *Gannett News Service* reprint, "Equality: America's Unfinished Business," interviewed American blacks for their perspective on American society, 1981.

1-408 *Evening Independent* (St. Petersburg) article shows how that city's realtors segregate the community through unfair housing practices, February 1979.

1-308 *The Record* (Hackensack, N.J.) tests real estate agents for discrimination and finds blacks are shown fewer homes in fewer neighborhoods, etc., January 1979.

1-3194 *KDKA-TV* (Pittsburgh) examines the employment agency industry and finds that agencies and employers practice subtle forms of discrimination in screening applicants, 1979.
1-2627 *The Clarion-Ledger* (Jackson, Miss.) series investigates broad question of justice in racially hostile Northern Mississippi; discusses racially motivated murders, resurgence of the Klu Klux Klan, quality of law enforcement, and harsh economic realities that both whites and blacks face, December 1978.

DIVESTITURE

1-2689 *Columbia (Mo.) Daily Tribune* publishes article on the debate over South African investment by the University of Missouri, June 9, 1985.

DOCTORS

See also:
abortion
Army
cancer
hospitals
medicine
military

1-2158 *The Milwaukee Journal* article explains how Wisconsin doctors who had had their licenses revoked for wrongdoing managed to get them back, April 3, 1985.
1-2805 *The Plain Dealer* (Cleveland) examination reveals the Ohio Medical Board, which is charged with overseeing doctors in the state, has an appalling record of protecting the reputations and livelihoods of the state's medical outlaws instead of the public, April 7-13, 1985.
1-2842 *The Plain Dealer* (Cleveland) looks into the past performance of a doctor charged with deliberately poisoning several Illinois people; years earlier, while he was at Ohio State University Hospital, there were reports of misconduct but the university did not inform law enforcement officials; OSU botched its investigation of the doctor, January-April 1985.
1-2002 *Philadelphia Daily News* publishes series on the failure of the Pennsylvania Medical Board to keep incompetent doctors from practicing, Feb. 19-22, 1985.
1-283 *The Kansas City Star* does articles on an incompetent surgeon; 60 percent of the women whose breasts he removed did not have cancer; he also had a terrible record on breast implants; inadequacy of the Kansas Board of Healing Arts, February 1985.
1-3116 *WCCO-TV* (Minneapolis) reports of sexual abuse of young psychiatric patients by doctors at a private hospital and the failure of the Minnesota Board of Medical Examiners to properly police doctors, October-December 1984.
1-3087 *WKBW-TV* (Buffalo) series on the inadequacies of New York's system of investigating medical misconduct by doctors centers on a Buffalo doctor with a particularly poor record who is still in practice, November 1984.
1-227 *Roanoke Times and World-News* five-part series uses disciplinary records, state Freedom of Information Act, court documents and interviews to show the Virginia Board of Medicine ineffective in protecting the public from incompetent and/or unethical physicians, Oct. 6-10, 1984.

1-2858 *The Virginian-Pilot* (Norfolk) articles expose deceptive and illegal practices at an abortion clinic where a doctor was performing abortions on women who were not pregnant; reporter and colleagues submitted to exams at the clinic and were told they were pregnant when they weren't, July-September 1984.

1-3081 *KAKE-TV* (Wichita) series looks at problem of bad doctors—alcoholics, incompetents and the failure of good doctors to report on the bad, as well as the difficulty of disciplining doctors, June 1984.

1-2600 *Boston Magazine* article uses one couple's journey from the delivery room to the courts to tell the story of the growing incidence of malpractice in obstetrics and the state's neglect in disciplining doctors, June 1984.

1-2846 *KPRC-TV* (Houston) details numerous cases of anesthesia mistakes that often killed or severely injured patients in Houston hopsitals; mistakes are often covered up by altering medical records, May 9-12, 1984.

1-2841 *Detroit Free Press* series examines Michigan's system of dealing with bad physicians; each of the 205 doctors who came before the Michigan Board of Medicine on formal charges from 1977 through 1982 was studied, April 1-8, 1984.

1-3103 *WHA-TV* (Madison) tells the tale of an incompetent doctor with 12 malpractice cases, his faked death and the failure of Wisconsin's Medical Examining Board, 1984.

1-585 *Tampa Tribune* runs articles on how more than 100 people purchased phony medical degrees from two Dominican Republic medical schools, 1984.

1-2592 *The Plain Dealer* (Cleveland) series investigates practices of Dr. Richard M. Levin, pioneer in surrogate parenting; series finds he runs a slipshod operation, has various legal problems and ethical improprieties, November 1983.

1-2609 *Ypsilanti (Mich.) Press* investigates area doctors who prescribed addictive drugs to patients who didn't need them, October 1983.

1-2424 *Asbury Park (N.J.) Press* runs series on the growing number of New Jersey physicians with drug and alcohol problems, doctors who are abusing their prescriptions privileges and dealing in drugs, August 1983.

1-2598 *Phoenix Gazette* examines state's system of policing doctors, finds state does little to prevent dangerous doctors from practicing medicine, 1983.

1-2218 *The Courier-Journal* (Louisville) series, "Nobody's Watching," finds Kentucky Medical Licensure Board a paper tiger; board made little effort to find dangerous doctors, forgets about the few cases it initiated, doctors allowed to keep licenses after going to prison, etc., July 1982.

1-3286 *WBZ-TV* (Boston) looks at the "other" drug pusher — the doctor, Feb. 19, March 4-5, 1982.

1-2332 *The Record* (Hackensack, N.J.) series, "Dangerous Doctors," looks at how incompetent doctors are protected by fears of lawsuits from hospitals and fellow doctors, the ability to move from one state to another and the failures of New Jersey's policing of doctors, April 1981.

1-3323 *KING-TV* (Seattle) airs series on problems in the Washington system of disciplining bad doctors, Sept. 29-Oct. 6, 1980.

1-3322 *WISN-TV* (Milwaukee) in-depth series examines gross deficiencies in the Wisconsin Medical Examining Board, May 19-June 10, 1980.

1-761 *The Record* (Hackensack, N.J.) traces the less-than-sterling records of two physicians who made a bundle of money performing unnecessary surgery on

Medicaid patients and dispensing ineffective experimental cancer cures, June 1980.

1-3160 *KNXT-TV* (Los Angeles) investigates the illegal medical practice of Robert Bennett, who performs chemical face peels for exorbitant fees, 1980.

1-261 *The Courier-Journal* (Louisville) uses Medicare records to make detailed comparison of doctors' fees; charges vary widely for same services, October 1979.

1-827 *Las Vegas Sun* runs articles on "gross malpractice" of a Nevada osteopathic physician who performed cosmetic surgery despite insufficient training, July 1979.

1-265 *The Des Moines Register* finds Iowa board of medical examiners doesn't discipline drug-addicted or alcoholic physicians, October 1977.

1-304 *The Record* (Hackensack, N.J.) runs article on improprieties of a New Jersey acupuncturist, 1974.

DRAFT
See military

DRUG ABUSE
See also:
drugs
sports

1-2944 *The Montgomery County (Md.) Sentinel* sends a reporter undercover to high schools to determine how easy it is to buy drugs, Oct. 3, 1985.

1-2755 *Philadelphia Daily News* publishes series on drug trafficking in Philadelphia and how it has affected life in the city; series shows how both law enforcement efforts and drug treatment programs are haphazard and ineffective, Oct. 22-29, 1984.

1-95 *Columbia (Mo.) Missourian* interviews with drug and alcohol users, dealers, producers, police, scholars and counselors give insight into drug scene in college town, April 1984.

1-2692 *Daily Camera* (Boulder, Colo.) series on cocaine use in Boulder presents legal and medical facts on the problem and asks the community its views on cocaine abuse and what can be done about it, March 18-21, 1984.

1-3014 *WBRZ-TV* (Baton Rouge) airs documentary on the widespread use of cocaine among doctors, lawyers, professional and business people and the lack of prosecution by the district attorney, 1983.

1-2179 *The Detroit News* investigates the death of a woman who was given so many free drugs under Medicaid program that she died from them, finds 178 Medicaid drug-related deaths in 21-month period, July 1982.

1-2098 *Mother Jones* article, "How AT&T's Workers are Drugged, Bugged and Coming Unplugged," looks at AT&T's management techniques, August 1981.

1-499 *Soho Weekly News* illustrates the dramatic growth of heroin abuse and addiction among artists, musicians, and other creative people, May 1980.

1-706 *Independent Journal* (Marin County, Calif.) runs series on the widespread use of cocaine in the San Francisco area and its fallout, including overdose deaths, robberies, burglaries, money laundering and other crimes, May 1980.

1-243 *Kearney (Neb.) Daily Hub* series looks at drug abuse in local public schools, January-February 1979.

DRUG DEALERS
See also:
drug abuse
drugs
drug smuggling

1-3325 *WOTV-TV* (Grand Rapids, Mich.) airs series on the cocaine trade in that city, Feb. 16-20, 1981.

1-3324 *WVUE-TV* (New Orleans) airs two series on that city's illegal drug world, 1980.

1-266 *The Miami Herald* inside story on multi-agency sting operation to net drug dealers illustrates how law enforcement does and doesn't work, May 1979.

DRUG SMUGGLING
See also:
drug abuse
drug dealers
drugs

1-4031 *The Wall Street Journal* reports on how the airlines combat drug smuggling on their planes, Dec. 18, 1985.

1-2845 *The Wall Street Journal* article describes "drug diversion," a highly profitable practice where companies buy excess drugs from someone other than the manufacturer, typically a non-profit hospital, and then resell them; some drug diverters encourage hospitals to order more drugs than they need, and set up phony charities to buy drugs cheap, Aug. 6, 1985.

1-2806 *The Houston Post* series, "Drug War: A Report from the Front," examines the cocaine trade from its origin in South America, smuggling route into the United States, distribution here and the troubles it causes, Jan. 16-Feb. 10, 1985.

1-2720 *The Times* (Gainesville, Ga.) goes into the background of three ex-lawmen who all quit their jobs when their department instituted a policy of giving lie-detector tests to weed out officers involved in drug smuggling, 1984.

1-258 *The Miami Herald* shows drug-related graft in the Bahamas goes all the way from the police to Parliament; uses records, wide range of sources to trace the corruption, September 1984.

1-2662 *Fort Myers (Fla.) News-Press* runs articles on involvement by members of county sheriff's department in drug smuggling operations; reporter uses many public documents, including bill of sale filed with Federal Aviation Administration of a plane sold by sheriff deputy to known smuggler — this is apparently what sparked the investigation, June-October 1984.

1-3105 *WGRZ-TV* (Buffalo) series reports Customs and Immigration Service agents are helping smuggle drugs (and people) into the United States from Canada, September 1984.

1-160 *Family Weekly* tells how Cuban Navy bases are being used to smuggle Colombian cocaine into the United States; Fidel Castro and fugitive American financier Robert Vesco are involved, April 29, 1984.

1-2060 *Richmond Times-Dispatch* runs article on the use of Amtrak to transport cocaine from Florida to the northeastern United States; questions why so many arrests are made in one town, April 1984.

1-741 *Tropic* (The Miami Herald) article shows how Cuban government and military officials help Colombian drug smugglers get drugs into Florida, Nov. 20, 1983.

1-3053 *ABC News Close-Up,* "The Cocaine Cartel," examines the 12 Colombian crime families that manage the cocaine trade in the United States, 1983.

1-2505 *Fort Lauderdale News and Sun-Sentinel* does series of investigations into links between drug smuggling and prominent sports figures, including National Football League players, offshore powerboat racers and car racers, June 1982.

1-2385 *St. Petersburg Times* describes drug smuggling into Dixie County, a rural, Florida county, where drugs are the leading business, 1981.

1-705 *The Evening Tribune* (San Diego) does article on the investigation of a drug smuggling ring that involved two Bakersfield, Calif., associates of Billy Carter, October 1980.

1-490 *The Journal-Bulletin* (Providence) takes first-hand look at drug traffic into the United States from Colombia, June 1980.

1-403 *KTVI-TV* (St. Louis) exposes a hundred-million dollar drug-smuggling ring headquartered in that city whose members are suspected of committing bribery and contract killings, June 1980.

1-498 *The Tribune* (San Diego) article looks at marijuana trade and forecasts dramatic increases in Colombian smuggling, May 1980.

1-555 *Roanoke (Va.) Times and World-News* series investigates drug-trafficking network in the Southeast and Montgomery County, Va., involving businessmen and public officials, April 1980.

1-2300 *The Miami Herald* documents the impact of the marijuana smuggling trade in Key West; finds corruption of law enforcement, breakdown of the justice system and use of drugs by county prosecutor; series also looks at the economic impact of huge infusions of illicit cash, March 1980.

1-91 *Fort Lauderdale News* explores legitimate businesses that cater to drug smugglers' needs, January 1980.

1-48 *Newsday* (Long Island) finds New York organized crime trading guns for drugs in Latin America, October 1979.

1-809 *New Florida* runs article on probe into cocaine queen Libia Cardona.

DRUGS

See also:
drug abuse
drug dealers
drug smuggling
Food and Drug Administration
police
prisons

1-4032 *Los Angeles Times* runs series, "The 'Plant of Plants,'" on Latin America's cocaine industry, Dec. 1, 1985.

1-2945 *Columbia Journalism Review* looks at how the media promote the "miracles" of new drugs on the market and overlook their potentially harmful side effects, July/August 1985.

1-829 *St. Louis Post-Dispatch* articles say O'Neal, Jones & Feldman Inc. ordered the manufacture of a drug despite being told it could "kill a few infants;" marketed the product as a nutritional supplement instead of as a drug to avoid government approval regulations and was still seeking information about proper dosage of the drug three weeks after infant deaths associated with the drug were reported to the firm, March 1985.

1-3108 *WPVI-TV* (Philadelphia) report finds sloppy waste disposal practices at city-run health centers allow children to get at discarded syringes and hypodermic needles, October, 1984.

1-258 *The Miami Herald* shows drug-related graft in the Bahamas goes all the way from the police to Parliament; uses records, wide range of sources to trace the corruption, Sept. 23-28, 1984.

1-2844 *Reader's Digest* article details how Bulgaria trades guns to Middle Eastern nations for drugs that it then sells in the West, November 1983.

1-2843 *Newsweek* article looks at the problem of people using drugs on the job, Aug. 22, 1983.

1-2004 *Fort Lauderdale News and Sun-Sentinel* runs series on the problems created by the federal government's policy of using methadone to halt heroin addiction, June 1983.

1-3005 *WBBM-TV* (Chicago) airs investigation of the two prescription drugs that when taken together make a cheap substitute for heroin; doctors, pharmacists and clinics are using professional status to deal the drugs, billing Medicaid for thousands of dollars, 1983.

1-3028 *WZZM-TV* (Grand Rapids) airs series on a doctor who runs a "one-man prescription mill," pushing prescriptions for profit, 1983.

1-3051 *ABC News 20/20* investigates danger to children of an anesthetic drug, Nisentil, approved by the Food and Drug Administration and widely used in pediatric dentistry; the manufacturer, Hoffman-La Roche, promoted it despite knowledge it can paralyze, 1983.

1-2095 *Gannett News Service* reprint, "War on Drugs: A Domestic Vietnam," finds American battle against drugs a disaster; overview of drug policy says there is inadequate legislation, underfunding, bad management, lax judges and politically spawned policies, December 1982.

1-3304 *KTVI-TV* (St. Louis) series reports on the marijuana-growing business in Missouri, Sept. 28-30, 1982.

1-3305 *KTHV-TV* (Little Rock) series reports on the marijuana-growing business in Arkansas, September 1982.

1-2203 *The Denver Post* articles indicate chief narcotics agent of Colorado's Organized Crime Strike Force was on the payroll of Michael Howard, editor of the Rocky Mountain News and a cocaine addict; also, reports of drug use at the Rocky Mountain News, 1982.

1-2339 *Newsday* (Long Island) series, "Hazards for Export," documents the double standards by which many U.S. firms operate abroad in ways that would not be allowed at home, including firms marketing drugs banned in the United States, December 1981.

1-2096 *The Miami Herald* series looks at the failures of America's war on drugs; looks at drug agents, informants, courts, etc., November 1981.

1-2164 *The Arizona Daily Star* (Tucson) articles say Arizona Narcotics Strike Force parlayed a couple of glamorous drug busts into larger, much more expensive role for itself; money was spent lavishly and role shifted from law enforcement to public relations; director ran his own personal domain, March and May 1981.

1-2384 *Buffalo Evening News* investigation of the prescription drug black market tells where drugs come from and how they are distributed, April 1981.

1-717 *The Chronicle-Telegram* (Elyria, Ohio) series investigates violations of proper medical procedure that occurred at a 24-hour doctor's clinic at which licensed physicians and unlicensed practitioners prescribed massive amounts of drugs to patients and undercover reporters; series resulted in a grand jury investigation, June 1980.

1-777 *Quad-City Times* (Davenport, Iowa) reporter goes undercover for series presenting an overview of drugs in Quad-Cities, June 1980.

1-2323 *Mother Jones* describes how Benedictin, a drug prescribed to pregnant women for nausea, may have caused thousands of Thalidomide-like birth defects; reports of this in the files of Richardson-Merrell, the drug's manufacturer, and the Food and Drug Adminisrtration may have been ignored by both concerns, allowing widespread use to continue, 1980.

1-663 *The Village Voice* article examines the abuses in the U.S.-subsidized drug war in Mexico known as "Operation Condor," which includes systematic brutality, corruption and human rights abuses, June 1979.

1-2146 *Willamette Week* (Portland) runs article on Eli Lilly & Co.'s marketing of a "new" drug; article says Lilly introduced new drug, which is essentially the same as the one it is to replace, because its patent is running out, which means doctors could prescribe cheaper generic drugs as a substitute; Lilly also doubled price of new version, February 1979.

1-395 *The Daily Olympian* (Olympia, Wash.) story gives chronology of a major drug bust, November 1978.

1-113 *The Miami Herald* shows how pharmacies are collecting windfall profits on state generic drug law, designed to save consumers money, August 1978.

1-360 *The New York Times* article says paraquat-laced marijuana is less prevalent and less contaminated than earlier reported, August 1978.

1-416 *KSL-TV* (Salt Lake City) airs investigation of that city's role as the distribution center for the eastern U.S. heroin market, July 1978.

1-2815 *WHA-TV* (Madison) reports on the possible link of Benedictin, an antinauseant used to treat morning sickness, and birth defects.

DRUNK DRIVING

1-2956 *The Hartford (Conn.) Courant* magazine focuses on Connecticut's counseling programs for drunken drivers, Oct. 6, 1985.

1-2764 *Atlanta Journal and Constitution* article lists the loopholes in Georgia's drunk-driving law that allowed offenders to avoid penalties; series resulted in state action to close the loopholes, Oct. 21, 1984.

1-30-91 *WXYZ-TV* (Detroit) series shows how repeat drunk drivers manage to stay on the road; how one drunk driver managed a double driving identity that slipped by police, January 1984.

1-3030 *WCCO-TV* (Minneapolis) airs series on drunk driving and the leniency of prosecution and judges, November 1983.

1-2120 *WJAR-TV* (Providence) uses a computer analysis of drunk-driving cases throughout the state to report on the ineffectiveness of Rhode Island drunk-driving law; profiles the drunk driver and reports on breathalyzer controversy and the effectiveness of individual police departments in dealing with drunk drivers, October 1982.

1-80 *Beaver County (Pa.) Times* shows how few drunk drivers are charged or sentenced, and the county coroner's role in that problem, June 1982.

1-529 *The News & Leader* (Springfield, Mo.) reports on the unwillingness of local prosecutors and juries to clamp down on drunk drivers, even repeat offenders, April 1982.

1-2276 *The Charleston (W.Va.) Gazette* exposes lax enforcement against drunk drivers through series "Licensed to Kill," February 1981.

1-477 *Newsday* (Long Island) series, "Drunk Driving: The Dismal Record," finds drunk drivers are treated leniently; drunk driving treated as a social problem, instead of a criminal one, June 1980.

1-396 *Quad-City Times* (Davenport, Iowa) uses computer to analyze handling of drunk driving arrests in Scott County; study reveals only 55 percent lose their licenses when 90 percent should have, April 1979.

1-2139 *The Charleston (W.Va.) Gazette* series finds enforcement of drunk driving law lax in the state capital, most drunk driving charges reduced, October 1974.

1-370 *The Wenatchee (Wash.) World* series on the handling of drunk driving cases in north central Washington finds judges too lenient, November 1973.

ECONOMY

1-217 *The Texas Observer* looks at the effect of Reagonomics on Texas, August 1984.

1-2022 *The Wall Street Journal* special section takes in-depth look at international debt crisis, June 1984.

1-171 *Minneapolis Star and Tribune* publishes comprehensive overview of Minnesota's economy and economic outlook, April 1984.

1-2377 *The Orlando Sentinel* special section, "Florida's Shame," looks at present and future growth in the state and effects of Florida's continuing development, April 1984.

1-2494 *Telegraph Herald* (Dubuque, Iowa) special section, "Dubuque's Economy: Changing Direction, Changing Shape," examines the city's troubled economy, September 1983.

1-2271 *Gannett News Service* studies the Midwest's economy in decline; collapse of the region's economy, the political quick-fix attitude, coping with change and the future, December 1982.

EDUCATION
See also:
schools
teachers
universities

2973 *The San Francisco Bay Guardian* reports on the controversies surrounding former San Francisco Superintendent Bob Alioto; also looks at city's two teacher's unions, Nov. 20, 1985.

1-4033 *APF Reporter* publishes article on the racist beliefs of the inventor of the Scholastic Aptitude Test, Carl Campbell Brigham, Winter 1985.

1-275 *The News Chief* (Winter Haven, Fla.) runs series on problems of policing the teaching profession; failure of teacher screening, poor handling of misconduct cases, September 1984.

1-649 *WTVH-TV* (Syracuse) reports on how a Board of Cooperative Educational Services instructor used student labor to build several homes for relatives, March 12-15, 1984.

1-2407 *The Star-Ledger* (Newark, N.J.) does series on how state education officials mismanaged, misused and diverted millions of dollars in federal education aid, January 1983.

1-209 *The Miami Herald* runs overview of Florida public education; issues and trends, 1983.

1-2099 *The Clarion Ledger* (Jackson, Miss.) issues reprint on the 1982 legislative battle over education reforms in Mississippi; state had one of worst education systems in the country, December 1982.

1-778 *Macon (Ga.) Telegraph and News* looks at the lucrative and federally unregulated private special education field, after exploring local controversy, November 1980.

1-821 *New Jersey Monthly* does in-depth article on how the Educational Testing Service covered up its own findings that scores on its tests could be lifted by coaching, March 1979.

ELDERLY
See also:
dance studios
housing
insurance
Medicaid
Medicare
nursing homes

1-2963 *The Pittsburgh Press* issues reprint highlighting the problems in Pennsylvania's state licensing laws and programs for personal care homes for the elderly, March 1985.

1-2634 *Buffalo News* does series on the problems created by the move toward home health care, which is unlicensed and unregulated for the elderly; among the problems: patient abuse, robbery and neglect, March 1983.

1-463 *New Jersey Monthly* does article on troubles faced by residents of a large, exclusive planned retirement community when new owners took control, November 1980.

1-3136 *KPNX-TV* (Phoenix) looks at insurance fraud against the elderly, 1980.
1-812 *Chicago Tribune* issues reprint "Growing Old in America," on problems faced by the elderly, October 1978.
1-347 *Quad-City Times* (Davenport, Iowa) runs articles on insurance salesmen who say they are representatives of a senior citizens organization to sell nursing home coverage to its members August-October 1978.

ELECTIONS
See also politicians
1-172 *The Wall Street Journal* finds post-Watergate election finance loopholes allow politicians to get around limits of campaign contributions, July 1984.
1-2008 *Los Angeles Times* describes changes in nature, makeup and distribution of American electorate that is altering the nature of politics and the outcome of elections, December 1983.
1-2546 *Telegraph Herald* (Dubuque, Iowa) examines voter turnout among school district employees in an effort to examine the problem of voter apathy, September 1983.
1-3015 *WLS-TV* (Chicago) series investigates how illegal aliens acquire voter registration cards and purchase social security cards from government employees; also, employers taking advantage of illegal alien employees, 1983.
1-2615 *Delaware (Pa.) Daily Times* investigation uncovers evidence that powerful county Republican leaders rigged a Democratic primary election, paid off candidates and then tried to cover it up, 1983.
1-487 *Augusta Chronicle* reports that two major changes in state election procedures and one proposed change violated the Voting Rights Act of 1965, which requires that proposed changes be cleared by the Justice Department, September 1980.
1-645 *The Eunice (La.) Gazette* uncovers evidence of illegal voting practices in St. Landry Parish; nine people were indicted for voting fraud after state and federal authorities investigated the allegations, October 1977-December 1979.
1-3196 *WAFB-TV* (Baton Rouge) investigates charges of vote fraud in St. Helms Parish, where, as in many Louisiana parishes, votes are brought and sold, 1979.

ELECTRIC UTILITIES
See public utilities

EMBEZZLEMENT
See also loans
241 *Philadelphia Magazine* gives an up-to-date dossier on the last 10 years of Robert Vesco's life, and tells story of John Lewis, the Philadelphia attorney who has doggedly pursued him, January 1983.

EMERGENCY MEDICAL SERVICES
See also:
ambulances
hospitals
1-2962 *The Wasington Monthly* looks at the trauma center in the Cook County Hospital in Chicago; also examines other trauma centers, November 1985.

1-2960 *The Pittsburgh Press* issues reprint of series on trauma and the problems of emergency medical care in southwestern Pennsylvania, Feb. 10-14, 1985.

1-2038 *Roanoke (Va.) Times & World News* shows Roanoke's antiquated volunteer rescue squad system does not consistently provide speed necessary to save lives, April 1983.

1-2207 *New Jersey Monthly* article says state's ineffective ambulance system unnecessarily loses a thousand lives a year; instructors abuse power to certify their friends in emergency training, EMS workers mistreat patients, November 1979.

EMPLOYMENT
See job training

ENDANGERED SPECIES
1-2661 *Fort Myers (Fla.) News-Press* article tells story of a Seminole Indian indicted for shooting a rare Florida panther; reporter treats questions of Indian sovereignty and endangered species designation, Dec. 9, 1984.

ENERGY
See also:
coal
gasoline
natural gas
nuclear energy
oil
public utilities
synthetic fuels

1-51 *The Philadelphia Inquirer* publishes series on energy anarchy, December 1980.

1-142 *The Washington Monthly* finds the "energy crisis" is really an oil pricing crisis; examines oil and coal industries, 1980.

1-402 *The Denver Post* issues reprint on the energy industry builders who are changing Denver's destiny, August 1977.

ENVIRONMENT
See also:
acid rain
agriculture
air pollution
automobiles
carcinogens
chemicals
hazardous substances
toxic wastes
water pollution
waste treatment systems

1-2959 *TWA Ambassador* presents "A Layman's Guide to Modern Menaces," which include overpopulation, soil erosion, deforestation, the greenhouse effect, ozone, acid rain and toxic waste, October 1985.

1-2905 *The Courier-Journal* (Louisville) devotes an entire magazine to an examination of indoor pollution in Kentucky and Southern Indiana; the paper examines national studies and runs thousands of tests on indoor air, drinking water and food in homes and businesses across the region, Sept. 15, 1985.

1-2957 *The Wall Street Journal* describes the frustrations and dangers Environmental Protection Agency officials encounter when they try to enforce environmental policies, January 1985.

1-2758 *The Reporter Dispatch* (White Plains, N.Y.) covers a controversy involving a county garbage-burning plant that initially exceeded federal emission limits; reporters look into the steps taken behind the scenes by county officials and the EPA to raise the pollution limits, November-December 1984.

1-3096 *CBS News* reports on the failure of the Environmental Protection Agency to inform the public of the danger of radon exposure, which comes from radium in the soil, December 1984.

1-2957 *United Press International* investigates the Environmental Protection Agency controversy; allegations of wrongdoing by top agency administrators, including their subversion of agency's role, 1983.

1-556 *The Oregonian* (Portland) issues special report on the Mount St. Helens eruption — its prediction and its impact on the region's environment and people, October 1980.

1-2273 *The Ledger* (Lakeland, Fla.) does series on Polk County pollution, more than half of which comes from phosphate chemical fertilizer complexes; EPA says many of the pollutants are hazardous to health; so do people living near some of the industrial plants; industry denies any hazard, June 1980.

1-88 *The Capital Times* (Madison) says National Research Council report on Seafarer, a Navy communications network, whitewashed environmental hazards, February 1978.

1-419 *The Register-Guard* (Eugene, Ore.) series looks at the problem of loss of jobs versus the environment in the closing of a Weyerhauser pulp mill in Everett, Wash., January 1972.

1-2097 *Gannett News Service* reprint, "Selling Our Natural Resources: The Watt Legacy," says the Reagan administration's zeal to bolster commercial production from federal lands is sacrificing other important values.

ENVIRONMENTAL PROTECTION AGENCY (EPA)
See environment

ESPIONAGE
See also Central Intelligence Agency

1-2847 *The Wall Street Journal* reports on Francesco Pazienza, a highly placed Italian political operator and spy with contacts in many governments who was put out in the cold, August 7-8, 1985.

1-30 *The Register* (Orange County, Calif.) runs series on the activities and death of Edward Lee Cooperman, a California State University scientist who was an operative for Vietnam, December 1984.

1-2581 *San Diego Magazine* article describes increasing Soviet spy activity in and around San Diego due to the area's high-tech industry and large military complex, 1984.

1-3022 *WMAQ-TV* (Chicago) series investigates how KGB-sponsored Polish spies have infiltrated Chicago, discredited Polish individuals, stolen industrial secrets and trailed citizens, 1983.

ESTATES
1-2278 *The Wall Street Journal* article details the rising misuse of estates by the conservators charged with overseeing them; conservators are rarely prosecuted for misusing estate money, July 15, 1985.

EVANGELISM
See also:
cults
religion
1-2785 *The Charlotte Observer* article is about a Charlotte-based television ministry known as "PTL" whose leaders spent more than a half-million dollars on expensive cars and real estate in California while pleading for donations from viewers to keep the ministry going, Oct. 5, 1984.
1-549 *Pittsburgh Post-Gazette* runs article on "The Way," an evangelical church whose questionable religious status and dubious financial statements are under investigation by the Ohio IRS, July 1980.
1-2155 *The Charleston (W.Va.) Gazette* series, "Gospel Millions," reports the millions of dollars raised through evangelical broadcasts and promotions is often misused; also, related articles by the same reporter, September 1979.

EXPORTS
1-1-5 *The Kansas City Star* reports on how a former U.S. soldier managed to obtain secret high-tech weapons components from U.S. manufacturers and illegally export them, July 7, 1985.
1-610 *Industrial Research and Development* shows U.S. high-tech sales to the Soviet Union have enabled the Soviets to build awesome war machine, July 1980.

EXTRADITION
1-184 *The Wall Street Journal* shows governors' extradition decisions vary radically; there is indication that politics enters into some decisions, May 1984.

FARMERS HOME ADMINISTRATION (FMHA)
See also agriculture
1-511 *Bakersfield Californian* series looks at the collapse of Tex-Cal Land Management Inc., which received more than $50 million in FmHA loans; why did

FmHA lend Tex-Cal so much? What happened to the money? Who was behind Tex-Cal? May 1985.

1-2489 *Gannett News Service* reprint finds Farmers Home Administration lending millions to the rich and politically well-connected; as a result, whole regional farm economies are nearing bankruptcy, December 1983.

1-2027 *Bakersfield Californian* runs series on Tex-Cal's (FmHA's largest borrower) internal fights for control of company, illegal diversion of funds, July 1983.

1-744 *The Tulsa Tribune* series examines waste, mismanagement and violations of agency rules that resulted in a history of bad loans by the Oklahoma FmHA, June 1980.

1-251 *Sun-Times* (Chicago) shows political concerns cause FmHA to crumble under pressure to underwrite financially shaky ventures; millions in tax dollars wasted, June 1980.

FARMING
See agriculture

FEDERAL AVIATION ADMINISTRATION (FAA)
See also air traffic controllers

1-2537 *The Wall Street Journal* investigates the allegation that J. Lynn Helms (chief of Federal Aviation Administration in December 1983), while president of Piper Aircraft Corp., tried to keep the FAA from finding out about alleged safety defects in one of the company's planes, December 1983.

1-552 *The Tribune* (Oakland, Calif.) article uses Federal Aviation Administration documents to examine controller errors and violations of regulations that contributed to the death of four Bay area residents in plane crash, August 1980.

FEDERAL BUREAU OF INVESTIGATION (FBI)
See also police

1-2940 *The Wall Street Journal* examines cases in which undercover FBI agents suffer from psychological problems resulting from their assignments, Nov. 4, 1985.

1-3300 *ABC News Closeup* presents in-depth look at J. Edgar Hoover, June 3, 1982.

1-2040 *Gannett News Service* reprint, "Abscam: The Scandal Within The Scandal," investigates the conduct of the Justice Department in the Abscam investigations; evidence that an innocent man was knowingly indicted was withheld, videotapes altered, etc., 1982.

1-483 *Camden (N.J.) Courier Post* details the workings of "Operation Kingfish," the FBI's elaborate attempt to bring millionaire fugitive Robert Vesco to U.S. jurisdiction, May 1980.

1-841 *Jacksonville Journal* runs articles on problems with a flamboyant FBI informant and a federal probe of white-collar crime in Jacksonville, 1980.

1-437 *The Indianapolis Star* runs series on racketeering among local teamsters and the involvement of local police and politicians; series details the FBI's examination of the crime network and the agency's failure to prosecute those involved, January 1979.

FEDERAL GOVERNMENT
See also:
Congress
foreign policy
lawyers
regulation
specific federal agencies, by name

1-4034 *The New Yorker* article tells of the negotiations betwen Chrysler and the federal government over a bailout of the troubled auto-maker and the controversy over an equity kicker in the final agreement, Jan. 7, 1985.

1-436 *The Wall Street Journal* article examines the practice of federal officials briefing investor groups about government policy and future government actions behind closed doors, January 1985.

1-2037 *Fortune* shows H. Ross Perot is banking on federal government mega-contracts to make his Electronic Data Systems Inc. the leader in computer services industry, October 1983.

1-2076 *The Kansas City Star* article finds abuses in use of Intergovernmental Personnel Act, which was designed to strengthen coordination between federal government and state and local governments by letting them borrow employees; instead program has been used to get rid of unwanted federal bureaucrats; assignments often have little connection to department's programs and goals, March 1982.

1-538 *Dayton Journal-Herald* finds members of the Reagan Cabinet and their aides went against a presidential order forbidding office redecorating and spent thousands of dollars on upgrading their personal quarters, August 1981.

1-537 *The Washington Post* runs series on federal contracting: a documented saga of squandered funds, conflicts of interests, sweetheart deals, June 1980.

1-189 *The Kansas City Times* undercover series details waste and inefficiency at Kansas City regional Health, Education and Welfare office — and the resulting fallout from the series, December 1979.

1-765 *Federal Times* exposes neglect, mismanagement, bureaucratic empire-building and slush fund in General Services Administration-run National Archives, April-December 1979.

FEDERAL RESERVE BOARD
See also banks

1-623 *Gannett News Service* demystifies one of the country's most powerful, least understood institutions and examines its current policies and controversies surrounding them, 1981.

FIRE DEPARTMENT
See also:
arson
cigarettes

1-731 *The Daily Herald* (Arlington Heights, Ill.), follows up the fire that destroyed the Arlington Park Race Track, examines the track's fire inspection records; finds hundreds of violations which should have kept the park from opening; the state racing board ignored its own inspection rules and failed to monitor Illinois's tracks, Aug. 6 and 11, 1985.

1-2810 *The Hartford Courant* investigation finds Connecticut's fire protection system deeply flawed: inspections never take place, fire code is rarely enforced, fire marshals cannot meet requirements of state fire law, June 20, 1985.

1-2811 *New Haven Register* issues reprint on fire code violations that contributed to a devastating apartment fire in East Haven, the inability of East Haven to inspect buildings and a fire inspector who doesn't do much inspecting, June 1985.

1-2086 *The Miami Herald* article finds a combination of decayed hotels for the elderly, a thinly stretched fire department and a city government that has allowed violations has weakened protection offered by Miami's fire safety code, May 1984.

1-2414 *The Register* (Orange County, Calif.) investigation, "Deadly Smoke," shows how the cancer rate among firefighters is rising dramatically because of the use of synthetic materials in buildings; also, the danger to firefighters of toxic chemical spills, December 1983.

1-2379 *St. Louis Post-Dispatch* reports that the chief of a St. Louis County fire protection district intercepted and cashed checks payable to the district, 1983.

1-2322 *Quad-City Times* (Davenport, Iowa) looks at the Bettendorf, Iowa, volunteer fire department; finds that equipment is located in the wrong part of town, the department often responds too slowly on nights and weekends, and there are lax work and training standards for the volunteers, May 1982.

1-2387 *St. Louis Post-Dispatch* investigation of St. Charles Fire District finds lax safety standards, conflicts of interests and nepotism in the district's financial dealings, 1982.

1-3150 *WDTN-TV* (Dayton) investigates the aftermath of a fatal fire at the Cambridge, Ohio, Holiday Inn and uncovers serious problems with fire safety and inspection protection, January-February and December 1980.

1-691 *The Fairpress* (Norwalk, Conn.) runs article on problems within Westport's fire department that range from inadequate training of firefighters to falsification of credentials by the deputy fire chief, September 1979.

1-221 *The Daily Breeze* (Torrance, Calif.) runs investigation of computerized fire and police dispatching system plagued with problems that result in reduced service to public, July 1979.

1-418 *KSL-TV* (Salt Lake City) looks at inadequacies in the training program and the lack of fitness of firefighters in the Salt Lake County Fire Department, September 1978.

FOOD
See also:
agriculture
foreign aid
inspections

1-3092 *WSMV-TV* (Nashville) airs series on how a meat-packing plant that was a chronic violator of federal sanitation standards continued to operate because of the government's poor inspection and enforcement system, August 1984.

1-2420 *Asbury Park (N.J.) Press* series traced illegal "bootleg" clamming network, which takes clams from polluted waters closed to clamming by the state; inadequacies of state enforcement, October 1983.

1-2246 *The Kansas City Times* series examines the meat industry; articles include disclosure of numerous violations by inspectors, safety hazards faced by workers, growing pains of meat packing cities, giants in the meat industry, May 1982.

1-47 *Newsday* (Long Island) shows organized crime infiltrates greater New York fish distribution industry, May 1981.

1-3326 *KSL-TV* (Salt Lake City) series describes a bait-and-switch operation used by a local meat supply outlet, Feb. 9-12, 1981.

1-715 *The Record* (Hackensack, N.J.) examines how organized crime has penetrated the Midwestern cheese-producing industry and the northern New Jersey pizzeria business, October 1980.

1-814 *Mesa (Ariz.) Tribune* runs series on how state meat inspectors ignore shoddy practices in meat plants; conflicts of interests in the State Livestock Sanitary Board, 1979.

1-3223 *WRC-TV* (Washington, D.C.) reports on rip-offs by bulk meat retailers who use bait-and-switch tactics around the country, costing consumers $2 billion a year, 1979.

1-3214 *WBZ-TV* (Boston) finds lax enforcement of quality standards and inspector conflicts of interests throughout the Massachusetts supermarket monitoring program, 1979.

1-433 *The Minneapolis Tribune* does series on how billions of dollars worth of food are wasted due to food industry inefficiencies, errors and competition, November 1978.

1-210 *The Miami Herald* finds organized crime infiltrates bagel business through Bagel Nosh restaurant chain, June 1977.

1-42 *Newsday* (Long Island) shows organized crime heavily involved in food we buy at local stores, September 1971.

FOOD AND DRUG ADMINISTRATION (FDA)
See also food

1-2849 *Common Cause* reveals serious problems with the government's approval of the sugar substitute NutraSweet, July/August 1984.

1-3079 *CBS News* series reports on questions surrounding NutraSweet, the sugar substitute: possible connection to insomnia, nervous disturbances, brain seizures and the sweetener's controversial route to FDA approval, 1984.

1-2089 *The Plain Dealer* (Cleveland) runs series of articles about the FDA under the Reagan administration; agency sides with industry and is steadily dismantling public safety programs that have been years in the making, July 1983.

1-206 *Foundation for National Progress and Center for Investigative Reporting* look at Food and Drug Administration and the breakdown of regulatory system for testing drugs and consumer products; also examines FDA's performance regarding 31 of the largest U.S. pharmaceutical and pesticide companies, reliance on phony test results, 1982.

1-2178 *Mother Jones* article says millions of women in Third World countries are being injected with Depro-Provera, a contraceptive, under U.S.-sponsored programs, despite it being linked to tumors in animals; the FDA refuses to approve it for domestic use, November 1981.

1-2146 *Willamette Week* (Portland) publishes article on Eli Lilly & Co.'s marketing of a "new" drug; article says Lilly introduced drug which is essentially same as one it is to replace because its patent is running out; Lilly doubled price of new version, February 1979.

1-3231 *KOIN-TV* (Portland) looks at FDA delays in approving DMSO, a drug that has been shown to be effective in treating a variety of medical ailments, 1979.

1-3222 *WRC-TV* (Washington) reports the dangers of using Neo-Mull-Soy and Cho-Fru baby formulas, each of which has been shown to cause long-term health effects; report points to poor FDA nutritional controls for baby formulas, 1979.

FOOD STAMPS
See welfare

FOREIGN AID
See also:
charities
contraceptives

1-2790 *The Christian Science Monitor* series details the political and social impact of humanitarian aid from the U.S. Agency for International Development on the country of El Salvador; reporter found that food aid was sometimes used as weapon of war and that AID was funding the sterilization of thousands of Salvadoran women, often without their consent, Ja. 10-13, 1984.

1-2047 *The Kansas City Times* prints special report, "The Hunger Game, Our Wasted Foreign Aid," on the failure of American programs to combat world hunger, October 1983.

1-2201 *The Miami Herald* series, "Haiti: Foreign Aid Gone Awry," finds U.S. food aid is being smuggled out of Haiti and sold in Miami groceries and peddled in Haiti's black markets; corruption in the Haitian government is a major obstacle to development, December 1982.

1-198 *The Philadelphia Inquirer* reprint, "Feeding on the Hungry," deals with problems of relief effort to East Africa; half of relief food is stolen before it gets to the hungry; Somali government uses its hungry people to fatten its economy; aid is creating long-term dependence, September 1981.

FOREIGN CORPORATIONS
See business

FOREIGN POLICY
See also individual countries, by name

1-816 *APF Reporter* does article on the suppression of dissent in the State Department and the declining use of the department's "dissent channel" because of fear of retribution, Winter 1985.

1-270 *The New York Review of Books* investigates the circumstances that led to the shooting down of Korean Airlines flight 007, April 1985.

1-758 *Bulletin of the Atomic Scientists* runs article on how U.S. officials concealed the histories of Nazi scientists to bring them into the country to work on military and space projects, April 1985.

1-2799 *Newsday* (Long Island) article examines what went wrong during the period of American military presence in Beirut that caused it to be a major foreign policy defeat, April 8, 1984.

1-2441 *Albuquerque Journal* series looks into Salvadoran death squads; who belongs to them, their ties with political leaders in El Salvador and their ideological connections with the United States, December 1983.

1-2590 *The New York Times* articles disclose Reagan administration's plans for major escalation of American military involvement in Central America, 1983.

1-205 *The New Republic* investigation traces massive corporate lobbying campaign — orchestrated by Saudi Arabia and its American agents — that resulted in sale of AWACs to Saudi Arabia, despite Senate opposition, February 1982.

1-2338 *Newsday* (Long Island) series, "Hazards for Export," documents the double standard by which many U.S. firms operate abroad in ways that would not be allowed at home; firms market drugs banned in the United States, subject foreign workers to occupational hazards and pollute the environment, December 1981.

1-2255 *Los Angeles Herald Examiner* series says State Department suppressed fact that the lone civilian taken hostage in Iran was a drug dealer with Mafia connections who had gone to post-revolutionary Iran as the representative of a company owned by the family of the Shah, March 1981.

1-2280 *Washington Journalism Review* day-by-day account of how the ABC broadcast — "America Held Hostage: The Secret Negotiations" — was put together, 1981.

1-460 *Politics Today* article says the Carter administration helped undermine the Shah of Iran by cutting off long-standing system of CIA subsidies to Iran's Islamic groups, March/April 1980.

1-832 *Santa Fe Reporter* series includes information on the U.S. Office of Public Safety, which was linked to torture of political prisoners in countries around the world, 1980.

1-3235 *WABC-TV* (New York) "America Held Hostage: The Secret Negotiations" offers a detailed look at secret discussions involving dozens of world leaders and diplomats in their efforts to free American hostages, 1980.

1-333 *St. Louis Post-Dispatch* runs article on how Central Data Corp. skirted a presidential embargo on the sale of certain goods to South Africa, March 1979.

1-26 *Newsday* (Long Island) reporter shows difference between public and private U.S. foreign policy during Carter years, August 1978.

FOSTER CARE
See also juveniles
1-2348 *The Kansas City Star* reprint looks at widespread problems in Missouri's foster care system, June 1985.

1-89 *The Evening Tribune* (San Diego) publishes series about structure of foster home system, April 1972.

FRAUD
See also:
clinics
repair ripoffs
securities
telephones sales, fraudulent
1-773 *The Sun-Tattler* (Broward County, Fla.) does series on phony professionals

— from supposed building contractors and insurance agents to phony doctors, April 1985.

1-2452 *The Wall Street Journal* runs story on con-man Bernard Striar, who has led at least five different lives and been wanted by the FBI for nearly 20 years for the successful frauds he pulls off, December 1984.

1-3109 *WOKR-TV* (Rochester, N.Y.) investigates a chemical distributorship scam that promises people the opportunity to make thousands of dollars delivering chemicals to area customers, October 1984.

1-2792 *The Record* (Hackensack, N.J.) series covers a large discount-diamond retailer in New York City that used deceptive sales techniques, including phony appraisals and fake discount sales, June 3-5, 1984.

1-3061 *KCTV-TV* (Kansas City) series investigates Gypsy palm-reading and fortune-telling ring that bilked people out of thousands of dollars, 1984.

1-3126 *WCBS-TV* (New York) airs series on phony therapists, psychologists, etc., and the ease with which anyone can claim to be a therapist and then steal from and abuse patients, 1984.

1-4035 *Texas Monthly* article details the exploits of Eugene Anderson, a big league con artist who claims his "chemical reactor block" can change water into fuel, September 1983.

1-3029 *WZZM-TV* (Grand Rapids) airs investigation of Auston's Modeling & Finishing Schools, which operate nationally; the company promises successful careers, no matter how clients look, September 1983.

1-2167 *The Indianapolis Star* article says scam promoters are telling people they can make money raising rabbits and selling meat and furs; says $2,000 investment can make up to $30,000, then sell rabbits at ridiculous prices, August 1983.

1-2633 *Minneapolis Star and Tribune* runs articles from investigation of two operators who claimed they had struck oil; articles expose past shady dealing of the two, January-April 1983.

1-3010 *WSMV-TV* (Nashville) airs series on a sophisticated multi-million dollar coal investment fraud that was copied nationally, 1983.

1-3054 *WTVJ-TV* (Miami) investigates scam wherein companies sell "recommendations" about federal government leases, 1983.

1-2472 *The Evening Gazette* (Worcester, Mass.) investigates Sunshine Publications Inc., a rental listing operation, for fraudulent business practices — selling useless apartment lists, October 1982.

1-2512 *Fort Lauderdale News and Sun-Sentinel* investigates David H. Ruch, a prominent and influential businessman; reveals that he never obtained a college degree, never worked for the CIA, never was a commercial pilot and never had entered the U.S. military — all of which he claimed, April 1982.

1-573 *The Honolulu Star-Bulletin* does series on the Paradise Palms, a time-share apartment rental business that engages in questionable business practices including misrepresentations, March-July 1981.

1-3354 *WISN-TV* (Milwaukee) airs stories on problems with a firm that, for a fee, promotes entertainment shows for charity groups; shady backgrounds of the promoters, bills left unpaid, 1980.

1-543 *Albany Times-Union* looks into the disappearance of a successful self-made businessman; finds he is a con man who owes at least $1 million, October 1979.

1-144 *Arlington Heights (Ill.) Herald* says growing earthworms at home turns out not to be a great way to make money; World Wide Worms, Inc. investigated by state and federal government on fraud charges, Oct. 18, 1978.

1-415 *The Record* (Hackensack, N.J.) series looks at a New Jersey radio preacher, Clinton White, who solicits funds from audiences to invest in pyramid schemes, September 1978.

1-99 *The Christian Science Monitor* shows magazine subscription rip-offs persist despite attempts to regulate, Nov. 14, 1977.

1-149 *Arlington Heights (Ill.) Herald* reports on federal investigation of false billings seeking payment for advertising in apparently fictitious business directories sent to tool companies, February 1976.

FUNERAL HOMES

1-237 *Spokesman-Review* (Spokane, Wash.) looks into allegations of unethical practices at Spokane funeral home, provides overview of laws for funeral industry, June 1984.

GAMBLING

See also:
animal abuse
charities
organized crime
police

1-4036 *Chicago Tribune* runs article on fears that organized crime will soon move in on unregulated, big-money Indian bingo, Dec. 1, 1985.

1-412 *The Tulsa Tribune* publishes series on the bingo industry in Oklahoma, a state with lax bingo regulation; how promoters rig the odds and cheat both players and the charities they represent; Indian bingo operates outside any regulation, allowing professionals to run their operations, May 1985.

1-467 *The Washington Monthly* runs article on the unregulated Indian bingo business, questionable "bingo management" firms and Mafia connections; other ways Indians use autonomy to reap profits, May 1985.

1-3062 *Channel 8* (Dallas) investigates charity bingo promoters; promoters are creating questionable charities to make money, offering charities money to use their licenses, siphoning off money from charities, October 1984.

1-182 *St. Petersburg Evening Independent* takes an in-depth look at the inability of Florida to enforce laws for parimutuel gambling in general and greyhound racing in particular, November 1983-May 1984.

1-2754 *Philadelphia Daily News* series concerns systematic discrimination by Atlantic City casinos against blacks who want to gamble; series finds that casino-bound buses are allowed to make few stops in most black neighborhoods in Philadelphia and other Eastern cities, April 25-26, 1984.

1-314 *The Pittsburgh Press* series offers some background on the numbers racket and police attempts to crack it, March 1984.

1-2495 *Times Leader* (Wilkes-Barre, Pa.) series looks at proposals to bring gambling to the Pocono Mountains; also, a look at the records of areas with legal gambling, September 1983.

1-2449 *Akron Beacon Journal* series details the financial troubles and racing violations at Northfield Harness Park, Ohio's largest harness track, June 1983.

1-2406 *The Oregonian* (Portland) runs series on how professional gamblers posed as ministers and charitable operators to take advantage of Oregon's social gambling laws, March 1983.

1-3019 *WTOL-TV* (Toledo) series invstigates illegalities in that city's bingo operations, 1983.

1-3039 *WBTV-TV* (Charlotte) investigation finds only a small fraction of bingo proceeds in Mecklenburg County goes to charity, most is diverted to professional bingo operators, 1983.

1-3069 *WOWT-TV* (Omaha) investigation of local charity bingo and pickle operations finds not all money is going to charity; they are paying outrageously high rents for halls and are illegally paying workers, 1983.

1-2286 *Channel 7* (Baltimore) examines Maryland's horse racing industry; the failure of the state racing commission to detect the widespread drugging of horses by trainers; trainers paying employees less than the minimum wage and failing to pay federal and state taxes; the racing industry's influence in the Maryland Legislature, Nov. 8-17, 1982.

1-3306 *News Seven* (Baltimore) series investigates Maryland's thoroughbred racing industry: drugged horses, lack of track security, the inadequacy of the state's system of drug enforcement, the cozy relationship between Maryland politicians and race industry leaders, Nov. 8-17, 1982.

1-2311 *Las Vegas Review-Journal* details how Nevada officials ignored years of substantiated evidence questioning the suitability of the David Funk family — linked with organized crime — to run a Nevada racetrack, February 1982.

1-659 *Rocky Mountain Business Journal* publishes article on Securities and Exchange Commission probe of American Leisure Corp., developers of an Atlantic City hotel-casino complex, May-June 1981.

1-2154 *Philadelphia Magazine* article looks at how amateur crooks fixed the Pennsylvania lottery and won $1 million; legal system worked out a deal in private to settle the case with least amount of embarrassment for state, March 1981.

1-3327 *WCCO-TV* (Minneapolis) series examines the operating techniques of organized professional bookmakers in the Twin Cities, Feb. 16-20, 1981.

1-3328 *WSMV-TV* (Nashville) airs series on that city's numbers racket, 1981.

1-801 *Arizona Republic* (Phoenix) does articles on improprieties in state's horseracing industry and failures of the Arizona Racing Commission, 1981.

1-842 *The Sun* (Baltimore) does articles on illegal amusement machine gambling (usually in taverns) and lax enforcement in Baltimore County; illegal financial links between amusement machine companies and tavern owners, March-November 1980.

1-519 *Erie (Pa.) Morning News* series investigates a drawing of the Pennsylvania lottery that some suspect was rigged, September 1980.

1-711 *Pasadena (Calif.) Star-News* series investigates illegal bookmaking activities at southern California race tracks and the failure of the California Horse Racing Board to investigate those activities, September 1980.

1-445 *Philadelphia Magazine* does article on organized crime's takeover of Atlantic City, April 1980.

1-654 *The Hartford Courant* follows up original investigation of Connecticut's jai alai industry; the series examines the connection of a Miami betting syndicate that fixes games, May-December 1979.

1-2070 *Reno Evening Gazette* and *Nevada State Journal* run series on Nevada gaming control and inability of state to control gambling industry, August 1979.

1-2458 *The Record* (Hackensack, N.J.) runs article on Bob Guccione, *Penthouse* founder, and his interests in Atlantic City; finds numerous links to the mob, both in his Atlantic City ventures and abroad, July 1979.

1-320 *The Hartford Courant* does article on Jimmy "The Greek" Snyder's gambling with bookmakers associated with some of the nation's leading mobsters; one sophisticated bookmaking operation works out of a Florida racetrack run by former FBI agents, April 1979.

1-3189 *Canadian Broadcasting Corp.* investigates Toronto organized crime connections in developing Atlantic City casinos, 1979.

1-202 *The Hartford Courant* runs series on unfolding scandal — including commercial bribery, player-fixing and handicap-fixing — in Connecticut's jai alai industry, May 1977-December 1978.

1-429 *Wenatchee (Wash.) World* article examines Seattle developers' attempts to co-opt public land for recreational and casino gambling uses in eastern Washington state, November 1977.

1-115 *The Washington Post* finds a lawyer used a job on a federal commission studying gambling laws to launch a career lobbying for Nevada casinos, February 1977.

1-289 *The Record* (Hackensack, N.J.) does article on visits of three gambling entrepreneurs with organized crime links to Atlantic City as it prepares for casino gambling, December 1976.

1-288 *The Record* (Hackensack, N.J.) article examines the corporate history of Resorts International, focusing on some questionable figures who have been associated with the company, October 1976.

1-36 *Newsday* (Long Island) finds charity gambling spreading on Long Island and the mob becoming involved, September 1976.

1-372 *The Daily Oklahoman* (Oklahoma City) reports that a major Las Vegas gambling figure with reported links to organized crime is operating two arcades in Oklahoma City, April-May 1975.

1-33 *Newsday* (Long Island) investigation ties crime boss to track takeover bid, December 1974.

GANGS

1-2530 *The Wall Street Journal* writes of the four big motorcycle gangs — Hell's Angels, Bandidos, Outlaws and Pagans — and law enforcement worries that they are becoming criminal syndicates akin to the Mafia, January 1984.

1-2518 *The Journal Gazette* (Fort Wayne, Ind.) reports that residents of a near-downtown Fort Wayne neighborhood fear that teenagers in the area were organized gangs for criminal activity; law enforcement officials disagreed with one another on the issue, July 1983.

1-2073 *The Charlotte Observer* series, "Biker Gangs: The New Mafia," finds organized crime more and more rooted in motorcycle gangs, particularly in the Carolinas; gangs are fighting for control of Charlotte, August 1981.

1-213 *San Jose Mercury-News* says the Hell's Angels seems to be taking over Bay Area industrial catering business; competitors victimized by arson, bombings and vandalism, June 1978.

GARBAGE
See refuse collection

GASOLINE
See also:
energy
natural gas

1-3123 *WCBS-TV* (New York) series reports on the pervasive problem of "bootleg gasoline" in New York; the use of inferior quality gasoline on which taxes have not been paid, 1984.

1-3027 *WTVH-TV* (Syracuse) finds that using ARCO gasoline, which contains methanol, can damage your car, 1983.

1-3023 *WCAU-TV* (Philadelphia) reports the methanol many small oil company and ARCO are using in their gasoline can seriously damage cars, 1983.

1-2140 *Newsday* (Long Island) does series on how gasoline retailers in New York state steal millions by not reporting gasoline tax collected from motorists; other tax evasion schemes, September 1981.

1-215 *Newsday* (Long Island) investigation finds that Carter administration and major oil firms had a heavy hand in causing and prolonging the gasoline shortage, and then blamed it all on Iran, 1979.

GENETIC ENGINEERING
1-319 *West (San Jose) Mercury News* article looks at "HGH," the hormone that causes humans to grow, now being made synthetically and about to be marketed to short people by Genentech Inc.; article questions when practicing medicine becomes engineering society; investigates the control of this, November 1984.

1-662 *Pacific News Service* article looks at the health and environmental risks associated with relaxing safety standards for recombinant DNA production.

GERM WARFARE
See chemicals

GRAND JURIES
See juries

GUNS
See:
handguns
weapons

HANDGUNS
1-443 *Regardie's* runs article on the Army's bidding process for the contract to supply its sidearms provides good background on U.S. handgun industry, May 1985.

1-2504 *Fort Lauderdale News and Sun-Sentinel* looks at the role of handguns in crime-ridden South Flroida, given that Florida maintains one of the loosest state weapons statutes in America; series includes experiences on several people whose lives were irrevocably changed by handguns, December 1982.

1-3257 *KTVH-TV* (Wichita) demonstrates how easy it is to buy a handgun in Wichita, 1982.

1-2274 *Herald-Telephone* (Bloomington, Ind.) looks at the proliferation of handguns in Bloomington and the state of Indiana; increase in violent crimes has led to record purchases of handguns in the area, November 1981.

1-2329 *Cox Newspapers* series, "Handguns in America," explores all aspects of gun use in crime, from legitimate gun industry to gun smuggling; computer analysis used to create profile of handguns likely to be used in crimes, 1981.

HANDICAPPED
See also automobiles

1-2583 *The Washington Times* series, "Baby Doe: The Politics of Death," reports the Justice Department and the Department of Health and Human Services have adopted a hands-off policy on prosecutions and even investigations into the questionable deaths of handicapped newborns, July 9-13, 1984.

1-2050 *Columbia (Mo.) Daly Tribune* runs article on controversy over firing of first blind deputy director of Missouri Bureau for the Blind; bureau charged he showed favoritism to a "radical blind group" and a blind training center, he says his philosophy differed from that of his boss, July 1984.

1-2850 *Conquest* (a monthly newsletter for the handicapped) looks at companies that advertise they employ the handicapped exclusively; questions their emphasis on hardship in their sales pitches, whether the companies could survive without the handicap pitch and their definitions of handicapped, October 1983.

1-665 *The Progressive* article looks into the wheelchair industry and how one California company has monopolized it, resulting in low quality, high prices for equipment and little design innovation, March 1979.

1-246 *WLS-TV* (Chicago) investigates neglect and abuse of handicapped children placed in nursing homes, January 1979.

HAZARDOUS SUBSTANCES

See also:
asbestos
carcinogens
chemicals
environment
refuse collection
toxic wastes

1-2800 *Newsday* (Long Island) reports on the Bhopal gas leak and its aftermath, goes into how it happened, whether it can happen elsewhere and what should be done to ensure that it doesn't, Dec. 9-31, 1984.

1-3095 *WHA-TV* (Madison) documentary reveals the inability of Wisconsin to enforce state regulations concerning the shipping of hazardous materials by truck; because so many state and federal agencies share responsibilities, and yet do not coordinate, programs accomplish little, October 1984.

1-2588 *Minneapolis Star and Tribune* issues reprint, "Toxic Harvest," on the health dangers to workers and consumers of fumigants used to rid grain of insects, Sept. 2-4, 1984.

1-2771 *The Leesburg (Fla.) Commercial* series on an Army air base that was used for testing and storing chemical weapons during World War II; after a local well-digger was burned when working at the site, reporter investigated the possibility that chemical weapons might still be buried there, July 13-16, 1984.

1-2749 *The Kansas City Star* series looks at EPA regulation of pentachlorophenol, a common wood preservative that contains dioxin, and finds the EPA did little to study its effects on users; series tracked some people afflicted from contact with the substance, June 3-5, 1984.

1-3071 *KOVR-TV* (Sacramento) reports on widespread illegal dumping of hazardous waste by automotive firms that generate waste, their failure to register with the state and poor regulation by the state; waste recycling companies are illegally handling chemicals, mixing them into recycled oil used on road, 1984.

1-3241 *WNRE Radio* (Circleville, Ohio) series investigates the legal, economic, social and environmental impact of a major hazardous waste incinerator in Circleville, May 12-Dec. 25, 1983.

1-2143 *60 Minutes* reports on the possible health risk of Chlordane, the pesticide used to kill termites, April 10, 1983.

1-79 *Newport Times-Herald* runs series on lead poisoning in tenements, April 1982.

1-2335 *St. Paul Dispatch* runs series on the dangers of exposure to formaldyhyde gas from products in the home such as particleboard and plywood, January 1982.

1-740 *Valley Advocate* (Amherst, Mass.) runs series on hazardous waste in western Massachusetts's Pioneer Valley — how much is produced and monitored, how dumping problems are ignored by oversight agencies, June 25, 1980.

1-714 *The Washington Star* article explains how the Arlington railroad yards are ill-equipped to handle hazardous waste accidents because of lack of water; yet the yards handle hazardous chemical traffic daily, March 1980.

1-2369 *Santa Barbara News-Press* says hazardous materials traffic was much greater than had been thought; a study of the dangers posed to Santa Barbara County by this traffic, May 1979.

HELL'S ANGELS
See gangs

HERBICIDES
See:
agriculture
chemicals

HEROIN
See drugs

HIGH SCHOOLS
See:
education
schools

HIGHWAY PATROL
See police

HIGHWAYS
See also:
public works
roads
1-2769 *Journal Tribune* (Biddeford, Maine) article shows how Maine State Police tampered with collection of speed data to conceal the state's poor record in enforcing the 55-mph speed limit, which is related to allocation of federal highway funds, Dec. 20, 1984.
1-2733 *St. Paul Pioneer Press-Dispatch* series uncovers irregularities in local land condemnation for highways; reporters found commissioners in one county directed millions of dollars in awards to their own real estate investment partners, resulting in inflated highway construction costs, August-September 1984.

HISPANICS
1-218 *San Jose Mercury-News* series gives overview of Mexican-Americans in the Southwest in general, San Jose specifically, Nov. 1-8, 1981.

HOMICIDE
See murder

HOMOSEXUALS
See also Acquired Immune Deficiency Syndrome
1-2563 *The Daily Chronicle* (Centralia, Wash.) looks at homosexuals in Lewis County — where they meet, how many there are, etc.; also examines the health and mental problems associated with being gay, November 1983.

HORSE RACING
See gambling

HOSPITALS
See also:
ambulances
army
asbestos
clinics
doctors
emergency medical services
medicine
mental hospitals
Veterans Administration

1-1948 *The Wall Street Journal* reports on how the nation's four giant for-profit hospital chains are restructuring their health-care systems, Oct. 10, 1985.

1-2808 *The Houston Post* investigation of a hospital set up as a public charity finds widespread improprieties by hospital officials, including insider and sweetheart deals, kickbacks, gambling trips and using estate property for personal entertainment, Jan. 13-May 4, 1985.

1-2668 *The Columbia (Mo.) Daily Tribune* runs series on mushrooming administrative costs of a county hospital due to excessive travel and entertainment charges by administrators; series led to resignation of some hospital administrators, Dec. 16-20, 1984.

1-2783 *The Denver Post* series following two deaths at a Denver hospital brought out evidence that they may have been caused by faulty anesthesia machines used in surgery; the series prompted a congressional investigation of unregulated medical devices and new rules for reporting such accidents to the FDA, August 1983-December 1984.

1-2669 *The Modesto (Calif.) Bee* does article concerning the death of a man who was transferred to different hospitals following a traffic accident because he was not insured and could not afford a $1,000 deposit at the first hospital, April 15, 1984.

1-2807 *The Houston Post* investigation of the Harris County Hospital District's plans to build a new hospital raises several conflicts of interests questions; plans to finance it by a hospital board member's bank without competitive bidding and a doctor payment system that favors another board member's university and costs the hospital an extra $4 million a year, 1984.

1-2103 *The Plain Dealer* (Cleveland) runs series probing hospitals in the city; topics include trustee conflicts of interests, violation of surgery safety rules by heart units, lack of regulation of heart units in Ohio, too many beds and expensive overstays in hospitals, June-December 1983.

1-2382 *Texas Monthly* article reconstructs events surrounding the deaths of several children in the care of licensed vocational nurse Genene Jones at a Texas hospital; failure of medical community to properly deal with a nurse who was murdering children, August 1983.

1-2501 *Columbia (Mo.) Daily Tribune* series examines what led to the decline of

86

the Ellis Fischel State Cancer Center and looks at what the future holds, May 29-June 5, 1983.

1-2605 *Birmingham Post-Herald* runs series on conflicts of interests between hospital board of directors and companies they control, May-June 1983.

1-2430 *Dayton Daily News* and *Journal Herald* series, "Hospital Wars," examines the continued rapid growth in the Dayton health care industry at a time of protracted economic recession and the implications for area residents, May 1983.

1-2152 *St. Louis Post-Dispatch* series finds hopsital costs 28 percent higher in the city than rest of country, wildly fluctuating costs to Medicare for the same operations, a new emphasis on sales drives by hospitals, May 1983.

1-2434 *United Press International* does series on long-standing improprieties, some of which led to patient deaths, at a California hospital; hospital's operating room death rate was more than three times the national average, March 1983.

1-3034 *KMOX-TV* (St. Louis) investigates St. Louis City Hospital and finds it expensive and poorly managed, 1983.

1-2456 *News-Star-World* (Monroe, La.) investigation into an accidental death at E.A. Conway Memorial Hospital reveals numerous hospital problems, including malfunctioning water filters in the dialysis unit that caused 15 deaths, 10-hour waits at the emergency room and more, all primarily due to the building and the budget, May 1982.

1-19 *The Sun* (San Bernardino, Calif.) finds inefficiency in San Bernardino county hospital trauma center may have led to deaths, March 1982.

1-2328 *Charleston (W.Va.) Gazette* series "Public Hospitals/Private Boards," and other articles examine the secrecy in the administration of public hospitals; reveals board of city-owned hospital that resisted giving financial data to the city officials spent lavishly on luxuries for itself, 1980-1982.

1-3131 *KUTV-TV* (Salt Lake City) finds Raleigh Hills alcoholic rehabilitation clinic charges exorbitant rates to vulnerable patients and often does not inform them of the cost of hospitalization, 1981.

1-494 *Taunton (Mass.) Daily Gazette* investigates a possible "mercy killing" of a woman by a deliberate overdose of morphine by three nurses, June-December 1980.

1-638 *Charleston (W.Va.) Gazette* series explores causes of high hospital rates in that state; finds excessive hospital construction, rivalry among hospitals and luxuries for hospital executives, May 1980.

1-2575 *Quad-City Times* (Davenport, Iowa) investigation into Davenport Osteopathic Hospital reveals that the hospital is in financial trouble; story also examines its surgical practices, which had come under criticism, April 1980.

1-86 *Call-Chronicle* (Allentown, Pa.) issues reprint on the battle between local business and religious leaders and the community over controversial decision to build a new hospital, July 1979.

1-2141 *Cleveland Press* series examines the quality of patient care at a 25-bed Ohio hopsital where several doctors and administrators face charges; Ohio is the only state that does not license hospitals, April 1979.

1-143 *The Courier-Journal* (Louisville) finds that two Humana hospitals made more gross profits in 1977 than eight other county hospitals combined, October 1978.

HOUSING
See also:
conflicts of interests
discrimination
mobile homes
real estate
slumlords
special districts

1-3044 *The Chicago Reporter* reports on widespread abuses in the allocation of subsidized housing intended for low- and moderate-income persons in suburban Chicago, September 1985.

1-4037 *Post-Bulletin* (Rochester, Minn.) in-depth series examines the ineffectiveness of the system of housing codes and its enforcement designed to protect renters, Sept. 7-13, 1985.

1-2809 *Detroit Free Press* series, "Slums and Money," traces deterioration of that city's housing caused by absentee landlords and failed government policies, June 16-20, 1985.

1-2964 *APF Reporter* runs article on how "tenant management" turned the run-down Washington housing project of Kenilworth into a well-kept development that no longer needs a federal operating subsidy, Spring 1985.

1-728 *Dallas Morning News* in-depth series, "Separate and Unequal," finds illegal segregation pervades the nation's subsidized housing, blacks getting lower quality housing than whites, February 1985.

1-2906 *The Journal-Bulletin* (Providence) runs detailed, computer-assisted investigation of the Rhode Island Housing and Mortgage Finance Corporation, a public bond-issuing agency set up by the state to help low- and moderate-income people find affordable housing; finds low-interest mortgages were issued to ineligible high-income people with political connections through a secret fund; the agency head grossly misspent agency money on luxurious travel and was tied to a bank that he allowed to break state rules to provide the low-interest mortgages, 1985.

1-2725 *Asbury Park (N.J.) Press* story with two teams of reporters — one white and one black — posing as apartment hunters finds outright discrimination against the blacks despite painstaking efforts to eliminate differences between the teams other than race, Dec. 30, 1984.

1-3084 *WTHR-TV* (Indianapolis) documentary investigates Indianapolis Housing Authority; many units uninhabitable; neglect, mismanagement allow supplies to be stolen and resold; waste and inefficiency among employees; segregation of employees, November 1984.

1-2688 *The Post-Standard* (Syracuse) surveillance finds most of that city's housing inspectors falsify work records so they can spend city time on personal activities or other jobs, Nov. 26-27, 1984.

1-2731 *The Miami Herald* series examines housing shortage for migrant farm workers in Belle Glade, Fla., where thousands live in run-down shacks; reporter found at least ten public officials owned slum property, Oct. 28-29, 1984.

1-2652 *The Standard-Times* (New Bedford, Mass.) runs series on problems in a low-income housing project designed to be model suburban project for poor; project deemed a failure due to poor planning, July 15-21, 1984.

1-2748 *The Kansas City Star* covers the misuse of public funds at a Kansas City housing project, including payments to a phony company for work that was never done; reporters used land records, loan agreements and work contracts to uncover the story, January-July 1984.

1-191 *APF Reporter* finds nation's public housing system crumbling as Reagan administration gives it the axe, Summer 1984.

1-2788 *The Washington Post* series on mismanagement at a D.C. housing development documents the misuse of millions of dollars in federal funds and how some city officials had work done on their own homes through the project, March 18-20, 1984.

1-2305 *Sunday Democrat and Chronicle* (Rochester, N.Y.) shows Rochester's low-income tenants are at the mercy of a system designed to protect them, with unsanitary and unsafe conditions; landlords, meanwhile, profit from weaknesses in the city's building code enforcement system, March 1983.

1-3181 *WBBM-TV* (Chicago) finds elevator servicing and maintenance in Chicago public housing is woefully inadequate and responsible for the death of at least one child, 1983.

1-3045 *KTVI-TV* (St. Louis) reports county building inspectors approved one of the most expensive housing developments in St. Louis County despite knowledge of many violations, 1983.

1-2375 *Akron Beacon Journal* examines the extensive involvement in the Akron Metropolitan Housing Authority by its former director, who is now its consultant, August 1982.

1-79 *Newport Times-Herald* series reports on lead poisoning in tenements, April 1982.

1-9 *Clearwater (Fla.) Sun* reports on misappropriation of public money in Florida housing authority, July 1981.

1-572 *The Kansas City Star* series on Haven Property Management documents investment schemes of a Kansas City slumlord, who invested more than $6 million from Oregon investors in sub-standard housing and in turn failed to provide services to residents, May-June 1981.

1-524 *New Castle (Pa.) News* does series on the decaying state of some city housing projects; the housing authority tolerates infestation, leaking pipes, clogged sewers, June 1980.

1-838 *The Sun* (Baltimore) series investigates inadequate housing in that city; topics include: inefficiency of the system, ease and manipulation of regulations by landlords and how landlords avoid prosecution, May 1980.

1-481 *Seattle Post-Intelligencer* series on corruption in Seattle Housing Authority programs finds housing projects incomplete, questionable loan practices, conflicts of interests, February 1980.

1-737 *Willamette Week* (Portland) article takes an in-depth look at housing in the Portland area, showing who owns substantial housing and how low-income housing developments have failed to address the poor's housing needs, 1980.

1-598 *The Bulletin* (Providence) runs series, "The Housing Game," on how Section 8 rent-subsidy program, designed to provide decent housing for the poor, is used to make enormous profits at little or no risk, September 1979.

1-567 *Fort Lauderdale News and Sun-Sentinel* looks at rental apartment finder services that employ bait-and-switch tactics and advertise rented apartments to unwitting clients who pay up-front for services, April-May 1979.

1-619 *The News-Sun* (Waukegan, Ill.) investigation finds houses rehabilitated with federal funds were sold to city hall officials and relatives of the housing chief who later sold houses for huge profits, January-February 1979.

1-504 *Charleston (W.Va.) Gazette-Mail* series examines living conditions and landlord problems student renters face in Morgantown, home of the University of West Virginia, February 1979.

1-3197 *WABC-TV* (New York) reports on the deplorable condition of proprietary houses for the needy in Long Beach; houses have become dumping grounds for the mentally ill, sick and poor aged; these people are often victims of sexual abuse, crime and suicide, 1979.

1-3186 *KYW-TV* (Philadelphia) finds the Gift Property Program, designed to turn abandoned houses over to the poor, was used by politicians to trade property for votes and by realtors to evade taxes, 1979.

1-15 *Detroit Free Press* shows con men in Detroit sell vacant homes that are actually owned by federal government, August 1974.

1-13 *Detroit Free Press* shows Detroit delinquent taxpayers lose homes for as little as $18 in back taxes, May 1971.

HOUSING AND URBAN DEVELOPMENT (HUD)

1-2945 *The Wall Street Journal* looks at Reagan administration on civil rights; explores fair housing problems and how the Department of Housing and Urban Development and the Department of Justice are dealing with them, Oct. 8, 1985.

1-2949 *Syracuse (N.Y.) Herald-Journal* reports that the Department of Housing and Urban Development is investigating Syracuse's Housing Authority for collecting subsidy payments for vacant apartments at the Hilltop housing project, April 1985.

1-733 *The Philadelphia Inquirer* issues reprint on how a Reagan administration HUD program designed to sell crumbling homes to private firms that would renovate them and sell them to the needy backfired, leaving the poor in lousy housing, the federal government out of millions of dollars, while speculators profited handsomely, January 1984.

1-2206 *Chicago* article examines the political activities that led HUD in 1982 to demand the resignation of the chairman of the Chicago Housing Authority; HUD originally intended to completely overhaul the Chicago agency, considered one of the worst-run in the country, July 1982.

ILLEGAL ALIENS
See also:
immigration
migrant labor
refugees

1-2593 *The Wall Street Journal* series includes problems faced by the U.S. Immigration and Naturalization Service in trying to keep illegal aliens out of the country; understaffing, poor record keeping, administrative confusion, conflicting purposes; also, the importance of illegal immigrants to the economy of the Southwest; a highly efficient underground employment system flourishes, May 1985.

1-2697 *Stockton (Calif.) Record* series investigates the work of the U.S. Border Patrol in California and the problems of undocumented workers in the San Joaquin Valley; reporter worked peach orchards to talk with workers about Border Patrol raids, February-April 1984.

1-3015 *WLS-TV* (Chicago) series investigates how illegal aliens acquire voter registration cards and purchase social security cards from government employees; also, employers taking advantage of illegal alien employees, 1983.

1-2224 *The Miami Herald* runs series, "The People Smugglers," on the smuggling of illegal aliens into the United States, one of the most dangerous and lucrative of the nation's illicit industries, December 1982.

1-3329 *WPLG-TV* (Miami) series on the smuggling of illegal aliens into Florida, Aug. 10-14, 1981.

1-2326 *Los Angeles Herald Examiner* series examines use of illegal aliens in California's garment industry and the labor and health code violations they face, January 1981.

1-232 *The Midland (Texas) Reporter-Telegram* series gives overview of illegal aliens, their impact on local economy, December 1978.

1-71 *Sun-Times* (Chicago) finds Nazi death camp guard who lied to get into the United States, August 1978.

1-328 *Fort Myers (Fla.) News-Press* does articles on a lawyer who, operating as the American Bureau of Citizenship, ripped off illegal aliens by charging them for help getting alien employment applications he knew would be denied, April 1978.

1-40 *Newsday* (Long Island) finds Mafia smuggles Sicilians into the United States, December 1970.

IMMIGRATION
See also:
illegal aliens
refugees

1-2904 *The Wall Street Journal* article reports on ethnic Albanian gangs, centered in New York and heavily involved in the heroin trade among other criminal activities; the new problems these gangs create for American law enforcement, Sept. 9, 1985.

1-3105 *WGRZ-TV* (Buffalo) series reports Customs and Immigration Service agents are helping smuggle drugs and people into the United States from Canada, September 1984.

1-2383 *Washingtonian* article looks at the effects of the influx of hundreds of thousands of Third World immigrants on the District of Columbia, May 1984.

1-2011 *San Diego Reader* tells how two Solidarity refugees escaped from Poland through use of forged documents, a paper company and bribes, February 1984.

1-153 *The Miami Herald* issues special sections, "The Cubans, a People Divided" and "The Cubans, a People Changed," December 1983.

1-3003 *WSOC-TV* (Charlotte) investigates sham marriages — foreigners taking

American spouses only to stay in the United States, and the marriage mills that help arrange such marriages, 1983.

INCOME TAX
See taxes

INDIANS
See:
gambling
Native Americans

INDUSTRIAL DEVELOPMENT BONDS
See:
bonds
special districts

INSPECTIONS
See also:
city government
county government
federal government
food
housing
state government

1-2812 *The Hartford Courant* runs special section on bridge inspections in Connecticut a year after a fatal bridge collapse; probe finds the state's revamped bridge inspection program marred by falsified records, wasted time, inconsistent performance and poor supervision; a model surveillance effort, June 24, 1984.

1-2066 *The Kansas City Star* investigation finds not one of 18 building inspectors followed reported the work he did; instead inspectors loaf; city spends less on building code enforcement despite pledge after Hyatt Regency Hotel disaster to beef up program, January 1983.

1-2594 *The Plain Dealer* (Cleveland) series, "Amusement Parks: The Safety Gap," says no one inspects Ohio's amusement parks; parks make concerted effort to keep accidents quiet and lobby to keep inspectors out, August 1983.

1-3004 *WSOC-TV* (Charlotte) follows county building inspectors on their rounds and finds many of them loaf for hours, 1983.

1-2204 *The Kansas City Star and Times* investigation, "The Hyatt Papers: Documentation of a Disaster," examines documents surrounding construction of the Hyatt Regency; indicates trouble signals were missed, contractor faced bankruptcy, skywalks were never inspected, October 1982.

1-2252 *Greenville (S.C.) Piedmont* does series on the failures of South Carolina's restaurant inspection program; state fails to revoke health permits even after series and repeated violations; state routinely neglected to follow up inspections, March 1982.

1-3267 *WJKW-TV* (Cleveland) investigation reveals payoffs and forged records in the city building department; violations were overlooked by inspectors in exchange for cash; one bribe was captured by a hidden camera, February 1982.

1-2247 *The Kansas City Times* examines Hyatt Regency disaster; finds earlier construction accidents, skywalk design changes, wiring problems; also, looks at city's inspections of construction, July 1981.

1-472 *Post-Bulletin* (Rochester, Minn.) series examines failure of carnival ride safety and inspections, July 1980.

INSURANCE
See also:
arson
automobiles
business
Medicaid
Medicare
organized crime
redlining

1-2947 *The Wall Street Journal* illustrates how inadequately some insurance companies police salesmen; focuses on estate conservation policies, Jan. 4, 1985.

1-2861 *The Evening Sun* (Baltimore) series looks at Blue Cross and Blue Shield health insurance corporations and their troubled relationship in the state of Maryland, Oct. 10-11, 1984.

1-2025 *The Denver Post* runs article on financial woes of Capitol Life, Colorado's largest life insurance company, May 1984.

1-267 *Knickerbocker News* (Albany) looks at redlining practices of Albany insurance companies, who deny fire and homeowner coverage to "undesirable neighborhoods," May 1984.

1-141 *American Banker* examines the "house of cards" insurance organization that forced the failure of two banks and the near failure of a third in Wyoming, South Dakota and Montana, August 1983.

1-3252 *WSB Radio* (Atlanta) looks at problem of lack of health insurance among the nation's unemployed, and extent of the problem in Atlanta, March 28, 1983.

1-3048 *WXYZ-TV* (Detroit) airs series on phony insurance agencies selling phony no-fault auto insurance policies; phony insurance certificates go undetected by the state; fraud going on for years but no law enforcement agency would act, 1983.

1-3180 *KCRG-TV* (Cedar Rapids) details an elaborate insurance scam in which Prudential salespeople sold policyholders additional insurance using the cash holdings of the first policies to pay for the second, thereby jeopardizing their original policies, 1983.

1-223 *The Evening Sun* (Baltimore) investigative series, which led to resignation of state insurance commissioner, uncovers serious abuses of power, February-December 1982.

1-2470 *Asbury Park (N.J.) Press* runc examination of insurance executive Jack Goepfert and the web of fraud in which he is accused of dealing; also looks at the FBI's investigation of him, October 1981.

1-672 *Sun-Times* (Chicago) runs series on a $3 billion-a-year auto accident swindle operation; reporters went undercover to examine the elaborate racket involving ambulance chasers, crooked lawyers, doctors and clinics conspiring to collect huge insurance sums, thereby raising insurance rates by as much as one-third, February 1980.

1-596 *The Indianapolis Star* series examines problems in insurance programs sold by auto dealers, February 1980.

1-3234 *WLS-TV* (Chicago) reports auto accident insurance swindling is a $3 billion-a-year business in which crooked lawyers, doctors and claimants conspire to defraud insurance companies; policyholders pay up to 30 percent more in premiums to cover these phony claims, 1980.

1-3136 *WXIA-TV* (Atlanta) looks at insurance fraud against the elderly, 1980.

1-3191 *KMOX-TV* (St. Louis) series on arson for profit focuses on how MFA Insurance of Columbia, Mo., used questionable practices to prove policyholders set fire to their houses, 1979.

1-347 *Quad-City Times* (Davenport, Iowa) runs articles on insurance salesmen who represent themselves as representatives of a senior citizens organization to sell nursing home coverage to members, 1978.

1-371 *The Daily Oklahoman* (Oklahoma City) story links an Oklahoma City-based insurance firm with organized crime figures purchasing controlling interest of the company, October-December 1975.

1-409 *Boston Herald American* series details how insurance commissioner appointed by former Gov. Ed King filed false financial disclosure statements.

INTERIOR, DEPARTMENT OF
1-32 *Sports Illustrated* two-part series details James Watt's policies, 1983.

INTERNAL REVENUE SERVICE (IRS)
See also:
nonprofit organizations
taxes

1-3067 *KMGH-TV* (Denver) investigation finds the IRS lied, cheated and stole from a businessman it tried to stick with phony tax fraud charges; federal prosecutors tried to blackmail several people in the case, 1984.

1-600 *The News World* (New York) discusses fear and loathing in the IRS; tactics of intimidation and regarding itself as being above the law, April 1980.

1-138 *The Clarion-Ledger* (Jackson, Miss.) reporter notes an unusual string of tax audits — 27 in all — of civil rights activists, October 1976.

INVESTMENTS
See:
bonds
fraud
securities

ISRAEL
See also:
foreign aid
foreign policy

1-2163 *The Nation* article indicates about 1,500 U.S. companies participated in the Arab boycott of Israel with the tacit encouragement of the Commerce Department, October 1983.

1-749 *The Philadelphia Inquirer* Pulitzer prize-winning series by Richard Ben

Kramer, "Report from the Mideast: A Human Drama," evokes the lives, politics, and cultural crossfire of the Mideast, March 1978.

JAILS
See prisons

JOB TRAINING
1-4056 *San Antonio Light* series finds officials at the Gary Job Corps Center, the nation's largest, let violence, racism, drug trafficking and prostitution exist and kept ghost students on the rolls in an attempt to keep a $20 million job corps contract, Sept. 15-17, 1985.

1-2508 *The Clarion-Ledger* (Jackson, Miss.) runs story on the handling of federal Comprehensive Employment and Training Act (CETA) funds in Mississippi; results show political handpicking to receive funds, dollars spent on impossible goals, and more, April 1979.

JUDGES
See also:
bail bondsmen
courts
criminal justice
juries
lawyers
trials

1-2974 *St. Louis Post-Dispatch* reports that a former Scott County circuit judge and his family were involved with drug trafficking and money laundering, Dec. 1, 1985.

1-2946 *TWA Ambassador* explores the New Right's efforts to throw out judges who are "too liberal" and replace them with conservatives, November 1985.

1-2711 *The Providence Journal-Bulletin* series delves into the background of state Supreme Court chief justice and finds the judge has extensive and long-standing ties to organized crime figures; reporters made use of public records and did physical surveillance, December 1984.

1-710 *The Pittsburgh Press* series details weaknesses in the oversight of state judicial conduct and the heavy influence of attorneys in financing judicial election campaigns, October 1984.

1-222 *Milwaukee Magazine* surveys, interviews trial lawyers on judging the judges, from the worst to the best, October 1984.

1-168 *Detroit Free Press* finds sex crime convictions bring disparate sentences depending on attitudes of judges, June 1984.

1-817 *The Plain Dealer* (Cleveland) examines increasingly powerful chief justice of Ohio Supreme Court; scrutinizes politicization of state's highest court, April 1984.

1-2596 *Tampa Tribune and Times* articles investigate two Florida circuit court judges for accepting bribes to reduce sentences and bails, February-December 1983.

1-2626 *The Clarion-Ledger* (Jackson, Miss.) series documents how defendants in a district justice court, which handles misdemeanor and small claims matters, were hauled in nights or weekends and forced to pay fines immediately or be jailed without the right to an attorney or a formal trial, October 1983.

1-2492 *The Daily Chronicle* (Centralia, Wash.) evaluates judges in Lewis County by surveying Bar Association members, October 1983.

1-2408 *Detroit Free Press* series studies all sentences for manslaughter in Michigan in 1982 and finds sentencing based more on judges' personal philosophies than on the crime, the killers or the victims, October 1983.

1-2106 *Richmond Times-Dispatch* study and research analysis of sentencing for criminal prosecutions in Virginia show widespread disparities across the state; newspaper analyzed 94 variables in each case, October 1983.

1-2604 *Oakland Press* (Pontiac, Mich.) investigation of county circuit court judge finds he has fathered nine children outside his marriage, May-October 1983.

1-2063 *The Tennessean* special report finds U.S. bankruptcy system in chaos because its judges are seeking status equal to federal district judges, who don't want bankruptcy judges as equals, August 1983.

1-2565 *Akron Beacon Journal* analysis of chief federal judge reveals he steered large sums of money to friends and relatives by way of lucrative court appointments, primarily through bankruptcy court; conflicts of interests arose repeatedly, April-July 1983.

1-45 *Newsday* (Long Island) finds Long Island judges consort with organized crime members; series also examines other aspects of Long Island judiciary that taint justice, February 1983.

1-2496 *The Times* (Gainesville, Ga.) articles look at the conduct of a state court judge who has been dismissing valid cases for certain individuals before they reach court, 1983.

1-3179 *WCCO-TV* (Minneapolis) finds judges in the Hennepin District Court don't use their summer schedule as it was intended — to allow time for judges to handle backlogged cases, 1983.

1-2248 *Cleveland Press* series finds pattern of personal favoritism, illegal conduct and improper manipulation of the law by judges in U.S. Bankruptcy Court in Cleveland, April 1982.

1-3272 *KSN-TV* (Wichita) finds judges lenient with criminals; lack of programs for those accused of crimes such as rape and child abuse when they are released, 1982.

1-843 *The Indianapolis Star* surveys 446 lawyers to rate the 50 judges in local, state and federal courts in Indianapolis, May 1981.

1-548 *Pittsburgh Post-Gazette* does series on how Pennsylvania's Supreme Court justices politicize the court by trying to defeat fellow judges in their re-election bids as well as promote their own hand-picked replacements, December 1980.

1-316 *Gannett News Service* issues reprint on politics of selection process for federal judiciary, February 1979.

1-3215 *WBZ-TV* (Boston) discloses the abuses of two district court judges who systematically manipulated court records and conducted personal business on court time, 1979.

1-239 *Charleston (W.Va.) Gazette* series critiques judges and court inequities, including disparate sentencing, especially for black defendants, March 1976-April 1978.

1-613 *Courier-Post* (Cherry Hill, N.J.) runs article in which municipal court lawyers rate the judges in three New Jersey counties, October 1977.

1-122 *Soho Weekly News* articles show how to buy a judgeship, importance of political connections within judiciary in New York City, 1976.

JURIES (including GRAND JURIES)
See also:
bail bondsmen
courts
judges
lawyers
trials

1-2730 *The Miami Herald* articles make use of a computerized study of Dade Circuit Court's jury system and finds that, contrary to charges of being unfair and discriminatory against blacks, the system is actually racially balanced, July 15, 1984.

1-3271 *ABC News 20/20* interviews key members of the Watergate trial grand jury 10 years later, June 17, 1982.

1-136 *Midland (Texas) Reporter Telegram* reports a grand jury investigation is sidetracked from questions of the civil rights of a murdered jail inmate when county district attorney attacks Texas attorney general and threatens libel suits against local media, July 1978.

JUSTICES OF THE PEACE
See judges

JUVENILES
See also:
adoption
child abuse
day care centers
drug abuse
foster care

1-2085 *The Wall Street Journal* article finds youths who join traveling magazine sales crews often work long hours, get little sleep, poor food, little money and face constant pressure from crew bosses, September 1984.

1-109 *Allentown (Pa.) Call-Chronicle* reports on problems with child-support; legal system snarled, April 22-May 1, 1984.

1-3129 *WHA-TV* (Madison) airs documentary on the growing problem of evasion of child support payments, 1983.

1-2506 *Los Angeles Times* details widespread financial exploitation of cast-off children in group homes; reveals the variety of schemes operators used to enrich themselves at the expense of the children's well-being, June 1982.

1-2342 *The New York Times* issues reprint on juvenile crime and the judicial and corrections system for juveniles, March 1982.

1-3330 *WIBW-TV* (Topeka) series looks into the workings of a rehabilitative facility for juvenile offenders: frequent runaways, the use of drugs at the facility, training of staff, the facility's effectiveness, Nov. 17-21, 1980.

1-545 *Albany Times-Union* series on St. Anne's Institute, a home for troubled girls, in which irregularities, including prolonged solitary confinement, were reported and ignored by the state and local bureaucracies, March 1980.

1-3167 *WWL-TV* (New Orleans) 23-part series on juvenile crime in that city shows how the police, courts and corrections system are woefully understaffed; the result is a revolving door for offenders, 1980.

1-3157 *WBBM-TV* (Chicago) reporter returns to Vietnam to examine the plight of children of mixed American and Vietnamese parentage and finds they are street people, panhandling and selling on the black market to survive, 1980.

1-2071 *Charleston (W.Va.) Gazette* series examines all aspects of juvenile crime and system of juvenile justice, November 1979.

1-753 *Arizona Daily Star* (Tucson) series looks at Vision Quest, a much-touted, profit-making program for "hard-core" juvenile offenders, and finds financial irregularities, questionable practices, April 1979.

1-3216 *WAST-TV* (Albany) series examines the Brookwood juvenile offender institution and the effects of tougher juvenile crime laws on residents of the institution, 1979.

KICKBACKS
See bribery

KU KLUX KLAN
1-2208 *Atlanta* article provides account and background of a Greensboro, N.C., shootout between members of the Community Workers Party and the Ku Klux Klan, April 1982.

1-582 *Clearwater (Fla.) Sun* runs article on the misuse of Klan funds by David Duke, national leader of the Ku Klux Klan, 1979.

LABOR UNIONS
See also:
migrant labor
organized crime
1-2759 *The Reporter Dispatch* (White Plains, N.Y.) looks into the excess labor

costs on the Metro-North Commuter Railroad; reporter found one conductor on the line made more than the railroad president, Nov. 12, 1984.

1-2042 *The Progressive* finds organized labor turns its back on migrant farm workers, August 1984.

1-2776 *The Pittsburgh Press* looks into the rise and fall of a union local of food and commercial workers; reporters found the local's extravagant expenditures, chaotic management practices and bitter political rivalry led to the organization's near-collapse, April 22-24, 1984.

1-2954 *St. Louis Post-Dispatch* looks at the union hierarchy of the International Typographical Union and why it stripped its first full-time vice president of his job, Feb. 19, 1984.

1-2132 *Mother Jones* does article on Lyndon LaRouche's U.S. Labor Party and its penetration of the Teamsters and indoctrination of its members in right-wing politics; article finds this success has provided a "frightening foothold" into the labor movement, January 1982.

1-2243 *The Plain Dealer* (Cleveland) runs articles on Teamster leader Jackie Presser getting cash kickbacks from a public relations firm that did business with the Teamsters, August 1981.

1-2079 *Common Cause* article, "The Reagan Teamster Connection," discusses Reagan's appeals to, and deals with, the union, June 1981.

1-848 *The Sun* (Baltimore) runs investigation of interference of United Mine Workers in the National Bank of Washington (which it controls), questionable loans that resulted and links to Maryland political figures, May 1980.

1-496 *The Des Moines Register* exposes a phony new labor newspaper — Mid-States Labor News — which apparently used ads from phone books and articles from a labor press service it doesn't subscribe to and carried a phony union label, March 1980.

1-595 *The Indianapolis Star* article says a racketeer receives payments from auto dealers for guaranteeing labor peace, March 1980.

1-634 *The Boston Globe* examines all aspects of the Massachusetts Bay Transportation Authority (MBTA) — from bus service, to employee hiring and pensions — and finds that an alliance between unions and politicians is responsible for making it the most expensive, least productive major transit system in the country, February 1980.

1-437 *The Indianapolis Star* runs series on racketeering among local teamsters that involved local police and politicians; the series also examines the role of the Federal Bureau of Investigation in failing to prosecute known members of the teamsters crime network, January 1979.

1-432 *Numerous article from various publications* on embezzlement, fraud and racketeering involving trust funds of the Laborers International Union of North America, January 1976-December 1978.

1-145 *The Kansas City Star* examines the investigation of a tax-exempt, not-for-profit Missouri corporation by labor leaders, legislators, and Internal Revenue Service for possible political support of right-to-work amendment, October 1978.

1-112 *Detroit Free Press* shows how Teamsters spent $1.3 million in a violent organizing campaign to get trucking companies to pay for labor peace, June 20, 1976.

1-844 *The Des Moines Register* does articles on how a Chicago union under investigation for labor racketeering and organized crime ties was collecting four percent of the wages of mentally and physically handicapped workers at a Clinton, Iowa, factory.

LAND
See also:
agriculture
land fraud
real estate

1-2517 *The Anchorage Times* reports that individuals — ranging from judges to doctors to Federal Bureau of Investigation agents to the governor — and companies are using state land without persmission and sometimes for profit, October 1983.

1-2219 *The Philadelphia Inquirer* series, "The Wasted Acres," says U.S. government is inefficient in management of land; government acquires land it doesn't need, holds on to property it doesn't use, gives away thousands of valuable properties it should sell, May 1982.

1-2288 *UPI and Better Government Association* illustrate how federal disposals of land are tied up for years by frequent political meddling, costly bureaucratic indecision and intense infighting among federal, state and local governing bodies, February 1982.

1-2568 *The Daily Oklahoman* (Oklahoma City) discovers that land in Oklahoma County is secretly owned by interests associated with the deposed Shah of Iran's family; their identities had been protected from the public through a trust, January 1980.

1-2515 *Harper's* survey of America's land tells who owns it, who controls it, how much is left, who tends it, who reaps the harvest, land legislation, January 1979.

1-358 *The Wenatchee (Wash.) World* tells about recreational land developers in north central Washington; gives layers of ownership alliances and power that make up a large recreational real estate empire; also discusses the legal and financial problems at one recreational place, September 1976.

LAND BANKS
See:
agriculture
banks

LAND FRAUD
See also:
land
loans
mortgages
real estate

1-3331 *KUTV-TV* (Salt Lake City) airs documentary on two fraudulent land companies and how they swindled more than two thousand land buyers, August 19, 1981.

1-2350 *Texarkana Gazette* runs series on hard-sell land fraud schemes and failure of state and federal agencies to protect consumers, April 1981.

1-334 *Eugene (Ore.) Register-Guard* series investigates financial collapse of a planned Utopian ecological community and losses of its idealistic speculators, April 1979.

1-69 *The Denver Post* investigates Colorado land developers Danny O'Keefe and Charles Baldwin, January 1977.

1-374 *The Daily Oklahoman* (Oklahoma City) reports that purchasers of resort property in the state may have been swindled by several persons and companies linked to a massive land fraud scheme in Arizona, April 1975.

1-423 *The Register-Guard* (Eugene, Ore.) publishes series on land swindles in eastern Oregon in which unwitting buyers purchased unusable ranchland, September 1973.

LANDLORDS
See:
housing
slumlords

LAW ENFORCEMENT
See:
Federal Bureau of Investigation
police

LAWYERS
See also:
bail bondsmen
conflicts of interests
courts
judges
juries

1-2679 *Beaumont (Texas) Enterprise* series tackles the topic of lawyer discipline by the State Bar of Texas and finds that what goes on in secret disciplinary hearings affects the public and should be open to public scrutiny, Oct. 28-31, 1984.

1-2316 *Newsday* (Long Island) reports political connections are proving profitable for some Long Island lawyers who are being appointed guardians to represent children and the disabled in estate cases, and to manage money for the incapacitated; fees are often exorbitant, October 1984.

1-2647 *The Journal-Gazette* (Fort Wayne, Ind.) story focuses on the legal but questionable practices by Fort Wayne city attorneys of billing the city above and beyond their normal salaries for doing certain legal work; reporters used city documents in the investigation, June 26, 1984.

1-2180 *American Lawyer* article on "monitors," lawyers hired by Wall Street firms not to influence pending legislation but to obtain inside information about it; raises questions about legality of insider-lawyers gathering and selling information that can be used to play the stock market, May 1984.

1-2083 *The Washingtonian* article, "Inside Washington's Legal Establishment," describes how each of Washington's "super lawyers" used a strategic job in a government agency to become an authority on one aspect of Washington law; other aspects of legal establishment, April 1983.

1-2282 *The Courier-News* (Bridgewater, N.J.) finds flaws in the New Jersey Public Contracts Law that allowed a private attorney to reap thousands of dollars in unearned payments from public coffers, April 1981.

1-2279 Charleston (W.Va.) Gazette presents an outline of the ways in which lawyers cash in on government and thrive on political connections, March 1981.

1-2741 *Des Moines Register* looks at law firm that has handled more public offerings than any other in Iowa over 16-year period; reveals deep involvement of lawyers in client companies; omissions are found in company prospectuses and business dealings between firm and clients are suspicious, August 6, 1978.

1-384 *WCAX-TV* (Burlington, Vt.) airs investigation of legal and financial problems of former Lamoille County state's attorney; charges include fraud in connection with real estate investments, January 1977.

1-392 *Charleston (W.Va.) Gazette* series examines rampant illegalities and wrongdoing by West Virginia's lawyers and the inability of the state's legal ethics committees to combat it, December 1974.

LEGISLATORS
See:
Congress
federal government
state government

LICENSING
See:
doctors
lawyers
regulation

LIE DETECTORS
1-333 *WKYC-TV* (Cleveland) airs series on how innocent people have lost jobs because of improper reliance on lie detectors, 1980.

LIQUOR
See also drunk driving
1-2498 *The Anchorage Times* publishes series on illegalities in a group of interconnected and racketeer-controlled Anchorage strip bars, June-July 1983.

1-2149 *The Philadelphia Inquirer* reprint, "A System Gone Bad," looks at the failures of Pennsylvania's Liquor Control Board; finds dishonesty, refusal to regulate and social consequences of these failures, November 1980.

1-462 *New Jersey Monthly* article investigates New Jersey's leading night club owner's illegal empire; finds he skirts state regulations that limit the number of taverns an individual can own by "fronting" club owners, October 1980.

1-53 *Springfield (Mass.) Valley Advocate* runs investigation of town's liquor industry; centers on how it's regulated, who profits from it, involvement of convicted criminals and organized crime, economic impact; also questions some controversial liquor license transactions, April-October 1980.

1-337 *WOR-TV* (New York) reports on chemical ingredients, including sulfur dioxide, in wine that are not mentioned on the wine labels, 1980.

1-470 *Honesdale (Pa.) Wayne Independent* series examines data put out by the Governor's Council on Alcohol and Drug Abuse and finds they are totally inaccurate; state officials knew they were inaccurate, February 1979.

1-299 *The Record* (Hackensack, N.J.) does article on failure of New Jersey's Division of Alcohol Beverage Control to regulate the liquor industry, May 1978.

LOANS
See also:
agriculture
banks
credit unions
embezzlement
Farmer's Home Administration
mortgages
savings and loans
scams
Small Business Administration

1-2975 *The Wall Street Journal* describes the rise and fall of Landbank Equity Corp., once known as the largest second-mortgage lender on the East Coast; company filed for bankruptcy, Nov. 25, 1985.

1-2753 *Philadelphia Daily News* investigates the Yellow Cab company in Philadelphia, which had come back from bankruptcy through a complicated loan scheme involving prospective drivers, March 22-26, 1984.

1-2908 *The Journal-Gazette* (Fort Wayne, Ind.) article describes a loan-finding scheme aimed at farmers rejected by banks; loan-finder left with the farmer's $25,000 fee, June 1984.

1-381 *Eugene (Ore.) Register-Guard* documents that a Nevada corporation is funneling money the government claims was obtained in illegal loans into its dormant Oregon Coast subdivision, July 1977.

LOANSHARKING
See organized crime

LOBBYISTS
See also:
Congress
federal government
politics
state government

1-2910 *The Wall Street Journal* article details the growing use of high-stakes lobbyists by foreign countries to affect U.S. legislation, Sept. 6, 1985.

1-2561 *Nevada State Journal* studies the influence of special interests on both the legislative and executive branches of the Nevada government; special interests examined include the greyhound racing industry, optometrists, mobile home park owners, hospital associations and more, August 1982.

LOTTERIES
See:
gambling
organized crime

MAFIA
See organized crime

MAIL FRAUD
1-2543 *Quad-City Times* (Davenport, Iowa) exposes a lucrative mail order organization with 15,000 paying members who believed they would one day be united in an idyllic retreat with 49 young women existing to serve the men's every need and pleasure, June 1983.
1-2264 *The Star-Ledger* (Newark) does series on the mail fraud empire of individuals in New Jersey who owned and operated more than 30 interlocking mail order companies involved in fraudulent promotions; explains why the Postal Service has been unable to curb mail fraud in the United States, June 1982.
1-754 *El Paso Times* series on the mega-business of mail fraud looks at everything from phony bust developers to weight loss scams and ministerial credentials, September 1979.

MALLS
See also construction
1-305 *The Record* (Hackensack, N.J.) series say malls are a bastion of crime, April 1977.

MARIJUANA
See:
chemicals
drugs

MARINES
See also military
1-2129 *The New York Times* series, "The Marine Tragedy," examines causes and responsibility for the deaths that resulted from the bombing of Marine barracks in Beirut; finds mission unprepared, security improvised, lack of guidance for officers, not enough evaluation of intelligence information, December 1983.
1-85 *Mansfield (Ohio) News Journal* shows an Ohio Marine recruiter cheats to meet enlistment quotas, July 1978.

MASSAGE PARLORS
See prostitution

MAYORS
See city government

MEAT
1-2364 *Chicago Tribune* does series on the turmoil the meatpacking industry is going through, with plants changing hands often or going out of business, and unions losing power and money; series includes historical perspective, June 1983.

MEDIA
1-2969 *Mother Jones* provides in-depth reports on three stories ABC News chose not to air in 1984; three stories were all about powerful Republican leaders: U.S. Information Agency Director Charles Wick, Nevada Senator Paul Laxalt and then-Secretary of Labor Raymond Donovan, November/December 1985.
1-2953 *The Philadelphia Inquirer* follows the city's newspaper strike, Oct. 25, 1985.
1-2950 *Columbia Journalism Review* examines how the media promote the "miracles" of new drugs entering the market while overlooking potentially harmful side effects, July/August 1985.
1-2935 *Advertising Age* profiles the "wheeling, dealing and unyielding dynamo" Jeffrey Gluck, publisher of the *St. Louis Globe-Democrat;* looks at his many acquisitions and subsequent rescues of failing publications, May 3, 1985.
1-2306 *Columbia Journalism Review* surveys Rev. Sun Myung Moon's far-flung media operations, most notably *the Washington Times,* November/December 1984.
1-2715 *The San Francisco Bay Guardian* reports on the two San Francisco daily newspapers — the *San Francisco Examiner* and the *Chronicle* — and how their merger has stifled the free flow of news in the San Francisco area, Oct. 10, 1984.
1-690 *St. Louis Journalism Review* runs in-depth report on the closing of the *St. Louis Globe-Democrat,* January 1984.
1-2621 *The San Francisco Bay Guardian* article investigates *feed/back,* a quarterly journalism review at San Francisco State University; publication is controlled by journalists from city's leading dailies and may be violating state law by operating on the campus without university approval, May 1983.
1-3298 *WNED-TV* (Buffalo) details deaths of daily newspapers in Buffalo, Cleveland, Philadelphia and Washington, D.C., and offers guidelines for survival of newspapers, Dec. 17, 1982.
1-2463 *Newsday* (Long Island) looks at the influence within Voice of America of its new chief, Kenneth Tomlinson, whose conservative views gained the support of the New Right; harsher anti-Soviet language and compromising of the integrity of the news are some products, staff members say, October 1982.
1-807 *Santa Fe Reporter* issues reprint, "The Newspaper That Was Murdered," on the practices used by Gannett to kill off a competitor in Salem, Ore., March 1981.
1-637 *Charleston (W. Va.) Gazette* critiques the newspapers of that state and finds little evidence of "watch-dogging," much evidence of greed and cronyism, June-August 1980.

1-482 *The Indianapolis Star* runs article on the use of *The Saturday Evening Post* as a propaganda device of the South African government and the role of the magazine's publisher in South African politics and business at the time of the Muldargate scandal, March 1980.

1-661 *Columbia Journalism Review* article investigates the financial dealings of Michigan publisher John McGoff, who was the subject of a grand jury investigation examining accusations that he worked as an unregistered agent for the South African government; the Securities and Exchange Commission also conducted an investigation into illegal uses of McGoff's publishing firm, Panax, to promote his personal business interests, December 1979.

1-762 *Soho News* investigates the plight of a freelance reporter who was prosecuted for bribery and rewarding official misconduct in the course of writing articles for the *New York Post* on Son of Sam; meanwhile, *The Post* abandoned him and other New York media outlets ignored him, February-September 1979.

1-766 *Washington Journalism Review* exposes the mismanagement and questionable financial practices of WETA-TV, Washington, D.C.'s public broadcasting station, which has led to mediocre programming and unresponsive attitude to local needs, minorities, January/February 1979.

1-163 *Newsday* (Long Island) runs series about controversy surrounding Pulitzer Prize advisory board's frequent overruling of jury selections, June 1978.

1-152 *Overseas Press Club Bulletin* discusses journalists missing after forcible arrests by foreign regimes, May 1978.

MEDICAID
See also Medicare

1-2966 *Columbia (Mo.) Daily Tribune* investigates a 21-year-old's death; her relatives blame the death on Missouri's Medicaid program, June 3, 1984.

1-2179 *The Detroit News* investigates the death of a woman who was given so many free drugs under Medicaid program that she died from them; finds 178 Medicaid drug-related deaths in 21-month period, July 1982.

1-3333 *WZZM-TV* (Grand Rapids, Mich.) airs series on how two firms under the same control were able to inflate Medicaid claims by charging themselves management fees that took Medicaid for an extra $3 million, Oct. 27-30, 1981.

1-724 *Lewiston (Idaho) Morning Tribune* examines the $64 million funding crisis in Idaho's Medicaid program that threatened nursing home care for 2,900 elderly and mentally disabled residents; the series shows how the system is rife with loopholes in spending limits, fraudulent claims and inspection violations, August 1980.

MEDICAL EXAMINERS

1-539 *The New York Times* runs series on pattern of cover-ups in police-custody cases by the New York medical examiner's office, January 1985.

1-2851 *WBBM-TV* (Chicago) in-depth examination of the Cook County Medical Examiner's Office reveals a pattern of mishandled cases in which medical evidence was destroyed, drug overdoses were missed and homicides went undetected, Sept. 9, 1984.

1-2560 *Ocala (Fla.) Star-Banner* exposes practices of medical examiners who secretly take corneas from eyes of dead bodies, without knowledge of next of kin, for Florida eye banks, July 1983-January 1984.

1-2554 *Beaver County (Pa.) Times* reveals operations of the county coroner: too many mysterious deaths attributed to heart attacks without inquests or autopsies, delays that hindered evidence gathering, an unwritten contract for body removal by the friend of a deputy coroner, March 1983.

1-542 *Springfield (Mo.) News & Leader* finds the county medical examiner is reluctant to order autopsies — many of which would have aided murder investigations, May 1982.

1-2067 *Akron Beacon Journal* reprint investigates Ohio's coroner system, February 1982.

1-2196 *The Courier-Journal* (Louisville) examination of Kentucky's coroner system finds it ineffective and corrupt; elected officials who investigate deaths are often untrained and incompetent; their failures allow people to get away with murder, May 1981.

1-3334 *WDIV-TV* (Detroit) investigtes the Oakland County Medical Examiner following a puzzling autopsy report by the examiner, 1981.

MEDICARE
See also:
hospitals
Medicaid
medicine

1-161 *The Washington Post* summarizes reforms proposed to prevent physicians from performing unnecessary tests and overcharging Medicare patients, January 1984.

1-3247 *WILL Radio* (Urbana, Ill.) examines impact of changes in federal Medicare program on patients and hospitals; effects of prospective payment plan and use of diagnosis-related groups in reimbursements are analyzed, Oct. 11 and Nov. 15, 1983.

1-2455 *Philadelphia Magazine* documents how the nation's Medicare system has created a pattern of exorbitant charges suffered by all members of the public; also studies the Pennsylvania Medicaid system in which 55 percent of the doctors refuse to treat indigent patients, August 1981.

1-751 *Chicago Tribune* describes non-profit home health-care scams that siphoned nearly $2 million in Medicare dollars from the government and hid more than half of it in various tax shelters; this is not a result of Tribune investigation, but a description of Senate subcommittee findings, May 1981.

1-261 *The Courier-Journal* (Louisville) uses Medicare records to make detailed comparison of doctors' fees; charges vary widely for same services, October 1979.

1-111 *The Columbian* (Vancouver) shows Washington State Clark County hospital is involved in Medicare/Medicaid fraud of pathology/lab work charges, August 1977.

1-2320 *The Clarion-Ledger* (Jackson, Miss.) series reports abuses by doctors under Medicare and Medicaid; one doctor charged Medicaid and Medicare for treating patients while he was out of the country, March 1976.

MEDICINE

See also:
Acquired Immune Deficiency Syndrome
chiropractors
clinics
dentists
doctors
emergency medical services
hospitals
Medicaid
Medicare
mental hospitals
military
Veterans Administration

1-4039 *The Wall Street Journal* article tells of danger of medical and dental X-rays due to badly maintained equipment and poorly trained operators, Dec. 11, 1985.

1-2952 *The Sacramento Bee* reports on the 10 most common lethal diseases in this country and what is being done (or not being done) to combat them, Sept. 15, 1985.

1-2760 *Gannett News Service* looks at the national immunization programs and how faltering federal policy results in regulatory problems and adverse results in vaccinating children against deadly diseases, Dec. 16-22, 1984.

1-837 *Atlanta Journal* article examines failures in the medical community's handling of the discovery of toxic shock syndrome and the multiple failures of the Center for Disease Control in investigating the cause of the disease, 1984.

1-2544 *Quad-City Times* (Davenport, Iowa) attempts to determine how fast medical costs are rising in the Quad Cities, why they are rising so fast and what is being done about it, May 1983.

1-70 *The Arizona Republic* (Phoenix) shows how medical profession kicks up prices to take advantage of government programs, May 1983.

1-2625 *The Times* (Hammond, Ind.) series, "Health — Can We Afford It?" looks at special interests and other forces driving cost of health care upward; includes angles from medical suppliers, users, providers and insurers, March 1983.

1-2199 *San Jose Mercury-News* series on Kaiser-Permanente Health Care Plan, the world's largest private provider of medical services, finds Kaiser keeps its costs low by providing as little care as possible; Kaiser is sued for malpractice about twice as often as private doctors, December 1982.

1-3259 *WRC-TV* (Washington, D.C.) shows that vaccine for whooping cough can cause severe brain damage in children; medical profession shunned reports; research resulted in lawsuits and legislation, April 19, 1982.

1-3260 *WLS-TV* (Chicago) series uncovers the failure of the state of Illinois to adequately inspect X-ray machines; findings include improperly calibrated equipment and machines operated by untrained workers, March 1982.

1-670 *San Jose Mercury-News* investigates improprieties in California's medical laboratory business that include physician kickbacks for unnecessary testing, defrauding stated-funded medical programs and double billing of patients, September 1980.

1-495 *Seattle Post-Intelligencer* does series on unnecessary surgery in Washington; incidence of caesareans, circumcisions, hysterectomies, and other operations are examined, June 8, 1980.

1-3152 *WBZ-TV* (Boston) conducted a three-month investigation of the medical laboratory business and uncovered sloppy testing and misdiagnoses; the investigation also shed light on poor governmental regulation of labs, May 1980.

1-3239 *WGR-TV* (Buffalo) reporter goes undercover at a blood plasma center to show how lack of medical training of staff and poor treatment of donors pose health risks, 1980.

1-3225 *Extra* show investigates chelation therapy, a cure for arteriosclerosis, and finds the process is potentially dangerous and can result in convulsions, even death, May 1979.

1-2147 *Willamette Week* (Portland) article finds a higher percentage of Oregon women have hysterectomies than the national average; appears many of them are unnecessary, April 1979.

1-3210 *KCTS-TV* (Seattle) reports on the inadequate care that premature infants receive once they leave the hospital, often due to the poverty of their mothers — many of whom are teenage girls, 1979.

MENTAL HOSPITALS
See also hospitals

1-2814 *The Houston Post* runs articles on how newly released mental patients from the Austin State Hospital, many of whom need supervision and medication, are dropped off at a downtown bus station, often without money or shelter, Dec. 1-6, 1985.

1-2909 *Columbia (Mo.) Missourian* article describes the lack of care for the chronically mentally ill in that city, June 1985.

1-400 *Newport News (Va.) Daily Press* and *Times-Herald* reprint examines problems created by releasing thousands of the mentally ill from mental hospitals; the future of care for the mentally ill, January 1985.

1-2765 *Scrantonian-Tribune* (Scranton, Pa.) looks at patient abuse at a state mental hospital; other problems include poor supervision and training and low employee morale, Dec. 3-22, 1984.

1-2853 *The Santa Fe Reporter* investigation reveals appalling negligence, mistreatment, mismanagement and corruption at the New Mexico State Hospital for indigent mental patients, August-November 1984.

1-2719 *The Montgomery (Md.) Journal* series investigates allegations of abuse of patients at a Maryland state institute for the retarded; series finds staff shortage, low pay and poor training and morale among employees leads to mistreatment of residents, Oct. 22-26, 1984.

1-2813 *The Tulsa Tribune* issues reprint of investigation into Oklahoma's archaic system of care for the mentally retarded; Oklahoma ranks last among the states in providing care for the retarded outside of institutions, Oct. 1-10, 1984.

1-2756 *The Cincinnati Enquirer* looks into group homes and developmental centers for the mentally retarded that are taking the place of larger institutions in Ohio; reporter finds some do a good job while others offer inadequate care, at times endangering the patients, Sept. 30-Oct. 3, 1984.

1-2044 *Columbia (Mo.) Daily Tribune* special report finds many mentally ill are released from the Missouri mental health system even though rehabilitation has failed, August 1984.

1-2043 *The Miami Herald* looks at poor living conditions for mentally ill released from Florida institutions, August 1984.

1-607 *Jacksonville (Fla.) Times-Union* investigation reveals problems at Northeast Florida State Hospital, a mental hospital; inadequate treatment and rehabilitation program, criminals using the program to escape criminal charges, older patients terrorizing children, understaffing, all hospital psychiatrists are foreigners, March 1984.

1-2664 *The Clarion-Ledger/Jackson (Miss.) Daily News* does series on the state of Mississippi's mental health system; reporters found inadequate funding meant Mental Health Department could not assure minimum care for patients in state's institutions; series resulted in considerable changes in the system, Jan. 15-22, 1984.

1-2268 *The Washington Post* examines involuntary mental institution commitment in Fairfax County and in Virginia, January 1984.

1-2784 *The Charlotte Observer* investigates patient care at the South Carolina state mental hospital and finds staff discipline lacking and sloppy patient care that sometimes proved fatal, January-November 1984.

1-2564 *The Courier-Journal* (Louisville) series examines Kentucky's system of care for the mentally ill; explores the jails, community mental-health agencies, the state hospitals, a look at Wisconsin's mental-health system — one of the most progressive in the country — and a personalized look at the troubled lives of the mentally ill, December 1983.

1-2432 *The Kansas City Star* does series on the failure of the state of Missouri to ensure the quality of staff and facilities in its mental health system, December 1983.

1-2416 *St. Louis Globe-Democrat* runs examination of treatment of mentally ill in Missouri, titled "Mental Illness: Missouri's System Needs A Cure," February 1983.

1-2409 *The Orlando Sentinel* does articles on results of Florida's shifting of severely retarded mental patients from two state institutions to community homes; fifteen people with complex medical problems died soon after the moves, 1983.

1-2478 *The Indianapolis Star* takes in-depth look at the deterioration of Indiana's mental hospitals and the poor care patients receive; also, the state is reluctant to spend money to aid patients; how the Department of Mental Health has become threatened by partisan politics, 1983.

1-2225 *Memphis Press-Scimitar* series, "Breakdown: Tennessee's Troubled Mental Health System," deals with horrors of "deinstitutionalized" mental patients, a psychiatric facility that has no board-certified psychiatrist, violations in boarding houses where patients live, August 1982.

1-2344 *The Philadelphia Inquirer* issues reprint on poor living conditions for mentally ill released from mental asylums, July 1982.

1-2176 *Columbus Dispatch* articles find Ohio law makes it difficult to hold a mentally-deficient criminal suspect, even where there is evidence that the suspect continues to be a danger to society; mentally ill found incompetent to stand trial for homicide allowed to walk streets, May 1982.

1-3175 *KOCO-TV* (Oklahoma City) finds widespread physical abuse of patients at state homes for mentally retarded children, 1982.

1-82 *The Press-Enterprise* (Riverside, Calif.) gives a portrait of the prisoners and staff at a state mental hospital-prison and examines the impact the facility has on the neighborhood where it is located, December 1981.

1-2354 *The Valley Times* (Pleasanton, Calif.) finds county jails are the new asylums for the insane who are turned out from state hospitals; laws passed to protect the mentally ill actually condemn them to the streets, cops, courts and then jails, where after having been given mind-numbing drugs, they become fair prey for robbery, sexual assault and murder, December 1981.

1-723 *Quad-City Times* (Davenport, Iowa) series evaluates mental health care in Iowa, including what problems there are in the delivery systems, the quality and costs of treatment, December 1980.

1-2618 *The Record* (Hackensack, N.J.) issues reprint on investigation of a private residential center for mentally handicapped children following the murder of a patient, finds negligence and physical and sexual abuse, 1980.

1-492 *The Evening Journal* (Lincoln, Neb.) investigation of three unlicensed homes for the mentaly ill finds poor living conditions and mistreatment of the patients, June 1980.

1-782 *Citizen-Journal* (Columbus, Ohio) finds officials of the Franklin County Mental Health and Retardation Board ran amuck and spent county funds on themselves and friends, January-April 1980.

1-3336 *WCIV-TV* (Charleston, S.C.) series looks into the plans Psychiatric Institutes of America, the nation's largest chain of psychiatric hospitals, has for the Medical University of South Carolina's psychiatric ward, which it is about to begin managing; series looks at what PIA has done in the past to win contracts, 1980.

1-521 *The Courier-News* (Bridgewater, N.J.) series examines abuses and problems (mainly patient and staff violence) at the New Jersey Neuro-Psychiatric Institute, a state school for the retarded, 1979-1980.

1-351 *The Ann Arbor (Mich.) News* series offers background on life inside two local psychiatric hospitals, drug prescription policies in them and general problems with the mental health care system, October 1979.

1-763 *The Kansas City Star* investigates policies that led to death-by-therapy for a retarded patient at a Missouri state mental hospital (she died after being forced to drink mass quantities of water, an unauthorized behavior-modification technique aimed at curing her of her compulsion to drink water), September-October 1979.

1-3200 *KPNX-TV* (Phoenix) reports on the Arizona State Hospital, where patients are often released despite their inabilities to care for themselves; staff negligence had led to patient deaths, 1979.

1-118 *California Journal* shows California mental hospitals are not in good condition; asks if Department of Health is to blame, November 1977.

METHADONE
See drugs

MEXICO
1-3280 *ABC News Close-up* examines Mexico's economic and political stability, July 25, 1982.

1-3281 *ABC News 20/20* looks at an arthritis clinic in Mexicali, Mexico, that promises cure for this incurable disease, March 1982.

MIGRANT LABOR
See also illegal aliens
1-2042 *The Progressive* reports organized labor turns its back on migrant farm workers, August 1984.
1-242 *KSL-TV* (Salt Lake City) series on federally funded company set up to help migrant workers uncovers mismanagement and abuse of funds, including kickbacks, January 1979.

MILITARY
See also:
Air Force
Army
Coast Guard
Central Intelligence Agency
defense
defense contracts
Marines
National Guard
Navy
nuclear weapons
weapons

1-4040 *Worcester (Mass.) Magazine* article details the impact the possible closing of Fort Devin, New England's last remaining military installation, would have on the surrounding community, Dec. 4, 1985.
1-2912 *The Wall Street Journal* article describes the outflanking of the Defense Contract Audit Agency, the agency charged with battling procurement abuse, by both contractors and others in the Pentagon, August 22, 1985.
1-2951 *Columbia (Mo.) Daily Tribune* debates the pros and cons of the draft, June 1985.
1-441 *The Washington Monthly* publishes excerpt, "Colonels in Every Corner," from Edward Luttwak's book *The Pentagon and the Art of War,* on the bloated ranks of mid-level officers and the effects: expense, overelaborate weapons, hostility toward innovation that doesn't require extensive research, make work, April 1985.
1-845 *The Wall Street Journal* runs article on a former Air Force major, now a leading consultant to defense contractors, who violated national security laws by supplying clients with classified budget and planning documents that the Pentagon didn't want released; also looks at the 20,000-member Association of Old Crows, a little-known but influential fraternity of electronic-warfare experts, U.S. military officers and corporate executives, March 1985.
1-835 *The New York Times Magazine* article examines increasing reliance of America's intelligence community on a supersecret network of spy satellites and the agency that oversees them: The National Reconnaissance Office, January 1985.
1-58 *Common Cause* runs article on how the U.S. commander of the Grenada invasion illegally brought back war booty and was promoted, while subordinates

who did the same went to jail, March/April 1985.

1-406 *Common Cause* article finds Defense Department engaged in partisan politics by unleashing a public relations campaign aimed at restoring faith in the Pentagon to coincide with the Reagan re-election campaign, November-December 1984.

1-4002 *Common Cause* article describes similarities between current Pentagon activities in Honduras and the early days of Vietnam, September/October 1984.

1-2742 *The Sacramento Bee* runs series on toxic chemicals leaking into the underground water systems from abandoned dump sites on U.S. military bases; reporters found the Defense Department program for dealing with the problem is inadequate, Sept. 30-Oct. 5, 1984.

1-2713 *The San Francisco Bay Guardian* reports on the quiet revival by the Reagan administration of Selective Service machinery, focusing on the San Francisco area; article says draft boards are prepared to draft 250,000 men in one month if they have to, July 18, 1984.

1-781 *San Jose Mercury-News* runs in-depth article on rapidly advancing chemical and biological warfare technology; how bioengineering could revolutionize warfare, April 1984.

1-2739 *The Orlando Sentinel* series investigates the crash of an Air Force helicopter off the Florida coast; reporter uncovers an Air Force and Navy cover-up of loopholes in inter-service communications that may have led to the deaths of five servicemen, April-December 1984.

1-2796 *The Wall Street Journal* uncovers a secret Soviet program to use genetic engineering techniques to create new biological weapons; reporter made use of secret U.S. and Soviet military documents, April-May 1984.

1-2793 *Army Times* reports on faulty results of the military's drug-testing program that led to the discharge, demotion, fine or imprisonment of thousands of soldiers, March-December 1984.

1-2129 *The New York Times* series, "The Marine Tragedy," examines causes and responsibility for the deaths that resulted from the bombing in Beirut; finds mission unprepared, security improvised, lack of guidance for officers, not enough evaluation of intelligence information, December 1983.

1-2622 *The San Francisco Bay Guardian* article says California's Sylvan National Forests are damaged by continual training and warfare games by the military and the National Guard, August 1983.

1-2571 *Los Angeles Times* issues special section on the Pentagon as employer, purchaser of goods and services, and bureaucratic monster; because of its size, the military-industrial complex makes politicians "captives," ultimately resulting in the breakdown of the system of checks and balances, July 1983.

1-801 *The Washington Monthly* does article on the rivalry between the Air Force and the Navy and how bureaucratic jealousies have been a major force behind the proliferation of nuclear weapons, May 1983,.

1-2091 *The Wall Street Journal* article says some congressmen saddle Pentagon with extra expenditures and requirements to bring money to their districts, April 1983.

1-640 *National Journal* runs articles on problems with Defense Department's five-year plans: persistent underestimation of defense costs, inefficient production rates and the imbalance between procurement and operations and maintenance costs, January 1983.

1-3047 *WXYZ-TV* (Detroit) series investigates military recruiting lies, fraud and deception; recruiters sometimes pressured into deception, other times explicitly told to deceive by superiors, 1983.

1-3009 *ABC News 20/20* report on military spending waste focuses on the expense of spare parts, "revolving door" problem — military watchdogs going to work for defense contractors — and waste and high-spending by one contractor, Pratt & Whitney, 1983.

1-2051 *The Washington Times* runs series on harassment and discrimination by superiors of a whistleblower at Defense Contract Audit Agency; articles also link generals to defense contractor Pratt & Whitney, 1983.

1-2100 *Science* runs series on response of United States to the vulnerability of missiles to Soviet Union; articles examine Reagan administration's response and alternatives, April 1982.

1-3279 *ABC News 20/20* investigates sales of the Hercules military aircraft to Libya, despite U.S. embargoes, January 1982.

1-2217 *The New York Times* articles outline classified strategic planning contained in "Defense Guidance," the Pentagon's classified blueprint; discloses decisions that United States should prepare to fight a protracted nuclear war, 1982.

1-2229 *Atlanta Constitution* series, "The Health of Military Medicine," finds excessive surgical deaths in Air Force's showcase hospital because of one incompetent surgeon and an Air Force cover up; also, a wider investigation finds inferior health care throughout the armed forces, December 1981.

1-534 *Dallas Morning News* article examines critical shortages in the U.S. miitary food stock and how mismanagement at a Chicago corporation contributed to the situation, August 1981.

1-2374 *The Anniston (Ala.) Star* series includes thirty-one stories on chemical and biological warfare; how the agents work, how they can be decontaminated, chemical warfare theory, a comparison of Soviet and American arsenals and a historical perspective, March 1981.

1-2272 *The New York Times* tells of former American intelligence agents and former military men who sell their connections and expertise for commercial profit — sometimes selling munitions and sophisticated technology to countries hostile to the United States, 1981.

1-698 *The Daily Oklahoman* (Oklahoma City) series shows how manpower and equipment shortages have impaired military preparedness, August 1980.

1-592 *The Atlantic Monthly* in-depth article examines the state of American defense and cost effectiveness of defense spending, October 1979.

1-508 *Military Journal* does article on American soldiers in Vietnam who deserted to fight with the North Vietnamese, 1979.

1-507 *Soldier of Fortune* article says U.S. government officials told returning POWs from North Vietnam to keep "totally quiet" about being tortured, May 1977.

MINING
See also coal

1-2761 *The Arizona Daily Star* (Tucson) tells the story of a copper miner who took on a giant mining corporation in a fight for mine safety, Dec. 9-16, 1984.

MINORITIES
See also:
civil rights
discrimination

1-4003 *The Riverfront Times* (St. Louis) article tells how Missouri's Highway Department regularly approves minority contracts for its minority road construction program that other governmental bodies reject as ineligible, July 31, 1985.

1-2816 *The Plain Dealer* (Cleveland) reprint finds white-owned construction companies have side-stepped government rules designed to encourage minority businesses and have set up front companies headed by minorities but controlled by whites, March 24-26, 1985.

1-2589 *Minneapolis Star and Tribune* runs series on the use of front companies by white male contractors to subvert government programs designed to help minorities and women, September 1984.

1-712 *The Plain Dealer* (Cleveland) examines conflicts of interests between minority leaders and city port authority; subjects include a Jesse Jackson campaign manager and other community leaders, April-September 1984.

1-458 *The Chicago Reporter* does article on women-owned "front" companies grabbing federal aid to minority businesses, January 1984.

1-3114 *WTTG-TV* (Washington) reports on the extra expense the District of Columbia incurs for contracts because of a program to aid minority businesses; also, bidding irregularities caused by the program, 1984.

1-3072 *KOVR-TV* (Sacramento) airs documentary on the use of women-owned "front" companies by small businesses to help land state contracts, 1984.

1-2436 *The Sun* (Baltimore) series examines breakdown in the traditional black family structure and how this breakdown is tied to poverty and welfare dependency, December 1983.

1-2410 *News American* (Baltimore) series, "Minority Contractors: Laws with Loopholes," finds front companies — firms purported to be minority owned that are owned and controlled by non-minority contractors — taking advantage of state and city minority business programs, August 1983.

1-2444 *The Post-Standard* (Syracuse) series details the success of several companies in setting up "fronts" to pose as minority-owned businesses and take advantage of affirmative action laws; also, weaknesses in the city's minority business enterprise program, April 1983.

1-3337 *WPLG-TV* (Miami) series, followed that city's May riots, examines the effectiveness of the system of federal programs aimed at improving life in Miami's black community since 1968, Oct. 13-17 and 20-23, 1980.

1-3155 *KUTV-TV* (Salt Lake City) examines minority hiring practices within the city's police department and finds systematic abuse of recruitment guidelines to hire women and minorities, September 1980.

1-491 *The Journal-Bulletin* (Providence) examines the Small Business Administration's efforts to assist disadvantaged businessmen through three major programs and finds several abuses, September 1980.

1-702 *Chicago Tribune* series, "The Black Tax," shows how members of the black community pay higher insurance rates and lose out on federal block grant funds and bank money as government officials and investors choose to funnel that money into "safer" investments in non-black neighborhoods of Chicago, June 1980.

1-442 *Fort Myers (Fla.) News-Press* series on the black community in Lee County examines the black power structure, housing and education problems and media discrimination, March 1979.

1-3195 *WCBD-TV* (Charleston, S.C.) examination of minority school system finds community apathy is responsible for chronic segregation, teacher incompetence and poor student achievement, 1979.

1-3218 *WRC-TV* (Washington) examines minority "front" businesses involved in construction of the Metro subway system, 1979.

MOBILE HOMES
See also housing

1-2968 *The Wall Street Journal* reports on mobile-home fraud investigations; the Veterans Administration and the Department of Housing and Urban Development are investigating fraudulent practices whereby mobile-home makers inflate invoices, receive payments and later return some of the money to dealers for taking their products; the practice adds thousands of dollars to the price of the homes, May 20, 1985.

1-368 *Los Angeles Herald Examiner* investigation of abuses in the mobile home industry in Orange County reveals illegal kickbacks, strangled competition and eviction of elderly persons, January 1979.

1-137 *Charleston (W.Va.) Gazette* discovers bait-and-switch scam involving young couples trying to buy mobile homes, Sept. 9, 1972.

MONEY LAUNDERING
See also music

1-720 *The Wall Street Journal* runs article on how the mob uses financial institutions to launder money and the growing number of financial institutions under scrutiny in connection with such activities, March 1985.

1-63 *New York* shows how crooks recycle $780 billion a year in dirty money, October 1982.

1-3187 *ABC News 20/20* investigation finds the International Children's Appeal, fundraiser for the International Year of the Child, is a money laundering front for drug and weapons merchants, 1979.

MORTGAGES
See also:
banks
credit unions
loans
redlining
savings and loans

1-54 *The Plain Dealer* (Cleveland) finds lenders charging higher-than-sanctioned mortgage fees, 1983.

1-783 *The Albuquerque Tribune* uses real estate records to expose hanky panky of "straw buyers," unqualified investors who buy up low-interest mortgages from qualified buyers, December 1980.

MOTOR VEHICLES
See:
automobiles
trucks
buses

MURDER
See also:
criminal justice
deaths

1-4004 *Knight-Ridder News Service* article examines the disturbed background of Leonard Lake, a murderer believed to have tormented and killed two dozen victims, June 30, 1985.

1-2976 *Columbia (Mo.) Daily Tribune* examines domestic murders in Boone County, Jan. 20, 1985.

1-2032 *St. Louis Post-Dispatch* issues reprint describing Charles Hatcher, the man who says he killed 16 children; the serial murderer's route left a trail not only of brutally murdered youths, but of imprisoned men who were mistakenly convicted, policemen who were rendered incompetent and mental health experts who were conned, Jan. 15-20, 1984.

1-804 *Akron Beacon Journal* tells story of the conviction of a man for murder by a rural county desperate for revenge; investigation uncovered numerous questionable practices; eventually the man was freed, January-July 1984.

1-3070 *ABC News 20/20* examines serial murders in the United States; what distinguishes them from other murders, who murderer and victim are likely to be, and how law enforcement agencies try to catch the serial killer, 1984.

1-230 *St. Petersburg Times* series on mass murderer Gerald Stano includes interviews with victims' families, in-depth profile of Stano, discussion of legal system that often allows most heinous criminals to plea bargain while others are executed, December 1982.

1-2107 *The New York Times* article on murders of Atlanta children indicates disputes between authorities and techniques used by investigators may have hindered the capture of killers; possibility that publicity aroused a new killer also discussed, March 1981.

1-699 *St. Paul Dispatch* runs series on the death of a St. Paul prostitute who turned police informant; her murder investigation was bungled by the police and prosecutors; the series offers evidence that information was withheld from grand jury and testimony of a key witness was destroyed, June 1980.

1-671 *The Journal-Times* (Racine, Wis.) series on a multiple murderer, Lawrence Dalton, traces his nine-year history in the Kenosha area including murders and incidents of sexual abuse, November 1979.

1-364 *Nevada Appeal* (Carson City) further investigates the shooting death of Argentine heavyweight boxer Oscar Bonavena and the court proceedings that followed, finding many facts not revealed during the court proceedings, September 1978.

MUSEUMS
1-2053 *The Washington Post* series, "The King of Gems," investigates the ethics of the curator of the Smithsonian museum's gems and mineral collection; curator broke donor's stipulations and traded items to better the collection; secret sales of items out of display cases; tax abuses by donors, March 1983.

1-255 *Wichita Eagle-Beacon* series on Wichita State Art Museum shows inflated appraisals can benefit wealthy art donors, August 1982.

1-554 *Cleveland Press* runs series on the city's historical society and how its trustees and staff members inflate appraisals on donations for tax purposes and use the society's collection of art for private purposes; reporters used price lists for antiques and tax records to expose these practices, February 1980.

1-11 *Detroit Free Press* series shows Detroit museum lends art to public officials for years, making it unavailable to the public; some art works are deteriorating, June 1974.

MUSIC
1-3055 *New Jersey Nightly News* investigates monopolization of concert promotion industry in the Northeast, 1983.

1-369 *Los Angeles Herald Examiner* reports on nationwide move by organized crime into the rock concert promotion business; focuses on hidden ownership by mobsters, laundering of illegally earned mob money and the skimming of profits, January 1979.

NARCOTCS
See drugs

NATIONAL AERONAUTICS AND SPACE ADMINISTRATION (NASA)
1-2373 *Reason* shows NASA's monopoly of the space transportation industry is posing problems for private entrepreneurs trying to develop low-cost alternatives; investigations show hardball pressure tactics by NASA to discourage this development, January 1985.

1-2081 *Reason* article finds National Aeronautics and Space Administration continued a program — Extraterrestrial Intelligence Research — that had been vetoed by Congress by hiding it under another name in its budget, August 1981.

NATIONAL ARCHIVES
1-765 *Federal Times* exposes neglect, mismanagement, bureaucratic empire-building and slush fund in National Archives, April-December 1979.

NATIONAL GUARD
See also military
1-120 *The Dallas Morning News* finds Texas National Guard has problems with theft, fraud, and low caliber members, 1981.

NATIONAL PARKS AND FORESTS
1-2762 *The Arizona Daily Star* (Tucson) goes into the management of the national forests in Arizona and the West by the U.S. Forest Service; series showed that Arizona's public forests had been logged abusively, and more intensively than those in other states, Feb. 5-13, 1984.

NATIVE AMERICANS
1-4041 *The Sacramento Bee* series describes the handling of the relocation of more than 10,000 Arizona Navajo Indians by the U.S. government as part of the settlement of a land dispute between the Navajo and neighboring Hopi Indians, Oct. 20-21, 1985.

1-467 *The Washington Monthly* article describes the unregulated Indian bingo business, questionable "bingo management" firms and Mafia connections: other ways Indians use autonomy to reap profits, May 1985.

1-2691 *The Bellingham (Wash.) Herald* series shows the disorganized nature of law enforcement and boundaries of criminal jurisdiction on the Lummi Indian Reservation in Washington state, Dec. 16-19, 1984.

1-2661 *Fort Myers (Fla.) News-Press* article tells the story of a Seminole Indian indicted for shooting a rare Florida panther; reporter treats questions of Indian sovereignty and endangered species designation, Dec. 9, 1984.

1-2105 *The Denver Post* reprint, "The New Indian Wars," says American Indians are the victims of mismanagement by the U.S. government and business, November 1984.

1-2817 *The Washington Post* series examines massive institutional breakdown at the Rosebud Indian Reservation in South Dakota; centers on three problems: rampant alcoholism and social deterioration, a court and legal system that, without the protections of the Constitution, is a sham, and a medical system run by medical misfits and impersonators, Sept. 9-11, 1984.

1-2522 *Hiawatha (Kan.) Daily World* finds extensive misuse of federal money, grants and property on the Kickapoo Indian Reservation; housing, Indian school operation and Housing and Urban Development projects were among the abused, January-December 1983.

1-2549 *Waterloo (Iowa) Daily Courier* shows thousands of dollars of federal funds were fraudulently diverted to private use by tribal officials at the Mesquakie Settlement at Tama, Iowa; accountability for those funds was virtually nonexistent, February-June 1983.

1-2726 *National Public Radio* covers the case of a young resident on a South Dakota Indian reservation facing life imprisonment for the fatal shooting of a white man; a prosecution informer later says state officials used him in the prosecution to support their political campaign; judge says state violated defendant's right to fair trial and case is thrown out of court, April 29, 1983.

1-3338 *KUTV-TV* (Salt Lake City) reports how oil royalties from the Wind River Indian Reservation are being stolen from the Indians, Jan. 11 and May 10, 1981.

1-2397 *The Denver Post* runs broad-based investigation of thefts in the oil industry; several major oil companies underpaid royalties to American Indians by more than $8 million; large-scale crude oil thefts and irregularities on federal and Indian oil fields are ignored by U.S. Geological Survey, 1981.

1-2183 *The Daily Oklahoman* (Oklahoma City) reprint, "The Legacy of Wounded Knee," investigates government aid to American Indians; finds mismanagement, waste, corruption, June 1980.

1-116 *The Progressive* shows how federal government neglects medical care on Indian reservations, February 1977.

1-2127 *The Riverside-Press Enterprise* (Orange County, Calif.) offers selections from its Pulitzer Prize-winning series "The Agua Caliente Indians and Their Guardians;" documents how Indians were ripped off by guardians who were supposed to help them manage valuable properties, 1968.

NATURAL DISASTERS AND RELIEF EFFORTS

1-3230 *WLBT-TV* (Jackson, Miss.) looks at human error that contributed to the severity of the 1979 flooding of the Pearl River in Mississippi and finds the weather service and the reservoir management did not inform residents adequately about the flood threat.

NATURAL GAS

See also energy

1-476 *The Dallas Morning News* reports neglect by Lone Star Gas Co. led to a series of natural gas-caused fires; government regulatory agencies failed to press the company to maintain its pipelines; consumers were paying for "lost" gas causing the explosions, October 1980.

1-98 *The Christian Science Monitor* examines whether a major natural gas discovery is truly what it seems, April 1, 1978.

NAVY

See also:
drugs
military

1-2419 *Asbury Park (N.J.) Press* runs series on shortcoming in security provided by civilian contractor for guard services at Naval Weapons Station Earle, one of two depots on the East Coast that service the Navy's Atlantic Fleet and a depository of nuclear weapons; also questionable bidding procedures, November 1983.

1-680 *Oceans* article says nuclear navies have hidden history of accidents, incidents and problems; U.S. Navy's assurances of safety are misleading, July 1983.

1-2448 *The Honolulu Advertiser* series documents conflicts of interests and contracting improprieties between the Navy and a major defense consulting firm, Harbridge House Inc., at Pearl Harbor and other naval facilities, July 1983.

1-2151 *Sacramento Bee* and *San Francisco Examiner & Chronicle* articles report on peacetime deaths of sailors; find letters from home were kept from sailor, Navy prevented newspapers communication between sailor and his family, Navy withholds information from parents after sailor's death, March 1983.

1-2064 *The Detroit News* Pulitizer Prize-winning series reprint investigates unexplained peacetime deaths of sailors; reveals scandalous conduct in Navy's procedures and an unwillingness to keep the public informed, 1982.

1-2301 *Buffalo Evening News* documents that the Navy forced more than 600,000 healthy sailors and Marines to take sulfa drugs during a World War II experimental program; today, many of these veterans are suffering from kidney disease and other ailments as a result, December 1980.

1-88 *The Capital Times* (Madison) says National Research Council report on Seafarer, a Navy communications network, whitewashed environmental hazards, February 1978.

NAZIS

1-4054 *Columbia (Mo.) Daily Tribune* article on the background of convicted murderer and self-avowed Neo-Nazi David Tate, Nov. 11, 1985.

1-3050 *ABC News* stories investigate the post-war activities of Nazi war criminal Klaus Barbie; connection to U.S. intelligence, visits to the United Sdates, etc., 1983.

NEPOTISM
See:
conflicts of interests
courts

NERVE GAS
See chemicals

NEWSPAPERS
See media

NONPROFIT ORGANIZATIONS
See also:
boy scouts
charities
hospitals
Internal Revenue Service
religion
universities

1-2437 *San Antonio Light* stories find a non-profit, city funded arts association created false contracts in order to divert funds that were supposed to be used for a series of free outdoor concerts, November-December 1983.

1-2415 *San Jose Mercury-News* runs investigation of how a drug rehabilitation and job training agency lied and falsified records over a two-year period to keep from losing federal and state grants, July 1983.

1-2241 *Los Angeles Times* series says leaders of a federally funded community organization, East Los Angeles Community Union, founded to fight poverty in East Los Angeles, have misused federal funds in setting up a $50 million corporate conglomerate, March 1982.

1-2148 *The Washington Post* reprint finds PRIDE, a non-profit self-help group, stole thousands of dollars from the federal government and low-income tenants; federal government ignored thefts and mismanagement, October 1979.

1-766 *Washington Journalism Review* exposes mismanagement and questionable financial practices at WETA, Washington, D.C.'s public broadcasting station, which has led to programming unresponsive to local needs, especially needs of minorities, January-February 1979.

1-3029 *WTVF-TV* (Nashville) reports on the growing role of the Red Cross in the for-profit plasma business; the volunteer organization has boosted its revenues while it keeps its not-for-profit status, 1979.

1-145 *The Kansas City Star* reports a tax-exempt, not-for-profit Missouri corporation is investigated by labor leaders, legislators and Internal Revenue Service for possible political support of right-to-work amendment, 1978.

NUCLEAR ENERGY

See also:
environment
public utilities

1-510 *St. Louis Post-Dispatch* series examines safety of six-month-old Callaway nuclear plant; looks at release of radiation and problem of inexperienced people operating the plant, March 1985.

1-528 *Amarillo News-Globe* does series on many aspects of the nuclear waste problem; special attention to Nuclear Regulatory Commission's proposed high-level nuclear waste repository and its effects if located in Deaf Smith County, Texas, one of the recommended sites, February 1985.

1-736 *The Philadelphia Inquirer* runs series, "TMI: Accident Without an End," on the failure to safely clean up radioactivity at the plant and the hazards faced by workers assigned that job, February 1985.

1-3099 *CBS News* reports internal studies done for the Department of Energy show an excess of deaths from cancer among nuclear defense workers exposed to uranium dust and radiation at numerous plants — which contradicts what the government says, October 1984.

1-178 *The Wall Street Journal* article finds Canadian nuclear power industry avoids chaos, inefficiency by using a single design, July 1984.

1-4005 *San Diego Magazine* article examines the adequacy of repairs to the shutdown San Onofre Nuclear Generating Station reactor and the role of mounting financial costs in the decision to restart the reactor, July 1984.

1-2055 *The Philadelphia Inquirer* two-part series examines rampant safety violations and regulatory breakdown that led to demise of William H. Zimmer nuclear plant in Ohio; says it was doomed by its own lax standards, January 1984.

1-2574 *St. Louis Post-Dispatch* reveals that although Nuclear Regulatory Commission inspectors discovered falsified quality assurance records for Commonwealth Edison's Byron nuclear power plant, they waited 2½ years before alerting other utilities to the problem, January 1984.

1-56 *The Philadelphia Inquirer* examines all aspects of nuclear waste problems, November 1983.

1-276 *Post-Bulletin* (Rochester, Minn.) series examines mishap at the Prairie Island nuclear power plant as symptomatic of problems plaguing the U.S. nuclear industry; includes examinations of scientific articles that predicted the accident 20 years ago, September 1983.

1-282 *Columbia (Mo.) Missourian* series examines safety of central Missouri's Callaway nuclear power plant, scheduled to go on line in 1985, August 1983.

1-2521 *Fredericksburg (Va.) Free Lance-Star* investigation reveals two nuclear reactors heating up a lake in violation of state standards, two counties putting partially treated sewage in a river and three local governments failing to responsibly protect state waters, February-August 1983.

1-2603 *New Orleans Gambit* reports on soaring construction costs at Louisiana Power and Light Co.'s virtually completed Waterford III nuclear plant and massive breakdowns in the safety and construction programs of several key contractors; also, concerted, systematic programs to hide problems from the public, 1983.

1-2292 *The Seattle Times* delves into the causes for the failure of four of five nuclear power plants to have been built by Washington Public Power Supply System (WPPSS); labor problems, spiraling costs, etc., resulted in the largest municipal bond default in American history; the only plant still being built was seven years late and $3 billion over budget, July 1982.

1-3282 *WXYZ-TV* (Detroit) series exposes potentially dangerous deficiencies at Midland Nuclear Power Plant near Detroit, 1982.

1-2338 *Newsday* (Long Island) reprint looks at the problems of the Long Island Lighting Company's Shoreham Nuclear Plant, the nation's costliest nuclear plant, which is still not in operation ten years after originally scheduled to be running, November 1981.

1-8 *Beaver County (Pa.) Times* series shows that nuclear power plant in Pennsylvania is worse than all others but one in terms of safety, April 1981.

1-247 *Harrisburg (Pa.) Guide* article on Three Mile Island uses undercover investigation and unpublished Nuclear Regulatory Commission document to show that TMI's failure to comply with NRC security regulation makes it a haven for the saboteur, February 1980.

1-657 *New West* runs article on the possible safety defects at the Rancho Seco nuclear power plant in Sacramento, Calif.; piece details engineering miscalculations and poor structural designs by Bechtel Corp., November 1979.

1-666 *Mother Jones* article tells how companies sell the nuclear power plants that nobody here wants anymore to countries such as the Philippines, August 1979.

1-2337 *The Philadelphia Inquirer* reprint, "Countdown: How the Nation's Worst Nuclear Accident Happened," looks at Three Mile Island in retrospect, April 1979.

1-678 *The Chronicle-Telegram* (Elyria, Ohio) series looks into efficiency rate of the Davis-Besse nuclear power plant, March 11-13, 1979.

1-3198 *WABC-TV* (New York) looks into safety and security problems at Long Island's troubled Shoreham nuclear plant, 1979.

1-435 *The Blade-Tribune* (Oceanside, Calif.) examines safety problems including lax quality control standards and poor site selection for a nuclear power plant in southern California, November 1977.

NUCLEAR POWER PLANTS
See nuclear energy

NUCLEAR WEAPONS
See also military

1-2979 *Discover* ushers in its new monthly Special Report section by focusing on "Star Wars" and how the Strategic Defense Initiative has become the United States' most ambitious scientific undertaking, September 1985.

1-2854 *The Asbury Park (N.J.) Press* reports that the Air Force failed to keep a highly contaminated nuclear warhead accident site off-limits, possibly endangering the health of numerous people, July 1985.

1-4006 *The Wall Street Journal* article on how pacifists harass the movement of nuclear weapons on the nation's highways provides background on the bomb-carrying trucks, Jan. 22, 1985.

1-2978 *Associated Press* explores the question of verification — the means (if there are any) of checking to see if the other side is holding up its side of a nuclear arms agreement, Jan. 6, 1985.

1-718 *The Progressive* runs article on how the Department of Energy secretly transports nuclear weapons in unmarked trucks on the nation's highways, November 1984.

1-2637 *Boston Magazine* article explores the tonnage and analyzes nuclear weapons arsenal at Pease Air Force Base near Boston, June 1984.

1-2863 *Boston Magazine* describes how inadequate testing of the Patriot ground-to-air missile system has led many to believe the system may not work, May 1984.

1-2638 *Science* does series on origins of the decision to deploy new nuclear missiles in Western Europe and the choices that lie ahead for North Atlantic Treaty Organization; deployment resulted from Western commercial and political forces, not a Soviet build-up; no further modernization or improvement of U.S. nuclear forces in Europe is feasible, 1984.

1-2480 *Los Angeles Herald Examiner* article says a radioactive cloud that drifted over the city in 1958, as result of atmospheric nuclear testing in the Nevada desert, was far more serious than previously reported, July 1983.

1-2977 *The Washingtonian* explains the process of choosing individuals to be "saved" in the event of a nuclear war; who does the choosing and how they make their choices are discussed, November 1982.

1-2184 *The Progressive* runs article presenting evidence that South Africa has acquired an atomic bomb, September 1982.

1-22 *New West* runs article on storage and moving accidents related to nuclear bombs in California, April 1981.

1-2118 *The Nation* article investigates growing threat posed by storage of nuclear weapons in this country; finds previously undisclosed accidents involving nuclear weapons, February 1981.

1-3168 *KQED-TV* (San Francisco) report, "Broken Arrow," examines the Concord Naval Weapons Station, a wildlife preserve 35 miles east of the city that houses an extensive arsenal of nuclear weapons; report concludes that poor planning resulted in locating the site near an earthquake fault and airport without any evacuation plans for the nearby city's residents, November 1980.

1-660 *New West* article, "Nuclear Nightmare," examines the use of homemade nuclear bombs for terrorist kidnapping threats; article also looks into the health and safety risks that use of such "dirty" bombs creates, December 1979.

1-594 *The Progressive* article, "The H-Bomb Secret: How We Got It; Why We're

Telling It," argues secrecy shields weapons not from foreign spies but from the American public, November 1979.

1-2371 *Albuquerque Journal* series examines the Los Alamos Scientific Laboratory, nuclear waste and radioactive contamination; looks at risk of atomic mishap, self-monitoring, elevated cancer rate, radioactive dumping and more, October 1979.

1-576 *San Jose Mercury-News* issues reprint, "The Bomb Builders," on the Lawrence Livermore Laboratory; the community, the laboratory's safety, the scientists who work there and competition between the Lawrence and Los Alamos labs, Sept. 23-27, 1979.

1-588 *The Deseret News* (Salt Lake City) runs articles on effects of radioactive fallout from atomic bomb testing in the 1950s and early 1960s, 1979.

NURSES
See:
hospitals
medicine

NURSING HOMES
See also elderly

1-770 *The Record* (Hackensack, N.J.) does series, "Nightmare of Neglect," on poor care, filth, understaffing and use of illegal immigrant employees at a New Jersey nursing home, March 1985.

1-4007 *Roanoke Times & World News* article reports on inadequacies at a Dublin, Va., nursing home, Jan. 13, 1985.

1-2698 *Kingsport (Tenn.) Times-News* coverage of a state probe into a Kingsport nursing home finds inexperienced staff, unsanitary beds, shoddy administration of drugs and failure to follow physicians' orders among serious, life-threatening problems at the home, February 1984-January 1985.

1-3093 *WSMV-TV* (Nashville) series reports lax enforcement of patient care regulations in Tennessee nursing homes, November 1984.

1-125 *The Tulsa Tribune* publishes investigation, based on documents and interviews, of nursing homes and boarding houses for the mentally ill and senile, February 1984.

1-2331 *Arkansas Democrat* (Little Rock) series reveals terrible conditions in Arkansas' boarding homes and the state's failure to deal with them, December 1983.

1-3245 *KMOX Radio* (St. Louis) looks at the high cost of nursing homes to Missouri and to its elderly; state officials say costs are driving the state toward bankruptcy; includes statistics on the trend of spiraling costs and increasing numbers of elderly in nursing homes, June 6-16, 1983.

1-4008 *Winston-Salem Journal* runs articles on a nursing home's attempt to cover up the negligence-caused death of an 80-year-old patient, 1983.

1-2614 *Dallas Times Herald* series investigates weaknesses in nursing home regulation in Texas; finds series of abuses linked to death and injury of the elderly, 1983.

1-3339 *WTSP-TV* (Tampa) reports on a new will left by a patient the day before his death in which he left a third of his estate to the administrator of the nursing home where he was a patient, August 10, 1981.

1-2230 *The Arizona Republic* (Phoenix) examines conditions in Arizona's private nursing homes for the indigent; conditions wretched but homes allowed to stay open, May 1981.

1-2238 *The Plain Dealer* (Cleveland) examines health care empire of the Coury family; finds abuses, illegalities, and state officials in business with those supposed to regulate nursing homes, May 1981.

1-2075 *The Courier-Journal* (Louisville) examines Kentucky's nursing home industry, "Till Their Dying Days: Inside Kentucky's Neglected Nursing Homes," May 1980; Update December 1980.

1-3161 *WTSP-TV* (Tampa) investigates the quality of nursing home care in the Tampa Bay area and finds patient neglect, financial mismanagement, and conflicts of interests in the state's Department of Health and Rehabilitative Services are commonplace, November 1980.

1-587 *Beaver County (Pa.) Times* series investigates poor conditions at a local nursing home, September 1980.

1-724 *Lewiston (Idaho) Morning Tribune* examines the $64 million funding crisis in Idaho's medicaid program that threatened nursing home care for 2,900 elderly and mentally disabled residents; the series shows how the system is rife with loopholes in spending limits, fraudulent claims and inspection violations, August 1980.

1-3340 *KSL-TV* (Salt Lake City) airs documentary on conditions in Utah nursing homes; reporters worked in nursing homes undercover, secretly installed cameras in homes and did long-term surveillance of nursing home operators, 1980.

1-615 *Mesa (Ariz.) Tribune* undercover investigation of nursing home finds abuse of patients, inefficiency of state regulatory agencies, July 1979.

1-246 *WLS-TV* (Chicago) airs news investigation of abuses and neglect of handicapped children placed in nursing homes, January 1979.

1-2507 *The Clarion-Ledger* (Jackson, Miss.) runs series on the Mississippi nursing home industry, including abuses due to little regulation, conflicts of interests with four state senators and the role of politics in the industry, November 1978.

1-3134 *WLS-TV* (Chicago) investigates the Illinois nursing home industry and finds there is little financial accountability, September 1978.

1-128 *The Philadelphia Inquirer* issues reprint on boarding homes and their problems; based on interviews, documents, February-May 1978.

OCCUPATIONAL SAFETY AND HEALTH

See also:
asbestos
carcinogens

1-736 *The Philadelphia Inquirer* series, "TMI: Accident Without an End," describes hazards faced by workers assigned the job of cleaning up radioactivity at the plant, February 1985.

1-424 *The Commercial Appeal* (Memphis) series finds government agencies charged with protecting workers from exposure to dangerous substances don't know when workers are exposed and are unable to force businesses to eliminate such exposures, May 1985.

1-4024 *Columbia (Mo.) Missourian* series examines chemical exposure of workers at the University of Missouri and the city's wastewater treatment and power plants and efforts being made to protect workers in an era of increasing chemical exposure, July 8-10, 1985.

1-4043 *The Progressive* article describes working conditions in high-tech Silicon Valley; workers receive low pay for tedious, dead-end jobs and often face conditions that are anything but clean and safe, October 1985.

1-3058 *WTSP-TV* (Tampa) uses Freedom of Information Act to show mismanagement, failures in inspections and the issuing of violations to employers, and the assessment of insufficient penalties in the Tampa OSHA office, 1984.

1-119 *The Kansas City Star* finds Occupational Safety and Health Administration director helped drop $12,000 worth of penalties against a local company whose parent firm had named him president, March 11, 1984.

1-2680 *Beaumont (Texas) Enterprise* series looks into worker safety at Texas oil refineries and finds that the number of safety violations vary greatly at different plants, March 18-22, 1984.

1-2057 *The Wall Street Journal* runs article on agency failure to take action on four dangerous chemicals, known as glycol ethers, still found in some paints; OSHA failed to act despite urgings from government scientists, June 1984.

1-2168 *The Kansas City Times* reprint, "Grain: A Harvest of Danger," looks at hazards of working in a grain elevator and the failure of industry and the government to work for greater safety; industry can actually profit from elevator explosions, July 1982.

1-252 *The Des Moines Register* series details increasingly serious health and safety hazards to which farmers are routinely exposed, September 1984.

1-2656 *The Saginaw (Mich.) News* runs series on worker health hazards at the GTE Valeron company due to cobalt dust, which is used as a metal-gluing agent, October-December 1984.

1-2639 *West Magazine (San Jose Mercury-News)* article looks at chemical hazards in the workplace in Silicon Valley; while the industry is thought of as "clean," the article suggests health of assembly line workers is being compromised in the name of greater productivity, August 1984.

1-4044 *The Wall Street Journal* article, in the wake of the Bhopal, India, Union Carbide disaster, looks at chemical-plant safety in developing nations, Dec. 13, 1984.

1-2761 *The Arizona Daily Star* (Tucson) tells the story of a copper miner who took on a giant mining corporation in a fight for mine safety, Dec. 9-16, 1984.

1-3128 *WPXI-TV* (Pittsburgh) airs series on poor safety conditions iron workers faced during a bridge reconstruction project; they were exposed to dangerous amounts of lead paint fumes for over a year; the contractor knew of exposure but did nothing for months; when the company did act, it used a questionable form of treatment, 1983.

1-2012 *Arlington Heights (Ill.) Daily Herald* finds that while the number of dangerous chemicals workers are exposed to in the workplace has exploded, government testing and regulation of those chemicals has lagged; many companies drop through the regulatory cracks, November 1983.

1-206 *Foundation for National Progress* and *Center for Investigative Reporting* find the domination of safety and testing standards by industry, and outright fraud in testing of products, conceal a world far more dangerous than it seems; includes articles on worker safety equipment, 1982.

1-2193 *Valley Advocate* (Hatfield, Mass.) runs article on how Monsanto exposes workers to cancer-causing chemicals at a local plant and the company's systematic effort to cover up information about exposure, January 1982.

1-2109 *Santa Cruz (Calif.) Phoenix* does article on lax safety standards at Berman Steel, the company that handles disposal of Pacific Gas & Electric's hazardous wastes; Berman's failure to explain to Spanish-speaking employees the danger of materials they handle; relationship between Berman and PG&E probed, May 1982.

1-102 *The Arizona Republic* (Phoenix) reprints series on asbestos poisoning controversy, September 1982.

1-2234 *News-American* (Baltimore) runs series, "The Disposable Workers," on the use of subcontracted day laborers for whom working condition regulations are loose; looks specifically at the case of an unskilled drifter hired to clean deadly chemicals — which trained employees would not touch — who died the same day, April 1981.

1-2253 *The Journal-Bulletin* (Providence) does in-depth report, "Working in Jewelry," on health, labor, safety and environmental problems in Rhode Island's leading industry, June 1981.

1-479 *The Charlotte Observer* finds many abuses by textile companies, including violating safety standards regarding cotton dust, concealing from workers that they had brown lung disease; also, industrial commissions processed compensation claims so slowly that many workers died before being compensated, February 1980.

1-3165 *ABC-TV News Close-up*, "The Uranium Factor," reports that the mining, milling and control of uranium pose severe health risks not only to workers but also to residents of areas where it is processed, April 1980.

1-709 *The Courier-Journal* (Louisville) does series on the effects of workers' exposure to vinyl chloride at the B.F. Goodrich factory in Louisville; death of a worker from a rare liver cancer raised questions about the monitoring systems and workplace precautions taken regarding this known carcinogen, August 1980.

1-650 *Cleveland Press* series on legacy of defunct Diamond Shamrock chromate plant finds Occupational Safety and Health Administration understaffed and overwhelmed, its standards out of date, and its inspections and enforcement inadequate, September 1979-January 1980.

1-531 *Atlanta Constitution* series on the underpaid and underprotected focuses on working conditions faced by the following occupations: turpentine men, ice toters, poultry farm workers and motel maids, December 1979.

1-2525 *Daily News Record/Fairchild Publications* (New York) runs series on the politics, tradeoffs and conflicting interests that the occupational disease byssinosis ("brown lung" disease, caused by the inhalation of cotton dust) has created in the American textile industry, 1978.

1-2355 *Fort Worth Star-Telegram* explores the situation in which a Missouri-Pacific Railroad switchman, previous year's recipient of a safety award, was diagnosed by the company psychiatrist as "overly safety conscious" and then fired because of his attempts to correct the company's practice of mishandling train cars loaded with hazardous materials, November 1978.

1-410 *Lewiston (Idaho) Morning Tribune* series reports on the failure of the Burlington-Northern railroad to enforce federal safety regulations for maintenance staff that resulted in the death of at least one worker, November-December 1978.

1-701 *The Philadelphia Inquirer* five-part series looks at the effectiveness of the Occupational Safety and Health Administration and how it fails to protect workers adequately because it is understaffed and does not enforce hazardous substance regulations, March 1976.

OIL
See also energy

1-2965 *The Wall Street Journal* reports that theft and fraud are getting out of hand in the oil exploration business; kickbacks and bribes come in the form of drugs, prostitutes, vacations and money, Jan. 15, 1985.

1-233 *Texas Monthly* takes a look at the shadowy world of the middlemen in crude oil sales — "spot market traders"; through their collective buying and selling, they play a major role in determining oil prices, October 1984.

1-3060 *KNBC-TV* (Los Angeles) investigates tactics Occidental Petroleum has used to try to drill for oil in Pacific Palisades, Calif.; company infiltrated an anti-drilling group, paid off politicians, allegations of bribery; the unusual circumstances by which Occidental acquired drilling rights and background on industrialist Armand Hammer, 1984.

1-2049 *The Denver Post* does article on entrance of Scientology Church — one of the wealthiest and most controversial religious organizations — into the oil business, November 1983.

1-2403 *Akron Beacon Journal* reprint examines the oil and gas drilling industry in Ohio; topics include impact of the industry on environment and the state's economy, political influence of industry with regulators and lawmakers, September 1983.

1-3293 *WDIV-TV* (Detroit) looks at controversial contract for fuel oil made with the city of Detroit that was engineered by the mayor and resulted in nation's highest oil prices, June and July, 1982.

1-2351 *The New Republic* finds four major oil companies have conducted a multimillion-dollar campaign to manipulate American public opinion; a pro-Arab, anti-Israel state is their goal; collusion with Aramco and key Saudi Arabian officials, May 1982.

1-2226 *The Tulsa Tribune* investigates America's emergency oil supply system and finds it a mess; quality of oil is subject to doubt as a result of Strategic Petroleum Reserve's failure to monitor private contractors, major oil companies allowed to default on deliveries without penalties, March 1982.

1-2169 *Alicia Patterson Foundation Reporter* series, "Lessons of the Oil Crisis," finds companies during 1979 oil crisis held excessive stockpiles; government was unable to obtain basic facts about the situation; internal government reports show the emergency oil-sharing plan is likely to fail if used during the next oil emergency, December 1981.

1-506 *The Daily Oklahoman* (Oklahoma City) runs articles on an oil and gas lease promotion and how investors lost millions of dollars, June 1981.

1-106 *San Francisco Chronicle* runs series on impact of huge profits from oil on state treasury and conflict over how to spend it, February 1981.

1-2397 *The Denver Post* runs investigation of thefts in the oil industry; among findings: several major oil companies underpaid royalties to American Indians by more than $8 million; large-scale crude oil thefts and irregularities on federal and Indian oil fields are ignored by U.S. Geological Survey, 1981.

1-51 *The Philadelphia Inquirer* publishes series on energy anarchy, December 1980.

1-620 *Parade* runs article by Jack Anderson who details the elements of greed, deception and political blackmail that led to U.S. oil crisis and the government's failure to deal with situation despite adequate warning, January 1980.

1-142 *The Washington Monthly* finds the "energy crisis" is really an oil pricing crisis; examines oil and coal industries, 1980.

1-3232 *KMGH-TV* (Denver) reveals how a western states oil and gas lottery is controlled by big oil companies; the companies hire people to bid on leases and then take the leases, 1980.

1-647 *United Features Syndicate* columnist Jack Anderson uses "secret governments" and interviews with U.S. and Iranian officials to piece together evidence that Henry Kissinger, David Rockefeller and the Shah of Iran formed an enormously powerful trio that was the brains behind the oil crisis, June-December 1979.

ORGANIZED CRIME

See also:
banks
Canada
charities
cigarettes
drugs
food
gambling
money laundering
music
pornography
prostitution
witness protection program

1-4045 *The Christian Science Monitor* series on organized crime examines activities of crime families, Justice Department efforts to prosecute high-level crime figures and the rise of a well-financed and unusually violent Colombian drug cartel doing business in the United States, December 1985.

1-720 *The Wall Street Journal* article describes how the mob uses financial institutions to launder money and the growing number of financial institutions under scrutiny in connection with such activities, March 1985.

1-2752 *Fort Lauderdale News and Sun-Sentinel* uncovers a Mafia scam to steal gasoline tax money from the state of Florida; after losing between $40 million and $200 million to the thieves, state government decided to change methods of tax collection, Dec. 9-20, 1984.

1-2711 *The Providence (R.I.) Journal-Bulletin* series goes into the background of state Supreme Court chief justice and finds the judge has extensive and long-standing ties to organized crime figures; reporters make use of public records as well as physical surveillance, December 1984.

1-2683 *New York Tribune* articles look into possible connections between John Zaccaro, husband of vice-presidential candidate Geraldine Ferraro, and organized crime figures and operations; articles use police and city records to show underworld figures and pornography distributors operate out of buildings owned or managed by Zaccaro, July-September 1984.

1-216 *Newsday* (Long Island) articles show that mob is knee-deep in Long Island garbage; city officials also involved in dirty business, September 1984.

1-4009 *Toronto Life* article reports on Toronto Mafia leader Paul Volpe's rise, criminal involvement and murder because of Atlantic City dealings, August 1984.

1-262 *Reader's Digest* article gives examples of how organized crime has found illegal dumping of toxic wastes profitable; shows how weak laws make it easy for the mob to move into the waste handling business, July 1984.

1-2530 *The Wall Street Journal* article on the four big motorcycle gangs — Hell's Angels, Bandidos, Outlaws and Pagans — and law enforcement worries that they are becoming criminal syndicates akin to the Mafia, January 1984.

1-2048 *The Denver Post* does article on theater-owner Donjo Medlevine's links to organized crime, November 1983.

1-2030 *The Milwaukee Journal* runs brief biographies of the defendants in Milwaukee's first racketeering trials, July 1983.

1-45 *Newsday* (Long Island) finds Long Island judges consort with organized crime members; series also examines other aspects of Long Island judiciary that taint justice, February 1983.

1-61 *Los Angeles Times* looks at Anthony Spilotro activities in San Diego, Orange County and Las Vegas in article, "The Mob Moves West," February 1983.

1-2611 *San Diego Daily Transcript* investigation of county Sheriff John Duffy, nominated to sit on President Reagan's Organized Crime Commission, finds he was cozy with organized crime members, 1983.

1-2318 *San Francisco Sunday Examiner & Chronicle* looks at the "yakuza," the Japanese equivalent of the Mafia, which controls much of the entertainment and construction industries in Japan, plus tourism, gun smuggling and drugs in Hawaii and Los Angeles; now they are staking out territory in San Francisco, Dec. 5, 1982.

1-3276 *WJAR-TV* (Providence) shows how men with ties to the Mafia commandeered illegal dumping of deadly toxic wastes from New Jersey into Rhode Island, September 1982.

1-253 *The Kansas City Times* uses documents, wide range of sources to explore links between Chicago's Pritzker family (Hyatt hotels) and mob, March 1982.

1-2311 *Las Vegas Review-Journal* details how Nevada officials ignored years of substantiated evidence questioning the suitability of the David Funk family —

linked with organized crime — to run a Nevada racetrack, February 1982.

1-2073 *The Charlotte Observer* series "Biker Gangs: The New Mafia," finds organized crime more and more rooted in motorcycle gangs, particularly in the Carolinas; gangs are fighting for control of Charlotte, August 1981.

1-47 *Newsday* (Long Island) finds organized crime infiltrates greater New York fish distribution industry, May 1981.

1-2400 *The Clarion-Ledger* (Jackson, Miss.) series finds Mississippi's Gulf Coast thrives on gambling and prostitution; law enforcement is lax and organized crime has crept into the area, March 1981.

1-834 *Several publications* from many states describe organized crime ties with SCA Services, Inc., the third largest waste disposal company in the country, and attempts by mobsters to move into hazardous waste disposal, 1981.

1-505 *The Dallas Morning News* runs articles on FBI sting operation against Carlos Marcello, who many believe operates the Mafia's most independent and elaborately insulated organization, 1980-1981.

1-3341 *WISN-TV* (Milwaukee) series investigates organized crime's links to the Wisconsin cheese industry, Nov. 11-14, 1980.

1-715 *The Record* (Hackensack, N.J.) examines how organized crime has penetrated the midwestern cheese-producing industry and the northern New Jersey pizzeria business, October 1980.

1-3342 *WOTV-TV* (Grand Rapids, Mich.) airs series on organized crime's operation in that city, May 1980.

1-461 *New Jersey Monthly* article, "The Mafia Road Map & House Tour," points out some of the leading Mafia landmarks in New Jersey, April 1980.

1-2304 *The Kentucky Post* (Covington) shows how one unsolved murder led to the discovery of organized crime in the American coal industry; included in the findings are murder, fraud, bribery, corruption, theft and narcotics trafficking, 1980.

1-742 *The Kentucky Post* (Covington) series investigates the murder of an international coal company president with ties to organized crime figures; series details his illicit campaign contributions to Reagan's presidential race in 1976 and also examines his firm's history of swindles; 20-month investigation relied on FBI, Securities and Exchange Commission and Bureau of Prisons documents, 1980.

1-839 *Burlington County (N.J.) Times* series examines organized crime activity in the county; surveys organized crime's ties to prostitution, illegal aliens, arson, gambling, etc., December 1979.

1-846 *The Indianapolis Star* does series on influence of organized crime in the city: how influence started, how it works and how it may spread, December 1979.

1-822 *New Jersey Monthly* investigation of that state's Urban Loan Authority finds many Mafia businesses getting loans from the program designed to serve as a lender of last resort to small businesses in decaying urban neighborhoods, December 1979.

1-606 *New Jersey Monthly* investigation of mysterious death of U.S. Treasury agent suggests the Mafia may have silenced him before he found out too much about gunrunning activities, July 1979.

1-2458 *The Record* (Hackensack, N.J.) runs article on Bob Guccione, *Penthouse* founder, and his questionable interests in Atlantic City; findings include numerous links to the mob, both in his Atlantic City ventures and abroad, July 1979.

1-627 *The Sun* (Atlantic County, N.J.) scrutinizes real estate transactions, practices and law providing basis for series about land speculation on parcels of casino land by organized crime in Atlantic City, January-June 1979.

1-646 *The Kansas City Star* series looks at the many facets of mob activity in Kansas City and profiles the mob's "board of directors," February-June 1979.

1-2166 *The Philadelphia Inquirer* series says racketeers and government officials have combined forces to build cigarette smuggling into organized crime's second biggest moneymaker; who was involved, how they did it, May 1979.

1-2181 *New Jersey Nightly News* airs investigation into Mafia infiltration of trucking industry, May 1979.

1-2856 *Newsday* (Long Island) reports on criminal investigation of organized crime boss leader Joseph Bonanno's criminal empire, April 1979.

1-651 *The Honolulu Advertiser* does follow-up series on Japanese organized crime syndicate that includes a discussion of their weapons and drug smuggling activities as well as illegal currency movement, February 1979.

1-369 *Los Angeles Herald Examiner* reports on nationwide move by organized crime into the rock concert promotion business; focuses on hidden ownership by mobsters, laundering of illegally earned mob money and the skimming of profits, January 1979.

1-3202 *WKYC-TV* (Cleveland) reveals organized crime's plot to assassinate former Mayor Dennis Kucinich and why contract was issued, 1979.

1-387 *The Honolulu Advertiser* runs article on the government's practice of giving new identities to people deeply involved in serious crime — especially with organized crime — for testifying in major criminal cases, November 1978.

1-411 *WCAX-TV* (Burlington, Vt.) details how a Canadian firm with ties to organized crime figure Joe Bonnano tried to get industrial development funds from the state, July 1978.

1-2967 *The Arizona Republic* (Phoenix) issues special edition of its year-long investigative report on mob activities in Arizona, June 25, 1978.

1-39 *Newsday* (Long Island) shows mob infiltrating postal service to tune of $70 million per year, May 1978.

1-38 *Newsday* (Long Island) runs investigation of mob and refuse collection, May 1978.

1-287 *The Record* (Hackensack, N.J.) article profiles the man it says organized crime has designated as peacemaker among rival factions in Atlantic City, April 1978.

1-398 *Albuquerque Journal* explores links between friends of the governor of New Mexico and a company thought by the FBI to be involved with organized crime figures, 1978.

1-389 *The Honolulu Advertiser* looks into a Japanese organized crime syndicate operating in Hawaii, 1978.

1-2162 *The Indianapolis Star* runs series on the influence of organized crime on that city, December 1977.

1-259 *Women's Wear Daily* finds Mafia is neck-deep in New York's multi-billion dollar apparel industry; Fairchild News Service uses 150 interviews, scrutinizes thousands of documents to make its case, August-September 1977.

1-280 *The Record* (Hackensack, N.J.) runs article on a New Jersey mobster who, like many in the state, moved to Florida to avoid subpoenas from the State Commission of Investigation, June 1977.

1-2249 *Cleveland Press* series, "Money and the Mob," investigates Mafia-controlled loan company and finds it has money invested in it from three Cleveland charities, 1978.

1-378 *Yakima (Wash.) Herald-Republic* investigates the involvement of organized crime in the pornography business in that city, March 1977.

1-42 *Newsday* (Long Island) says organized crime heavily involved in food we buy at local stores, November 1976.

1-288 *The Record* (Hackensack, N.J.) article examines the corporate history of Resorts International, focusing on some questionable figures who have been associated with the company, October 1976.

1-36 *Newsday* (Long Island) finds charity gambling spreading on Long Island and the mob becoming involved, September 1976.

101 *IRE* Arizona Project follows the trail of *Arizona Republic* reporter Don Bolles' murder and discovers ubiquitous network of organized crime tainting nearly every aspect of Arizona government and business, including the judiciary, real estate and public works; reveals lively underworld of drug smuggling, gambling and prostitution; investigation yields first documented connection between major heroin producer and organized crime figure, 1976.

1-371 *The Daily Oklahoman* (Oklahoma City) story links an Oklahoma City-based insurance firm with organized crime figures who purchased controlling interest of the company, October-December 1975.

1-377 *The Daily Oklahoman* does series of articles on a Kansas City lawyer, who had represented several organized crime figures, being retained by an Oklahoma City bookmaker who denies any link with the mob, April-November 1975.

1-393 *The Daily Oklahoman* (Oklahoma City) investigates inroads organized crime is making into Oklahoma, May 1975.

1-37 *Newsday* (Long Island) says New York mob steals millions of cigarettes, causing loss of millions of dollars, February 1975.

1-2855 *Newsday* (Long Island) series describes efforts by organized crime to penetrate management at the Suffolk Meadows horse racing track, December 1974.

1-2857 *Newsday* (Long Island) series details organized crime's involvement in the supermarket business, October 1971.

1-40 *Newsday* (Long Island) finds mob smuggles Sicilians into the United States, December 1970.

PARKING
See airports

PAROLE
1-2696 *Star-Gazette* (Elmira, N.Y.) series starts with articles about a shoot-out in which three people were killed; one of those involved was paroled from prison

despite evidence that he was planning the shoot-out while still in prison; series was instrumental in prompting investigation of the state's parole system, February-October 1984.

1-2365 *St. Louis Globe-Democrat* series looks at the Missouri parole and probation system and abuses thereof; investigation included a computer-assisted study of parole board records, July 1982.

PAYOFFS
See bribery

PCBs
See chemicals

PENSIONS
See also organized crime

1-4012 *St. Paul Pioneer Press-Dispatch* series, "Public Pensions: The Price & The Politics," investigates Minnesota's major public pension funds; finds ranking government retirees raking in too much, lower echelon and younger workers getting too little and the cozy relationship between pension fund officials and the legislative commission charged with monitoring them, Nov. 10-12, 1985.

1-4011 *The Sacramento Union* series describes the workings of California's lucrative legislative and judicial retirement systems, April 21-June 2, 1985.

1-697 *The Washington Monthly* runs article, "How to End the Federal Pension Scandal," on the reasons for high cost of both military and civil service pensions, May 1984.

1-2486 *The Sacramento Bee* articles discuss questionable lending and other transactions by trustees of the California State Teachers Retirement System, 1983.

1-688 *San Francisco Examiner* five-part series looks at the abuses in the city's disability retirement system that cost taxpayers some $2 million annually, November 1979.

PENTAGON
See military

PESTICIDES
See:
agriculture
chemicals

PHYSICIANS
See doctors

POLICE
See also:
arrests
Federal Bureau of Investigation
police brutality
sheriff

1-2981 *The Wall Street Journal* looks at some real "Miami Vice" cops — two homicide detectives working in Miami, Oct. 16, 1985.

1-4010 *The Boston Globe* investigation of a program designed to encourage Massachusetts police to seek higher education finds it merely provides hefty pay increases to officers who secure quick and easy college degrees, March 1985.

1-2980 *Syracuse (N.Y.) Herald-Journal* shows city's police force is understaffed, jeopardizing neighborhood safety; examination shows that the city budget is fraught with problems, Feb. 19, 1985.

1-3307 *WBTV-TV* (Charlotte, N.C.) airs stories on members of the Gatonia police department shaking down businesses for cash and gift contributions to their private Christmas party, Dec. 20 and 22, 1984.

1-2769 *Journal Tribune* (Biddeford, Maine) shows how Maine State Police tampered with speed data collection to conceal the state's poor record in enforcing the 55 mph speed limit so the state would receive federal highway funds, Dec. 20, 1984.

1-609 *Fort Lauderdale News and Sun-Sentinel* investigation of K-9 unit reveals spending discrepancies, forged receipts and the use of a K-9 sergeant's official trips overseas to purchase dogs for a sheriff's private commercial kennel, December 1984.

1-2720 *The Times* (Gainesville, Ga.) story goes into the background of three ex-lawmen from the Florida Keys who quit their jobs when their department instituted a policy of giving lie-detector tests to weed out policemen involved in drug smuggling, Nov. 4, 1984.

1-3074 *KMOX-TV* (St. Louis) reports on a St. Louis police officer who, while on duty, scalps theater tickets and runs a valet parking service for his customers, 1984.

1-3080 *CBS News 60 Minutes* investigates allegations that two Puerto Rican radicals were executed by Puerto Rican police and that the murder was covered up by the FBI and the U.S. Justice Department, 1984.

1-2519 *The Journal Gazette* (Fort Wayne, Ind.) follow-up on the police investigation of three city murders shows police had overlooked a few standard procedures in the investigation, December 1983.

1-2553 *The Denton (Ill.) Record-Chronicle* discovers incidents of sexual misconduct, cronyism and favoritism, misuse of city property and incompetence by the former Decatur police chief, October 1983.

1-3285 *WCBS-TV* (New York) paints sinister picture of one police informant who went on a crime spree while a pseudo-employee of the New York Police Department, January 1983.

1-3173 *WSOC-TV* (Charlotte) finds park police chief siphoned hundreds of dollars per month for private security work actually performed by officers working on city time, 1983.

1-3182 *KMGH-TV* (Denver) reveals Denver police arranged for bingo game sponsors to skim thousands of dollars from a travel fund for the junior police band, 1983.

1-74 *The Yonkers Herald-Statesman* finds police apparently charged $900 on credit card they confiscated from suspected thief, November 1982.

1-3268 *WMAQ-TV* (Chicago) shows the city police department uses secret files that permit coverups in murder cases, October 1982.

1-2353 *The Denver Post* says supervision of moonlighting Denver policemen — necessary to regulate possible conflicts of interests — has become so lax that a new system is being considered, one that would remove one police captain from his lucrative moonlighting business through which he controls up to 30 percent of off-duty police work in Denver, August 1982.

1-2215 *The Miami News* articles find police forging victim non-prosecution forms so they don't have to investigate crimes, August 1982.

1-2352 *The Denver Post* finds the Denver Police Department has commissioned more than 750 honorary lieutenants and captains since 1968; among those commissioned are political cronies, elected officials and a few convicted felons; article examines the abuses of these commissions, July 1982.

1-2391 *Saginaw (Mich.) News* series, "Raid," examines city police's drug raid conduct and effectiveness of local narcotics control effort; series based largely on statistical analysis of information from police and court records, March 1982.

1-2119 *The Indianapolis Star* investigation into a successful police "sting" operation that broke theft rings finds no rings at all; police actually created crimes in order to make arrests, police informants pocketed some of the operation's "buy" money, 1982.

1-2393 *St. Louis Post-Dispatch* investigation into that city's process of selecting a new police chief reveals behind the scenes jockeying that involved some of city's leading businessmen; confidential evaluations of candidates obtained by the paper show department's top officers to be under par and promoted because of connections, not merit, 1982.

1-3299 *KRON-TV* (San Francisco) gets policemen in Pittsburg, Calif., to discuss abuses in their department, 1982.

1-3291 *WBBM-TV* (Chicago) exposes massive cover-ups of crime by one Chicago police department, 1982.

1-7 *Middletown (N.Y.) Times Herald-Record* finds state police looking the other way when violator is another cop, December 1981.

1-3343 *WBBM-TV* (Chicago) reports on how Chicago police make it a policy to lie to the public and FBI about the city's crime statistics, 1981.

1-2398 *The Philadelphia Inquirer* investigation of that city's police decoy squad finds squad was deliberately framing innocent people on robbery charges, 1981.

1-3344 *KYW-TV* (Philadelphia) reports on a Philadelphia policeman who was the "personal cop" for a city councilman; the officer spent virtually all his on-duty time with the councilman while other officers covered for him, Nov. 13-14, 1980.

1-683 *The Boston Globe* series shows how that city's police force had a record of poor performance compared to other metro areas because of ineffective management and union-management struggles, October 1980.

1-3155 *KUTV-TV* (Salt Lake City) examines minority hiring practices within the city's police department and finds systematic abuse of recruitment guidelines to hire women and minorities, September 1980.

1-695 *The Evening Bulletin* (Providence) series examines corruption in the police department in which a police detective was allowed to retire even though he was under investigation for passing $30,000 worth of bad checks, June 1980.

1-755 *Minneapolis Star and Tribune* examination of police records finds politics had permitted an increase in prostitution and led to favoritism in the enforcement of vice laws and building code laws; the series prompted resignation of the police chief, overhaul of vice squad, July-December 1979.

1-617 *The News-Sun* (Waukegan, Ill.) uncovers police misconduct and hiring improprieties, September 1979.

1-3226 *WCBS-TV* (New York) examines the conflicts of interests in the purchase of bullet-proof vests for that city's police force and finds that the Policeman's Benevolent Association paid thousands of dollars more for them than they should have, May 3, 1979.

1-3203 *WTVJ-TV* (Miami) finds problems with the accuracy of radar guns in determining whether cars are speeding due to angling errors and operator misuse and abuse, 1979.

1-212 *The News* (Paterson, N.J.) shows how a group of local cops profits from buying tenements, inflating value by selling them to each other and raking in insurance premiums after suspicious fires gut them, 1979.

1-34 *The Daily Olympian* (Olympia, Wash.) runs story of police illegally bugging their jail, May 1978.

1-327 *Fort Myers (Fla.) News-Press* does articles on corruption and brutality in the Clewiston Police Department, September-November 1978.

1-385 *Courier-News* (Glendale Heights, Ill.) investigation reveals wrongdoing, questionable judgment and abuse of office for personal gain by Glendale Heights police chief, March 1978.

1-329 *Fort Myers (Fla.) News-Press* does articles on misconduct and corruption of North Port, Fla., police department, July-December 1977.

1-330 *The Times* (Shreveport, La.) investigation of that city's commissioner of public safety finds widespread abuses and illegalities, including embezzlement, 1976-1977.

1-397 *The Record* (Hackensack, N.J.) does article on municipal constables stretching the law and abusing their slim credentials, February 1975.

1-2161 *The Indianapolis Star* investigation of police corruption in the city produced this large collection of articles on wrongdoing by the city's police department — connections to organized crime, pay-offs, blackmail, etc.; also, questions about the conduct of the Marion County prosecutor, 1974-1975.

1-214 *The Wenatchee (Wash.) World* describes "courtesy policies" which allow state and city cops to avoid being cited for traffic violations, or being let off the hook later, December 1973.

POLICE BRUTALITY
See also:
police
sheriff

1-2818 *The Houston Post* looks into shootings by police officers and finds several officers with a proclivity for firing their weapons; suggests more officers should be indicted for shooting and killing people, July 31, 1985.

1-2023 *The Philadelphia Inquirer* investigation finds some K-9 officers deliberately fail to control dogs and sometimes command them to attack unnecessarily, June 1984.

1-2429 *The Daily Breeze* (Torrance, Calif.) runs series on police brutality in the Hawthorne Police Department, October 1983.

1-2566 *The Knoxville Journal* puts forth strong circumstantial evidence showing that a small cadre of Knoxville police officers regularly used excessive force; their names and actions were known but they were protected by colleagues and supervisors, July 1983.

1-2446 *The Post-Standard* (Syracuse) does articles on 32 instances of alleged brutality by state police at the New York State Fair, 1983.

1-2275 *The Journal* (Lorain, Ohio) looks at police brutality in Lorain, asking such questions as: Who polices the police? Who is responsible for their actions? October 1981.

1-3345 *KGO-TV* (San Francisco) airs series on police strip searches in the processing of minor-crime suspects, March 2-5, 1981.

1-2334 *Long Beach (Calif.) Press-Telegram* issues reprint of investigation into that city's police department for brutality, February 1981.

1-2232 *Long Beach (Calif.) Press-Telegram* does series on man stopped by police for speeding and found hanged in jail cell three hours later; police department had history of brutality, coroner's inquest found he "died at the hands of another," 1981.

11-725 *Republican-Eagle* (Red Wing, Minn.) seven-part series documents how a Minnesota police chief abused his power by threatening minors at gunpoint, using unnecessary force, and conducting illegal searches, September 1980.

1-3238 *KOIN-TV* (Portland) investigates police brutality in that city's police force, citing specific incidents and interviewing the people involved, 1980.

1-469 *News Journal* (Mansfield, Ohio) publishes series on police brutality and the failure of high-ranking department officials to investigate abuses, 1980.

1-694 *The Courier-Journal* (Louisville) examines unanswered questions surrounding the shooting of a man suspected of killing a Kentucky state trooper; questions include: Why did the arresting officer, a desk sergeant, pursue the suspect to Illinois? Was the shooting necessary? November 1979.

1-675 *The Miami Herald* series on police brutality in south Florida documents evidence of violence committed by a small band of officers that is sanctioned by the internal discipline system of the department, July 1979.

1-3204 *WMAQ-TV* (Chicago) reports that Skokie police often force women to undergo strip searches for minor traffic violations, 1979.

1-735 *The Philadelphia Inquirer* four-month investigation of Philadelphia's police homicide division reveals a pattern of beatings, threats of violence and intimidation, coercion and knowing disregard of witnesses' and suspects' rights, April 1977.

POLITICAL ACTION COMMITTEES
See campaign finances

POLITICIANS
See also:
campaign finances
city government
conflicts of interests
Congress
county government
elections
legislatures
lobbyists
politics
state government

1-2982 *The Wall Street Journal* describes House Banking Committee Chairman

Fernand St Germain's growing power, wealth; second article discusses his dealings in some legally dubious tax shelters, Sept. 11, 1985.

1-2983 *Syracuse (N.Y.) Herald-Journal* evaluates the impact of Syracuse Mayor Lee Alexander's announcement that he will not seek re-election, July 15, 1985.

1-431 *The New Republic* runs article on how the leaders of Lyndon LaRouche's National Caucus of Labor Committees won access to officials of the Reagan administration, and with it, respectability, November 1984.

1-2681 *Beaumont (Texas) Enterprise* covers indictment of a Texas state senator on charges relating to drugs, pornography and prostitution; charges were subsequently dropped because of possible bias among some members of the grand jury, July-November 1984.

1-2745 *Jack Anderson Enterprises* 10-part series investigates the involvement between Oregon Senator Mark O. Hatfield and Greek arms merchant Basil Tsakos; series also looks into Tsakos' relationships with other government officials, including CIA Director William Casey, July-October 1984.

1-2683 *New York Tribune* articles look into possible connections between John Zaccaro, husband of vice-presidential candidate Geraldine Ferraro, and organized crime figures and operations; articles use police and city records to show underworld figures and pornography distributors operate out of buildings owned or managed by Zaccaro, July-September 1984.

1-2653 *The Times-News* (Twin Falls, Idaho) runs series on the finances of Idaho Congressman George Hansen; article exposed Hansen's connections with Rev. Sun Myung Moon's Unification Church; Hansen subsequently lost reelection and was indicted for filing false financial disclosure records, May-September 1984.

1-2687 *Tallahassee Democrat* series covers the investigation and indictment of a former Florida state senator for laundering money made by drug smugglers; series also goes into the background of an FBI informant, May-June 1984.

1-2787 *The Charlotte Observer* article profiles a popular North Carolina state legislator with a questionable background; reporters use public records to find the man had various personal and government debts as well as business links to a known drug smuggler, April 1, 1984.

1-2156 *Sacramento Bee* articles on Nevada Senator Paul Laxalt indicate he receives campaign contributions from mob leaders; a casino the senator once owned skimmed money, November 1983.

1-2121 *The Record* (Hackensack, N.J.) reprint, "Behind the Donovan Affair," describes how the charges against the secretary of labor were magnified by mistakes by the FBI, misinformation from government informants, leaks from Senate committee, October 1983.

1-3020 *WMAQ-TV* (Chicago) documentary examines Jesse Jackson and the principal controversies he has been involved in — conflicts with civil rights leaders, disputes with the federal government over misuse of taxpayer funds by PUSH, trade agreements he has concluded with corporate America, October 1983.

1-741 *The Village Voice* does article on John Rees, a con man, who among other things started rumors that the nuclear freeze movement was controlled by the Soviet Union, Rees's influence on the New Right, August 1983.

1-2091 *The Wall Street Journal* article says some congressmen saddle Pentagon with extra expenditures and requirements to bring money to their districts, April 1983.

P

1-2485 *United Features Syndicate* series says current and former members of Congress were involved in the purchase of narcotics from a ring that sold drugs on Capitol Hill; Justice Department blocked a grand jury investigation and prevented the trial of the arrested pushers, 1983.

1-2511 *Fort Lauderdale News and Sun-Sentinel* delves into the practices and finances of Doyle Conner, the state's agricultural commissioner; findings include abuse of airplane privileges, secret and unreleased personal bank accounts and more, July 1982.

1-3278 *ABC News 20/20* finds that the Institute of American Relations, a conservative think tank directed by Jesse Helms' aides, may not deserve tax-exempt status, March 1982.

1-2177 *UPI* and *Better Government Association* do 10-part series, "American Royalty," on government officials and agencies living high on the hog at taxpayer expense; topics include Congressional overseas travel abuses, unauthorized use of military transport, expense account double-dipping, Pentagon supplying free travel and expensive entertainment to its Congressional watchdogs, White House travel abuses, taxpayers footing bill for National Aeronautics and Space Administration space shuttle promotions, February 1982.

1-2461 *Columbia Journalism Review* publishes close look at the prime funder of the media-savvy New Right — Richard Mellon Scaife — who uses his immense wealth to shape today's political climate, July/August 1981.

1-486 *Seattle Post-Intelligencer* finds a front-running candidate for attorney general had stolen money from the estate of a dead client, October 1980.

1-626 *The Evening Sun* (Baltimore) uses data on legislators' expense accounts, financial disclosure statements, General Accounting Office audits and vouchers to reach conclusion that it costs taxpayers an average of $1 million per congressman and senator to keep each one paid and comfortable each year, September-October 1979.

1-616 *Springdale (Ark.) News* uses public documents to show that state senator falsified and covered up his residence outside district in which he was elected, March 1979.

1-2367 *Boston Herald American* runs investigation of Tip O'Neill's involvement in a partnership that had a federal loan guarantee on a nursing home it owned, apparently in violation of the federal conflicts of interests law; October-December 1978.

1-65 *Columbia (Mo.) Daily Tribune* looks at effectiveness of U.S. Representative Richard Ichord, May 1978.

1-2469 *The Daily Oklahoman* (Oklahoma City) articles profile Oklahoma Senator Gene Stipe; focus is on the investigation of Stipe by the FBI in connection with a government-backed bank loan that a frozen foods company had and defaulted on, May 1978.

1-298 *The Record* (Hackensack, N.J.) article says Rep. Matthew J. Rinaldo, R-N.J., illegally received about $7,000 in campaign contributions from part-time congressional employees; also, Rinaldo juggled payroll to beat congressional spending limits, September 1976.

1-380 *The Daily Oklahoman* (Oklahoma City) profiles the governor's race in Oklahoma with a focus on the scandal-rocked administration of then-Gov. David Hall, August 1974.

141

POLITICS

See also politicians

1-2366 *Ottaway News Service* does story on the awakening of political involvement among the young, moneyed and formerly apolitical executives of the high-tech, high-risk industries that dominate the Silicon Valley, November 1984.

1-2475 *Palouse Empire Daily News* (Pullman, Wash.) explores the behind-the-scenes political machinations of a Pullman church, which tried to place three members on the city council and one on the school board, October 1983.

1-516 *Gannett News Service* issues reprint, "The Rise of the New Right," on the growing alliance between political and religious conservatives and its impact on American politics, 1980.

POLLUTION

See:
acid rain
agriculture
air pollution
environment
foreign policy
water pollution

PORNOGRAPHY

See also organized crime

1-2582 *Family Weekly* runs articles on the growth of child pornography in the United States; why pornography rings flourish, organized crime involvement and whether law enforcement doing enough, June 1985.

1-29 *The Wall Street Journal* runs article on the smart business techniques and evasion of obscenity laws by Reuben Starman, who operates the nation's largest pornography distribution network, May 8, 1985.

1-183 *The Knoxville Journal* finds organized crime making big bucks selling pornography in Knoxville; looks at pornography power structure in that city, August 1984.

1-3110 *WBTV-TV* (Charlotte) reports on links of local adult book stores to organized crime and the failure of law enforcement agencies to prosecute, 1984.

1-2631 *The Boston Globe* conducts investigation of the expanding pornography industry; topics include industry's growth, involvement of organized crime, industry's use of government loans, and law enforcement efforts, February 1983.

1-2453 *Philadelphia Magazine* takes a peek at the pornography business in Philadelphia; includes personal inspection of pornography establishments, documentation of organized crime's heavy involvement and the position of the law as it affects the pornography brokers, November 1981.

1-439 *The Call-Chronicle* (Allentown, Pa.) examines the business empire of pornography publisher John Krasner, who was murdered in Florida; the article makes extensive use of land deeds, court testimony and police records on Krasner, February 1979.

1-378 *Yakima (Wash.) Herald-Republic* investigates the involvement of organized crime in the pornography business of Yakima, March 1977.

POSTAL SERVICE

1-39 *Newsday* (Long Island) finds the mob infiltrating postal service to the tune of $70 million per year, May 1978.

1-382 *The Register-Guard* (Eugene, Ore.) does series on why the nation's mail system is beset with so many problems; a basic survey of the whole system, April 1975.

POVERTY
See welfare

POWER STRUCTURES

1-2705 *The Reporter* (Amsterdam, N.Y.) series looks at the informal exercise of economic and political power in a small community through the use of federal economic development money by the Amsterdam Industrial Development Agency, April 25-28, 1984.

1-2052 *Tallahassee (Fla.) Democrat* series goes into the Tallahassee area system of power brokers, profiling eight local business people and how they influence city and area affairs, Jan. 22-25, 1984.

1-199 *The Sun* (Baltimore) explores the city's "shadow government," the unelected officials who run the city from behind the scenes, July 1980.

1-3273 *WXYZ-TV* (Detroit) looks at who rules Detroit, Feb. 23-March 3, 1982.

1-2125 *Texarkana Gazette* issues reprint, "Sculptors of Power: Texarkana's Decision Markers," December 1981.

1-636 *San Jose Mercury-News* uses research methodology formulated by political sociologists to shed light on the individuals and institutions exerting inordinate influence on public policy in San Jose, August 1979.

1-322 *The Columbian* (Vancouver) runs series on the most powerful people in Clark and Skamania counties, September 1978.

1-72 *The Standard-Times* (New Bedford, Mass.) shows who's who in that city, August 1978.

1-2136 *Columbia (Mo.) Daily Tribune* article, titled "Power," looks at the most powerful people in Columbia and the ways they exercise influence, October 1977.

1-41 *The Indianapolis Star* shows who's who in Indianapolis, May 1976.

1-83 *The Des Moines Register* shows who's who in Des Moines, 1976.

1-155 *The Kansas City Star* tells who runs Kansas City, June 1975.

PRESCRIPTIONS
See drugs

PRIMARIES
See elections

PRISONS

1-4046 *The Sacramento Bee* series, "Life on the Line," examines the strained conditions California prison guards work under, how it influences their treatment of inmates and their own mental health, and the future design of prisons in the United States, Nov. 24-27, 1985.

1-2985 *The Progressive* reports that up to twenty thousand men may be raped in prison each day, November 1985.

1-2984 *Detroit Free Press* runs a series that examines Michigan's prisons and parole board; reporters did computer analysis of thousands of released prisoners and found overcrowding and other factors resulted in early release of many dangerous people, Sept. 22-28, 1985.

1-559 *Texas Monthly* in-depth article argues Texas prisons must be returned to disciplinary code courts recently said were cruel; new discipline code has made the prisons more dangerous, quadrupled costs and made it more difficult to control prisoners, May 1985.

1-2819 *The Washington Post* does series on how drugs and hot goods are smuggled into the Lorton reformatory, a Virginia prison where drug use is high and official concern about it is low, March 4-7, 1985.

1-2341 *The Washington Post* runs series on the political and public opinion origins of the current prison building boom and their results, March 1985.

1-2722 *Houston Chronicle* series looks in-depth at state of chaos and violence in Texas prisons; series found much of the violence was caused by inmate gangs that enjoyed extensive degree of control within the state's 26 institutions, Nov. 18-22, 1984.

1-2041 *The Progressive* examines prisons-for-profit; big bucks being made on inmates and prisons, September 1984.

1-2721 *Lexington (Ky.) Herald-Leader* story on county jail found that at least 22 inmates had died between 1976 and 1984; many of the deaths were not adequately investigated by authorities despite evidence that some of the deaths could have been prevented, July 15, 1984.

1-2491 *Indiana News* (Marion County) articles examine brutality of sheriff's deputies and denial of medical treatment in the Marion County jail, Nov. 10-Dec. 31, 1983.

1-2490 *The Kansas City Star* series on the prison death by prescription drugs of a mildly retarded inmate reveals much about life inside a Missouri prison, December 1983.

1-170 *The Tulsa Tribune* overview of Oklahoma prison system paints picture of waste, failure of system, May 1983.

1-2479 *The Indianapolis Star* does series on rapes in Indiana prisons, March 1983.

1-2607 *St. Albans (Vt.) Messenger* article documents the events leading up to the suicide of a federal prison inmate who earlier had tried to escape, March 1983.

1-2236 *The Washington Post* publishes series, "Rape in the County Jail," on violent gang rapes in a Maryland county jail; guards take no action, warden denies a problem exists, 1982-1983.

1-2212 *The Philadelphia Inquirer* runs series on fire deaths of seven men in a cell for the emotionally disturbed; guards waited more than 20 minutes before calling fire department, guard froze in panic, jail had many fire safety warnings but prosecutor found jail acted promptly and without negligence, December 1982.

1-2259 *The Register* (Orange County, Calif.) examines that county's jail; topics include high death rate, quality of medical care, financial and managerial problems, prisoner overcrowding, under-staffing, October 1982.

1-2392 *Arizona Daily Star* (Tucson) runs series, "The Convicted," on the state's troubled corrections system; *Star* sent two reporters inside the system, one as a supposed murderer, the other as a prison guard, August 1982.

1-2202 *The Washington Times* investigation of the death of a gay inmate in the Washington County Detention Center indicates he was beaten and killed by the guards, July 1982.

1-2058 *The Inter-Media Investigative Group* runs series, "Hell on Earth," about life inside the New Mexico Penitentiary; murder, torture, and blackmail are rampant, September 1981.

1-493 *The Commercial Appeal* (Memphis) investigation of a prison patronage officer reveals numerous instances of questionable practices and focuses on procedures at the prison farm, October 1980.

1-732 *The Waldboro (Maine) Weekly* runs series on the lockdown at the Maine State Prison and the aftermath of the crisis, June 1980.

1-681 *Herald-Dispatch* (Huntington, W.Va.) runs investigative series on the pervasive physical abuse of prisoners at the Cabell County jail that required extensive hospitalizations, and the great expense to taxpayers for medical bills, May 1980.

1-3154 *KRMA-TV* (Denver) takes a comprehensive look at Colorado's maximum security prison and finds physical violence and inmate abuse abound, 1980.

1-832 *Santa Fe Reporter* does series on problems, including low worker morale and weak security, in the New Mexico prison system; special attention is given to investigation of the new head of the system, a former employee of the U.S. Office of Public Safety, which was linked to torture of political prisoners in various countries, 1980.

1-769 *Iowa City Press Citizen* probes death of inmate at Iowa State Penitentiary and finds major problems with medical care at prison, December 1979.

1-520 *The Clarion-Ledger* (Jackson, Miss.) publishes series, "Jails: Mississippi's Worst Punishment," on poor conditions and problems in the state's county and municipal jails, December 1979.

1-757 *The Times-Picayune* (New Orleans) series uses records, interviews to investigate Louisiana's clemency system and finds that political influence runs deep in this life-and-death game, March-April 1979.

1-208 *Poughkeepsie (N.Y.) Journal* says that polyurethane mattresses, which burn quickly and emit toxic fumes, are used in New York prisons and other state institutions, January 1979.

1-586 *The Sentinel-Record* (Hot Springs, Ark.) investigation of failures of state medical examiner's office turns up cases of prison guards beating and killing inmates, 1979.

1-811 *Chicago Tribune* runs investigation of conditions at Pontiac State Prison; reporter took a position as a guard to write the series, October 1978.

1-211 *Columbus Dispatch* article gives overview of life in Ohio's Chillicothe Correctional Institute, May 1978.

1-33 *Labor Pulse* finds California's prison workers complaining of low pay, bad treatment, September 1976.

1-2467 *Pottsville (Pa.) Republican* looks at drug and alcohol trafficking in Pennsylvania prisons and how the flow has been stemmed, February 1974.

1-156 *The Kansas City Star* series looks at adult and juvenile correctional institutions in Missouri and Kansas; one *Star* reporter is an ex-convict, April 1973.

PRIVATE INVESTIGATORS
1-421 *The Wall Street Journal* article on private investigators centers on one private eye and the techniques he uses to help companies fight takeover bids, lawsuits and white-collar crime; his clients include the Moonies and Iran's revolutionary government, May 1985.

PROBATE
See also courts

1-2768 *Delaware County (Penn.) Daily Times* examines the dissolution of a $2.7 million trust and art collection that was left to the city of Chester by a wealthy resident, Sept. 23-28, 1984.

1-2325 *The Hartford Courant* articles detail abuses in the Hartford Probate Court, particularly with regard to favoritism in appointing people to control and manage lucrative estates, March 1981.

1-135 *Soho Weekly News* finds New York City probate court riddled with payoffs, August 1976.

PRODUCT SAFETY
See regulation

PROFESSORS
See universities

PROPERTY TAXES
See also real estate

1-2986 *Columbia (Mo.) Daily Tribune* reports on Missouri's property tax reassessment program; inequities have been corrected but problems remain, Sept. 22, 1985.

1-2738 *Sun-Times* (Chicago) publishes articles concerning irregularities in the tax assessment of a Chicago landmark building; shows the owners got a $1 million real estate tax break on the basis of false information they supplied to the Cook County Assessor, October and December 1984.

1-2562 *Sun-Times* (Chicago) does series on property assessment; includes explanation of the assessment method update and several "how to's" about assuring a fair assessment or filing complaints, November 1983.

1-3346 *KING-TV* (Seattle) airs series on how many of Seattle's new skyscrapers are under-assessed through irregularities and loopholes, costing the city millions of dollars in lost tax revenues, December 21-22, 1981.

1-484 *Seattle Post-Intelligencer* uncovers the widespread practice of businessmen taking advantage of a tax loophole by refusing to pay their property taxes — often for years, October 1980.

1-722 *Albuquerque Tribune* series investigates inequities in the state's tax reassessment program that differs radically from county to county and is subject to political influence, January 1980.

1-3347 *KYW-TV* (Philadelphia) airs in-depth series, "The Tax Dodgers," on the poor handling of the collection of delinquent property taxes by the city of Philadelphia, 1980.

1-3192 *KYW-TV* (Philadelphia) investigates real estate tax collections in that city and finds that delinquency in payments is pervasive and laws to enforce tax collections are ignored by tax collectors, 1979.

1-332 *Wheeling (W.Va.) Intelligencer* runs articles on large under-assessments of industrial property by the West Virginia Tax Department, October 1978.

1-331 *Lincoln (Neb.) Journal* series, "Assessing Assessments," finds great inequities in Lancaster County property tax assessments, September 1978.

1-352 *Sunday Call-Chronicle* (Allentown, Pa.) does article on how developers take advantage of a state property tax provision intended to give farmers a tax break, December 1977.

1-2529 *The Des Moines Register* study indicates that high-cost homes are assessed at far less than their value and that assessments are not raised even when homes sell for far more than valued — all resulting in ordinary home owners carrying a bigger tax burden, December 1976.

PROSECUTORS
See also:
courts
lawyers

1-3100 *WXYZ-TV* (Detroit) reveals county prosecutor dropped utility fraud investigation against several auto dealers after receiving a $5,000 campaign contribution from their political action committee (he had lost the election a week before), 1984.

1-2559 *The Star-Herald* (Belton, Mo.) shows possible political motives of the newly elected county prosecutor who had dropped, reduced or failed to prosecute an unusually high proportion of serious felony cases; retribution against political enemies appeared to be motivation, August 1983.

1-3006 *WFAA-TV* (Dallas) airs story of how county prosecutor and a sheriff's deputy took advantage of a retarded man and got him and another innocent man convicted of murder, 1983.

PROSTITUTION
See also organized crime

1-2221 *Sun-Times* (Chicago) series, "Sex For Sale," looks at Chicago's growing sex industry, August 1982.

1-2307 *Shreveport (La.) Journal* looks into prostitution in Shreveport, apparently a booming business; reporters interviewed people involved in all aspects of the business, February 1982.

1-3308 *WVUE-TV* (New Orleans) airs in-depth series on the male prostitution industry in that city, uses hidden cameras and microphones, 1982.

1-4013 *Willamette Week* (Portland) runs article on the increasing presence of pimps on high school grounds in attempts to lure students to prostitution, 1981.

1-3144 *WHEC-TV* (Rochester, N.Y.) uses hidden cameras to explore that city's male prostitution racket, September 1980.

1-699 *St. Paul Dispatch* runs series on the death of a St. Paul prostitute who turned police informant; her murder investigation was bungled by the police and prosecutors; the series offers evidence that information was withheld from a grand jury and testimony of a key witness was destroyed, June 1980.

1-755 *Minneapolis Tribune* examination of police records finds politics had permitted an increase in prostitution and led to favoritism in the enforcement of vice laws and building code laws; the series prompted the resignation of the police chief, overhaul of vice squad, July-December 1979.

1-658 *The Honolulu Advertiser* does article on a prostitution ring that caters to Japanese tourists and is well-screened from police investigations, August 1979.

1-745 *The Record* (Hackensack, N.J.) article examines the massage parlor industry in New Jersey and the lack of police enforcement to control it, May 1979.

1-376 *The Register-Guard* (Eugene, Ore.) finds a massage parlor is owned by a convicted Portland sex merchant and has been operating in Eugene in apparent violation of state law for more than five years, December 1978-January 1979.

1-434 *Minneapolis Tribune* series investigates go-go dancing and prostitution in cities and towns of the upper Midwest and what efforts police have made in trying to put an end to them, May 1978.

1-359 *South Idaho Press* (Burley) deals with prostitution in that city as a business and as part of a larger picture that includes gambling and drugs, June 1977.

1-446 *The Knickerbocker News* (Albany, N.Y.) publishes series on prostitution in Albany and links between prostitutes and police, 1977.

PUBLIC HOUSING
See housing

PUBLIC UTILITIES
See also:
energy
nuclear energy

1-4047 *The San Francisco Bay Guardian* article examines the efforts by Pacific Gas and Electric to persuade the California Public Utilities Commission that its customers, not its stockholders, should foot the bill for costly mistakes the company made in constructing its Diablo Canyon Nuclear Power Plant, Nov. 27, 1985.

1-2014 *Columbia (Mo.) Daily Tribune* says ratepayers of Union Electric have to pay for the utility's mistakes in building a nuclear plant, July 1984.

1-2712 *The San Francisco Bay Guardian* does article on the move by California utilities to gain free and permanent rights to sell power from public river systems at a time when 50-year leases granted by Congress are expiring, Jan. 18, 1984.

1-2263 *The San Francisco Bay Guardian* blasts Pacific Gas & Electric Co. in series that includes PG&E's influence in local politics and how PG&E robs San Francisco of cheap power; tells who owns PG&E, October 1982.

1-2256 *Los Angeles Herald Examiner* does series on problems of General Telephone Co.; series says GTE, which it says supplies the worst telephone services in California, has relied upon maintenance of out of date equipment rather than modernization; among other problems are transient and inexperienced workforce, financial corner-cutting, poor forecasting of telephone growth and inadequate planning, August 1981.

1-2165 *Newsday* (Long Island) series investigates telephone rate boundaries and calling charges on Long Island and compares them with other areas in New York;

finds major inequities and discrepancies in New York Telephone's rate structure, February 1981.

1-810 *New Florida* article examines Florida Power and Light Co.'s fuel adjustment charge and waste and inefficiency by the utility's management, 1981.

1-471 *New Times Weekly* (Phoenix) series documents surveillance of anti-nuclear protesters by the Arizona Public Service Company, August 1980.

1-608 *Cadence* (East Grand Rapids, Mich.) shows why power plant construction projects are usually characterized by cost and time over-runs: greed, deliberate labor slowdowns, and, in the case of one Michigan plant, theft, 1980.

1-669 *The Billings (Mont.) Gazette* runs article on the labor cost overruns at the Montana Power/Puget Sound Power and Light's Colstrip power plants that totaled nearly $6 million, September 1979.

1-2527 *The Anderson (S.C.) Independent* tells how a major utility operates during a time of high energy costs and cynicism and outrage brought on by rising utility bills, 1978.

PUBLIC WORKS

1-248 *Newsday* (Long Island) investigation results in allegations of bid-rigging and blackmail which allow five Long Island contractors to dominate major public works projects, November 1984.

1-2552 *Monroe (La.) News-Star-World* examines the political and financial problems in Richwood, La., reveals a string of technical state law violations and federal agencies reluctant to help out; one example is kids playing in a raw sewage-filled ditch while a $1.2 million sewer system sat unfinished, October 1983.

RACE TRACKS
See gambling

RACKETEERING
See organized crime

RADIATION
See also:
cancer
carcinogens
nuclear energy
nuclear weapons

1-2782 *The Philadelphia Inquirer* magazine looks at a medical program in San Francisco that screens American citizens of Japanese ancestry who survived the bomb on Hiroshima, Aug. 4, 1985.

1-510 *St. Louis Post-Dispatch* series examines safety of six-month-old Callaway nuclear plant; looks at release of radiation and problem of inexperienced people operating plant, March 1985.

1-736 *The Philadelphia Inquirer* does series, "TMI: Accident Without an End," on the failure to safely clean up radioactivity at the plant and the hazards faced by workers assigned that job, February 1985.

1-825 *Daily Herald* (Arlington Heights, Ill.) runs series on a cab company breaking federal and state safety regulations by transporting radioactive pharmaceuticals to unauthorized locations, illegally using passenger cabs to transport them, and doing so in cabs with a host of mechanical and safety problems, February 1985.

1-2616 *Science 84* publishes article on the worst radioactive spill in North America that took place in Juarez, Mexico, when workers mistakenly sold the radioactive core of a cancer therapy machine for scrap metal, December 1984.

1-3099 *CBS News* reports internal studies done for the Department of Energy show an excess of deaths from cancer among nuclear defense workers exposed to uranium dust and radiation at numerous plants — which contradicts what the government says, October 1984.

1-558 *Science Digest* article details the dangers of everyday exposure to low-level radiation; cancer risks are going up with spread of high-tech medicine and the nuclear industry, March 1984.

1-2371 *Albuquerque Journal* series examines the Los Alamos Scientific Laboratory, nuclear waste and radioactive contamination; looks at risk of atomic mishap, self-monitoring, elevated cancer rate, radioactive dumping and more, January 1984.

1-3269 *WLS-TV* (Chicago) runs series on failure of the state to adequately inspect X-ray machines; findings include improperly calibrated equipment and machines operated by untrained workers, March 1982.

1-2987 *Mother Jones* article tells of a NASA program to subject cancer patients, often without their consent, to large doses of radiation to learn of possible effects of radiation on astronauts, September/October 1981.

1-760 *Lewiston (Idaho) Morning Tribune* found federal agencies had been dumping large volumes of low-level radioactive liquid waste into the Snake River Aquifer, Idaho's major water table; a subsequent probe exposed major accidental spills, November-December 1979.

1-558 *The Deseret News* (Salt Lake City) does articles on effects of radioactive fallout from atomic bomb testing in 1950s and early 1960s, 1979.

RAILROADS
See also transportation

1-4014 *The Saginaw (Mich.) News* series investigates safety hazards of trains carrying dangerous chemicals; bad rails, bad container valves, poor emergency planning for chemical accidents, failure of industry to adequately inform emergency response units of potential problems, March 17-22, 1985.

1-2759 *The Reporter Dispatch* (White Plains, N.Y.) runs articles on the excess labor costs on the Metro-North Commuter Railroad; reporter found one conductor on the line earned more than the railroad president, Nov. 12, 1984.

1-410 *The Morning Tribune* (Lewiston, Idaho) series describes the failures of the

Burlington Northern railroad to enforce federal safety regulations for maintenance staff that resulted in the death of at least one worker, November-December 1978.

1-2355 *Fort Worth Star-Telegram* explores the situation in which a Missouri-Pacific Railroad switchman, previous year's recipient of a safety award, was diagnosed by the company psychiatrist as "overly safety conscious" and then fired because of his attempts to correct the company's practice of mishandling train cars loaded with hazardous materials, November 1978.

1-311 *The Record* (Hackensack, N.J.) investigation of a small railroad finds its owner's dealings brought him a hefty profit while bankrupting the railroad, June 12-26, 1977.

RAPE

See also:
criminal justice
prisons

1-2985 *The Progressive* reports that up to twenty thousand men may be raped in prison each day, November 1985.

1-631 *The Honolulu Advertiser* looks at the growing problem of tourist rape as well as tourist generated crime in Hawaii, July 1979.

1-3208 *KDVM-TV* (Washington, D.C.) examines the psychological trauma for rape and incest victims because of Health, Education and Welfare regulations that require medicaid patients to report their name and address; patients have had their privacy violated because of the reporting requirement, 1979.

REAL ESTATE

See also:
housing
land
property taxes
redlining
slumlords

1-2989 *The Wall Street Journal* reports on the troubled Equity Programs Investment Corp. (EPIC), a real estate investment firm whose poor financial management led to its collapse, Aug. 30, 1985.

1-4015 *The San Francisco Bay Guardian* article details connections and inside lobbying that resulted in the quick approval of a new city highrise; the failure of the city's board of supervisors to restrict real estate lobbyists, August 7, 1985.

1-2988 *The Kansas City Star* publishes article describing the genesis of a complicated $32 million real estate deal and a plan to renovate part of Kansas City's downtown, July 14, 1985.

1-2738 *Sun-Times* (Chicago) runs articles concerning irregularites in the tax assessment of one of Chicago's landmark buildings and how the building's owners got a $1 million real estate tax break on the basis of false information they supplied to the county assessor, October and December 1984.

1-3127 *WCBS-TV* (New York) airs series on how renters can be ripped off through phony advertising fees, application fees, fixture fees, etc., November 1984.

1-2056 *Columbia (Mo.) Missourian* series, "Who Owns Broadway," describes landlords and rents along eight-block stretch of downtown Broadway, January 1984.

1-3056 *KTNV-TV* (Las Vegas) investigates planned freeway construction and finds former Senator Howard Cannon owns property at two planned interchanges; the highway department failed to condemn a subdivision under construction in the freeway's path until the homes were sold and occupied, 1984.

1-2426 *The Dallas Morning News* runs series on how a handful of promoters developed a scheme to use drastically inflated appraisals and pyramid-type land transactions to obtain more than $500 million in loans to develop Dallas condominium projects, December 1983.

1-2562 *Sun-Times* (Chicago) does series on property assessment; includes explanation of the assessment method update and several "how to's" about assuring a fair assessment or filing complaints, November 1983.

1-2016 *Los Angeles Times* finds unchecked growth, real estate speculation and official neglect combine to produce slums in suburban Orange County, October 1983.

1-2266 *The San Francisco Bay Guardian* publishes issue devoted to "The Manhattanization of San Francisco, 1965-1983;" story topics include the politics of Manhattanization and the movers and shakers behind it, October 1983.

1-240 *West County Times* (Pinole, Calif.) explores shady dealings of companies trying to build huge condominium complex on a landslide-prone site, September 1983.

1-2602 *The Bakersfield Californian* series explores soil problems in affluent subdivision; residents discovered homes were on shifting soil and sued devlopers, who sued soils engineer, who sued city, February 1983.

1-2418 *Our Town News* (New York) does stories on the conversion of a federal Title I housing project to condominium status without the approval of the City Planning Commission and the Board of Estimate, as is legally required, 1983.

1-3008 *WSMV-TV* (Nashville) airs series, "The Homesnatchers," on a real estate swindle pulled on people who are behind in mortgage payments and facing foreclosure; they think they are signing loan agreements, but are actually signing deeds to their homes, 1983.

1-2213 *The Miami Herald* issues reprint on illegal activities by developers who sought to make North Key Largo a resort community; avoidance of zoning laws, conflicts of interests, developments approved illegally, July 1982.

1-257 *San Diego Reader* finds that city's records on public land transactions are a mess and that public land holdings mysteriously have shrunk to nothing, July 1982.

1-2209 *The San Francisco Bay Guardian* does article, "The Rental Crisis," on problems tenants face in San Francisco; in a city with a one percent vacancy rate landlords can charge what they want despite rent control ordinance; agency charged with enforcement of ordinance is powerless and controlled by landlord interests, January 1982.

1-3349 *WJLA-TV* (Washington) airs series on how urban developers took millions from the federal government for a housing development for the poor, and left subcontractors, the government and the poor out in the cold, November 1981.

1-2376 *The Honolulu Star-Bulletin* series investigates the use of "time sharing" plans, the selling of periods of time that a buyer can spend in an apartment or condominium, November 1981.

1-573 *The Honolulu Star Bulletin* does series on the Paradise Palms, a time-share apartment rental business that engages in questionable practices including misrepresentation to consumers, March-July 1981.

1-2092 *Chicago Tribune* series says fraud, government bungling and political favoritism have turned a government program to curb urban blight into a system that rewards real estate speculators with big profits and often actually contributes to neighborhood deterioration, May 1981.

1-2231 *Seattle Post-Intelligencer* runs articles on two lawyers who forced peoples' houses to sheriff sales and then bought them at rock bottom prices for over ten years, February 1981.

1-473 *Napa (Calif.) Register* investigation finds developers are buying property in Lake Beryessa and offering it for sale to foreign investors for four times the price they paid, September 1980.

1-466 *Texas Monthly* runs article on who owns real estate in Texas, June 1980.

1-3348 *KYW-TV* (Philadelphia) reports on how two prominent real estate developers used political connections to get the city council to pass legislation that required the city to pay for a sewer line to a housing development planned by the developers, Feb. 6-7, 1980.

1-3350 *WZZM-TV* (Grand Rapids, Mich.) airs series on how a rural county real estate developer managed to win great influence with officials throughout the county's criminal justice system, 1980.

1-3240 *KYW-TV* (Philadelphia) details the shady dealings of real estate tax delinquent Arat Ali, who purchased abandoned and run-down houses in a scheme to net thousands of dollars from phony mortgage loans, 1980.

1-627 *The Sun* (Atlantic County, N.J.) series uses close scrutiny of real estate transactions, practices and law as basis for series about land speculation on parcels of casino land by organized crime in Atlantic City, January-June 1979.

1-676 *Willamette Valley Observer* (Eugene, Ore.) does series on the county chief executive's government land swap that benefitted his private real estate development firm, March 1979.

1-2312 *Los Angeles Herald Examiner* tells of former used car salesman who becomes real estate tycoon by purchasing — often from unaware owners — distressed property cheaply, then foreclosing and selling the houses for their true value, March 1979.

1-3220 *WCBS-TV* (New York) examines the housing rental market in New York and finds discrimination and rip-offs by rental referral services, 1979.

1-300 *The Record* (Hackensack, N.J.) investigation of a county real estate appraiser finds he was copying the work of other appraisers (county law requires two or more appraisers make independent audits), September 1978.

REDLINING
See also:
insurance
mortgages
real estate

1-267 *Knickerbocker News* (Albany, N.Y.) looks at redlining practices of Albany insurance companies, who deny fire and homeowner coverage to "undesirable neighborhoods," May 1984.

1-702 *Chicago Tribune* series, "The Black Tax," shows how members of the black community pay higher insurance rates and lose out on federal block grant funds and bank money as government officials and investors choose to funnel that money into "safer" investments in non-black neighborhoods of Chicago, June 1980.

1-438 *The Saginaw (Mich.) News* series shows how real estate agents "steer" home buyers in Saginaw to maintain racially segregated neighborhoods; strategies that realtors use include withholding listings and giving buyers hard-sell lines on others, February 1979.

1-114 *Los Angeles* shows how illegal bank practices can lead to real estate speculation and redlining in poor neighborhoods, November 1976.

1-151 *The Kansas City Star* describes redlining practices of banks in inner-city neighborhoods, July 1975.

REFORMATORIES
See prisons

REFUGEES
See also:
illegal aliens
immigration

1-4048 *The Miami Herald* runs article on Haitian refugees recently ordered out of the Bahamas and the prospects for another wave of them arriving in South Florida, Dec. 9, 1985.

1-4049 *The Stuart News* (Florida) series examines the adjustment of Guatemala's Kanjobal Indians, a very primitive people who were driven from their homeland by civil war, to their new life in Indiantown, Florida, Oct. 13-17, 1985.

1-2990 *APF Reporter* tells of the problems of resettlement of the Hmong refugees of Laos, almost half of whom live in California's San Joaquin Valley, Fall 1985.

1-2820 *Minneapolis Star and Tribune* does special section on the struggle of Hmong refugees in the Twin Cities; thousands of Hmong were recruited and armed by the Central Intelligence Agency to fight the secret war in Laos, April 21, 1985.

1-3102 *CBS News* reports Vietnam has set up underground currency collection mechanisms throughout the United States to gather money from refugees; money is needed to help prop up the financially strapped Vietnam government, 1984.

1-700 *La Crosse (Wis.) Tribune* series investigates criminal abuses of Cuban refugees at the Fort McCoy, Wis., resettlement center; the abuses include assault, theft and harassment and are carried on by Cuban refugee security patrols while U.S. government officials ignore them, July 1980.

1-124 *The Philadelphia Inquirer* reprint tells of desperate plight of Cambodian refugees on Thai border, June 22-26, 1980.

1-575 *Fort Myers (Fla.) News-Press* does special supplement on Haitian refugees on the West coast of Florida; the report documents political and economic repression in Haiti that causes the flight of natives to the United States and the unwelcome reception they receive upon arrival, which often includes jail and deportation, December 1979.

1-321 *The Philadelpia Inquirer* issues reprint on the exodus of refugees from Southeast Asia, May 1979.

REFUSE COLLECTION
See also:
organized crime
toxic wastes

1-216 *Newsday* (Long Island) articles show that mob is knee-deep in Long Island garbage; city officials also involved in dirty business, September 1984.

1-3244 *KWY Radio* (Philadelphia) looks at the festering problem of trash accumulation, from transport to disposal to energy conversion, December 1983.

1-4 *The Sun* (Baltimore) does investigation of refuse collection abuse, March 1982.

1-2159 *Minneapolis Star and Tribune* runs series on the business of collection and disposal of waste in that city; describes price war that largest hauler, Browning-Ferris Industries, is waging against small haulers to increase its share of the business; also, private waste-burning firms' attempt to obtain business from city officials, 1982.

1-2235 *News-American* (Baltimore) finds city sanitation workers charging immigrant store owners for a free service, August 1981.

1-2192 *The Milwaukee Journal* investigation finds too much loafing by refuse collectors and too little management supervision, June 1981.

1-808 *The Milwaukee Journal* does articles on the failure of a "pioneer" garbage recycling plant owned by the American Can Co., and the added cost to the city, March 1981.

1-836 *San Diego Union* articles investigate trash hauling industry as the county prepares to award waste disposal contract, 1981.

1-738 *The Clarion-Ledger* (Jackson, Miss.) series profiles Browning-Ferris Industries, Inc., a giant in the waste disposal industry, which has earned a bad reputation because of poorly run dumps, alleged attempts to corrupt public officials and work-related health problems, December 1980.

1-38 *Newsday* (Long Island) runs investigation of mob and refuse collection, May 1978.

1-2514 *Newsday* (Long Island) does series on refuse disposal and the rising costs and health hazards associated with it; waste metals and energy and potential poisonous chemicals leaking from dumps are possible results, 1978.

1-426 *Trenton (N.J.) Times* runs series on municipal garbage collection monopoly and how the lack of competition costs taxpayers thousands of extra dollars, July 1977.

1-849 *The Indianapolis Star* articles say Sanitas Service Corporation, a national waste hauler, made thousands of dollars in "political payments" to monopolize area landfill business; also, national allegations of bribes, kickbacks and gifts by the company, May 1977.

REGULATION
See also:
federal government
state government

1-94 *The Milwaukee Journal* issues reprint of investigation of the Wisconsin Department of Regulation and Licensing which regulates a mixed bag of licensed occupations — including surgeons, surveyors, cosmetologists and private detectives; finds widespread failures and explains why, November 1984.

1-2757 *Roanoke Times & World-News* examines the Virginia Board of Medicine and how ineffectively it protects the public from doctors who are thought to be incompetent, impaired by drugs or alcohol, or dishonest, Oct. 6-10, 1984.

1-3098 *CBS News* reports on the danger of pools, hot tubs and whirlpools constructed with only one drain; if grate is missing powerful suction can entrap a person; no government agency requires that grates be maintained, August 1984.

1-2735 *Detroit Free Press* looks at the machinery for regulating physicians in the state of Michigan; reporter found the licensing system inadequate for protecting citizens from incompetent doctors, April 1-8, 1984.

1-2185 *The Des Moines Register* article indicates that under Reagan administration, American poultry industry is increasingly allowed to conduct its own testing for harmful chemical residues, to decide when potential problems should be reported to the government and other functions once handled by the U.S. Department of Agriculture, April 1983.

1-2123 *Mother Jones* and *Center for Investigative Reporting* reprint, "The Illusion of Safety," examines the entire public and private regulatory apparatus intended to guard the public by testing products; system is found to be bloated and ineffective, February 1983.

RELIGION
See also:
charities
cults
evangelism
nonprofit organizations

1-4050 *Mother Jones* article describes the strange marriage of America's Christian Right and the Reverend Sun Myung Moon's Unification Church, a union brought about by mutual interest in money and anti-communism; discusses the possible implications on American politics, January 1986.

1-4016 *The Progressive* publishes article on the religious television empire of Pat Robertson and the use of state-of-the-art broadcast techniques by right-wing Protestant fundamentalists, September 1985.

1-2306 *Columbia Journalism Review* publishes survey of Rev. Sun Myung Moon's far-flung media operations, including *The Washington Times*, November/ December 1984.

1-457 *The Chicago Reporter* articles assess the presence and commitment to that city of Catholic, Protestant and Jewish religious groups as white members move to the suburbs and city membership is increasingly made up of minorities, November 1984.

1-2785 *The Charlotte Observer* runs article on a Charlotte-based TV ministry known as "PTL" whose leaders spent more than $500,000 on expensive cars and real estate in California while pleading for donations from viewers to keep the ministry going, Oct. 5, 1984.

1-2640 *Williston (N.D.) Daily Herald* investigates operations of a California-based religious survivalist group with an active community in North Dakota, July-September 1984.

1-3107 *KXLY-TV* (Spokane, Wash.) series examines Fatima Crusade, a conservative offshoot of the Roman Catholic Church known for rigid discipline; exposes child abuse and sexual abuse, April 1984.

1-2670 *The Modesto (Calif.) Bee* runs series on the Universal Life Church, a mail-order ministry that sells diplomas and certificates of sainthood for small donations as a form of tax protest, March 11-16, 1984.

1-44 *The Press-Enterprise* (Riverside, Calif.) follows paper trail that leads to discovery of an unsecured, unrepaid loan of $225,000 in Roman Catholic diocesean funds; loan was made to man then on probation for mail fraud and later sent up for defrauding a savings and loan institution, February 1984.

1-2570 *The Wall Street Journal* looks at the financial empire of the Mormon church — its business holdings, business influence through board seats, and more, November 1983.

1-2049 *The Denver Post* does article on entrance of Scientology Church — one of the wealthiest and most controversial religious organizations — into the oil business, November 1983.

1-2475 *Palouse Empire Daily News* (Pullman, Wash.) explores the behind-the-scenes political machinations of a Pullman church, which tried to place three members in the city council and one on the school board, October 1983.

1-2035 *The News-Sentinel* (Fort Wayne) ties deaths of 52 people — most of them babies and children — to Faith Assembly, a new and rapidly growing church that teaches its members to avoid doctors, May 1983.

1-2434 *The Charlotte Observer* articles investigate the financial conduct of the PTL Club, a syndicated Christian ministry television show, headed by Rev. Jim Bakker; among other things, PTL offers receipts for donations that were never made to businesses it deals with, May 1983.

1-2447 *Flint (Mich.) Journal* reports on a "purification" center that is a front recruiting center for the Scientology Church; found improprieties by the church, February-April 1983.

1-2347 *The Denver Post* issues reprint, "Utah: Inside the Church State," on the control and influence of the Mormon church in Utah, November 1982.

1-2187 *The Sun* (San Bernardino) series examines loss of $21 million by the Adventist Church through the bankruptcy of developer Donald Davenport; close financial ties between certain church officials and Davenport violated church guidelines, May 1982.

1-2389 *Sun-Times* (Chicago) series investigates the misappropriation of church funds by Chicago's Cardinal John P. Cody; allegations church funds were illegally diverted to Cody's personal friends, September-November 1981.

1-2309 *The Record* (Hackensack, N.J.) series, "How Jerry Falwell Wants to Change U.S.," probes the background and dealings of the leader of the Moral Majority, June 1981.

1-643 *Dallas Times Herald* Sunday Magazine, *Westward,* profiles Oral Roberts and his calling to build a hospital despite money problems, law-suits and the criticism of the entire medical community of Tulsa, January 1981.

1-776 *The News-Sun* (Waukegan, Ill.) series investigates self-styled minister L.R. Davis and his nationally known Good News Singers; findings include evidence that Davis was pressuring sailors to desert, luring them into homosexual affairs and forcing them to turn over their paychecks, which he used for personal expenses, February-May 1980.

1-2102 *Gannett News Service* issues reprint on a small order of monks in rural Pennsylvania who squandered millions of dollars in donations, loans and investments through mismanagement and "immoral" lifestyles; Pope John Paul II quashed a five-year investigation, 1979.

1-415 *The Record* (Hackensack, N.J.) series looks at a New Jersey radio preacher, Clinton White, who solicits funds from audiences and parishioners to invest in pyramid schemes, September 1978.

1-349 *Quad-City Times* (Davenport, Iowa) runs series on a woman who wears a nun's habit and claims to have healing powers — who also has a habit of obtaining money and property from believers, May 1978.

1-104 *The Christian Science Monitor* examines church-run organizations that raised money through bond sales and are running into deep trouble, Dec. 5, 1977.

1-285 *The Record* (Hackensack, N.J.) runs article on the Church of Bible Understanding, which persuades young people to join its communes and pays them virtually nothing for working in the organization's rug cleaning business, September 1977.

1-281 *The Record* (Hackensack, N.J.) does article on The Order Ecumenical, an intensely religious organization that covertly sponsors seemingly non-religious, patriotic "Town Meetings" across the country; the meetings raise millions of dollars from corporations and are used to recruit members, July 1977.

1-278 *The Record* (Hackensack, N.J.) does articles on mismanagement and misconduct by a priest who ran a Catholic alcohol and drug abuse clinic, 1977.

1-343 *The News-Sun* (Waukegan, Ill.) runs articles on improprieties at a local Methodist Church; minister was misrepresenting himself as a therapist and conducting nude therapy sessions; minister stole church funds and was misusing a parishioner's personal funds, 1977.

11-279 *The Record* (Hackensack, N.J.) articles investigate improprieties of a pastor that contributed to the bankruptcy of his church, November 1976.

1-277 *The Record* (Hackensack, N.J.) runs series on corruption by two former officials of a Roman Catholic social service agency, June 1975.

1-249 *The Manitoba Tribune* explores the benefits and discounts available to anyone who has $10 to become an ordained minister by mail, September 1970.

RENTAL PROPERTY
See:
real estate
slumlords

REPAIR RIP-OFFS
1-3057 *KCTV-TV* (Kansas City) investigation of seven local television repair companies finds various unethical practices, including inflating repair costs and replacing good parts with bad ones, March 1984.

1-2462 *The Record* (Hackensack, N.J.) documents how a television repair shop routinely and systematically defrauds its customers through false billing and damaging televisions when customers declined repair after exorbitant estimates, June 1983.

1-2171 *St. Petersburg Times* series, "Hazardous to Your Home," looks at home repair rip-offs; agencies supposed to protect consumers are ineffective, December 1982.

1-3254 *WOKR-TV* (Rochester, N.Y.) shows how one Rochester repairman persuades homeowners to agree to expensive, unnecessary repairs and how the state may also charge customers for unnecessary services, Sept. 2 and Dec. 22, 1982.

1-6 *Newport News (Va.) Daily Press* finds cost of repairs of public vehicles inflated in that city, March 1981.

1-2528 *The Clarion-Ledger* (Jackson, Miss.) runs two-part series showing that flood victims were overcharged for electrical repair work; story stemmed from Action Line complaints, April/May 1979.

1-3 *The Charleston (W.Va.) Gazette* reports on roofing rip-off, January 1972.

RESEARCH

1-2991 *The Wall Street Journal* reports on research fraud; faced with intense competitive pressures, some scientists are faking data to publish findings and win grants, July 12, 1985.

1-2659 *The Journal-American* (Bellevue, Wash.) series documents how data from Nazi death camp experiments have entered the body of knowledge being used by modern scientists; series explores the scientific and moral dilemmas of using the information; reporter did extensive research through old scientific journals, April 15-17, 1984.

1-3265 *WAFB-TV* (Baton Rouge) studies secret drug research by the state and medical community and abuses of informed consent, May 27, 1982.

1-2473 *Lexington (Ky.) Herald* documents that Kentucky's Tobacco and Health Research Institute wasted millions of dollars on unnecessary and unpublished research and unneeded supplies; steered away from research on smoking and health; and allocated research funds on the basis of politics, not science, March 1982.

1-18 *The Kansas City Times* shows doctor at Veterans Administration hospital in Leavenworth, Kan., deceives some veterans participating in study and violates VA guidelines, 1981-1982,.

1-2368 *The News World* (New York) runs investigation into the misuse of millions of dollars of federal funds by the Eppley Cancer Research Institute; also contains criticism of the center's failure to make sufficiently substantial progress, October 1979.

RESTAURANTS
See inspections

REVENUE BONDS
See:
bonds
special districts

ROADS
See also construction

1-2294 *The Daily Oklahoman* (Oklahoma City) shows how that state lost about $28 million a year on highway construction because of bid rigging, lack of stiff competition among contractors and failure of transportation officials to get best deal for the money, June 1983.

1-2567 *Fort Lauderdale News and Sun-Sentinel* study shows faulty or improper designs resulted in premature deterioration of 200 miles of Interstate 10 in North Florida; also shows the nation's interstate system is wearing out faster than anticipated, largely because it was built with outdated research, March-June 1983.

1-3288 *WCCO-TV* (Minneapolis) looks at the average highway worker in Minnesota; does he repair roads quickly and efficiently or spend the day leaning on a shovel; evidence supports the latter, Oct. 11-14, 1982.

1-2111 *Sunday Call-Chronicle* (Allentown, Pa.) series examines 20-year history of a proposed 36-mile stretch of interstate highway now nearing completion; construction was blocked in courts and government bureaucracies, November 1979.

1-2314 *The Clarion-Ledger* (Jackson, Miss.) shows a Maryland firm was awarded a million-dollar highway contract, apparently as a result of political influence after two state highway commissioners met with two U.S. senators who knew the firm's president, February 1977.

1-117 *The Kansas City Star* shows that the company supplying crushed rock for highway construction juggled weights, costing taxpayers millions of dollars, 1975.

SAVINGS AND LOANS

See also:
banks
credit unions

1-176 *The Wall Street Journal* shows shaky foundation of IMI — Investment Mortgage International Inc. — which lures weak savings and loans into making tenuous investments, June 1984.

1-2065 *American Banker* story shows Federal Home Loan Bank Board overruled staff recommendation and approved thrift acquisition in which James G. Watt played a key role, May 1984.

1-2701 *Grand Forks (N.D.) Herald* runs series on the financial standing of area savings and loan institutions; one institution was shown to have had to merge with another because of major losses in real estate loans, Jan. 29-Feb. 1, 1984.

1-2088 *Sun-Times* (Chicago) series finds 298 savings and loans in Illinois lost a total of $300 million in the last six months of 1981, while only 41 earned a profit; computer analysis was used to examine financial statements of every federally insured S&L in the country and to trace patterns, May 1982.

1-130 *Charleston (W.Va.) Gazette* shows savings and loan scandal in West Virginia 1970-1975; ends in bankruptcy and president pleading guity to fraud, January 1971.

SCHOOLS
See also:
discrimination
drug abuse
education
teachers
universities

1-2992 *Syracuse Herald-American* explores teacher frustrations, student boredom and lack of quality in central New York classrooms, April 1985.

1-325 *The Charlotte Observer* runs articles on the rise of academic prep schools, fundamentalist Christian schools and private schools in general in the New South, April 1985.

1-612 *Macon (Ga.) Telegraph and News* runs series on incompetent teachers in the Bibb County school system; how they are identified, improved or removed from the system, February 1985.

1-2666 *The Clarion-Ledger* (Jackson, Miss.) series investigates abuses in leasing of school trust lands originally set aside for the financial benefit of public schools; reporters used public land-lease and deed records and found that much of the valuable land was being leased for pennies an acre, sometimes to the public officials in charge of managing the land, Nov. 11-16, 1984.

1-3115 *WREG-TV* (Memphis) series examines the waste of taxpayer dollars through federal grants and loans to proprietary schools and private business schools which often exaggerate job placement and put emphasis on financial aid while offering poor-quality education, November 1984.

1-2585 *The Chicago Reporter* assesses in-depth an "average" Chicago public high school in a way that assessment can be applied to schools citywide; minimal expectations were not being met and student attrition rate approached 80 percent, September 1984.

1-355 *The Chicago Reporter* runs article on the history of a West Chicago suburb that has gerrymandered and enlarged schools to stay segregated despite a growing black population, April 1984.

1-186 *The Charlotte Observer* overview of public schools in North and South Carolina shows neither state provides acceptable minimum standards of education for all children, December 1983.

1-2557 *The Jersey Journal* (Jersey City) finds that city's school board attorney who was also political campaigner for the mayor charged the board for work he never did, December 1983.

1-2541 *The Albuquerque Tribune* has an undercover "student" explore education from the inside at Albuquerque's largest high school; uncovers widespread use of drugs on school grounds, poor teaching and more, March-July 1983.

1-2431 *The Lousiville Times* and *Courier-Journal* do articles on school superintendent who wrote a check on a school account for her own use, then prepared false documents and stories to mislead investigators, June 1983.

1-2113 *The Kansas City Star* series, "K.C. Schools: On the Brink," gives overview of inadequacies of the city's school system, May 1983.

1-2395 *St. Louis Post-Dispatch* runs articles on irregularities in St. Louis County's Special School District board; closed door meetings, refusal to supply information to the public, no-bid contract system and hiring of friends, February-May 1982; updated 1983.

1-3002 *KNXT-TV* (Los Angeles) investigates taxpayer subsidization and regulation of trade schools and vocational colleges, 1983.

1-97 *The Boston Globe* publishes series on Boston public schools — their plight and future, June 1982.

1-2242 *The Philadelphia Inquirer* does series on city's school system; goes beyond the usual overview and examines teacher benefits, union control of school system, ethnic factions' control of bureaucracy and teacher pilfering, September 1981.

1-2296 *The News-Express* (San Antonio) investigation of political influence in San Antonio school district reveals pattern of political patronage — job assignments connected to political favor or disfavor, school officials expected to support the board's ruling clique, August 1981.

1-2278 *The Charleston (W.Va.) Gazette* studies political corruption in some rural West Virginia school systems, May 1981.

1-2078 *The Courier-News* (Bridgewater, N.J.) finds school board attorney overcharged the board thousands of dollars, April 1981.

1-3176 *KITV-TV* (Honolulu) investigates violence and vandalism in that city's schools and finds many occurrences of assault and vandalism are not reported to the state Department of Education, 1981.

1-3169 *WFAA-TV* (Fort Worth) reveals that the school district's transportation superintendent and others wasted $500,000 of taxpayer funds for purchase of unnecessary equipment and other items; information was obtained through use of computers to analyze district financial records, January-May 1980.

1-815 *Worcester (Mass.) Telegram* article finds high schools receiving kickbacks from photographers chosen for senior class yearbook projects, April 1979.

1-579 *Daily Hampshire Gazette* (Northampton, Mass.) runs articles on abuses by a school superintendent who managed the district as his own private fiefdom, 1979.

1-828 *Burlington County (N.J.) Times-Advertiser* runs articles on investigation of financial misconduct and child sex abuse by a teacher and township committeeman, 1979.

1-3195 *WCBD-TV* (Charleston, S.C.) examination of minority school system finds community apathy is responsible for chronic segregation, teacher incompetence and poor student achievement, 1979.

SECURITIES
See also:
bonds
commodities
fraud

1-2996 *The Wall Street Journal* studies the world of Wall Street's activist short sellers and the intricate strategies they use to shape bad news about a company for their own profit, Sept. 5, 1985.

1-2994 *The Wall Street Journal* reports that big money managers are relying more and more on the Keefe, Bruyette & Woods bank-rating scale; finds the rating service broadly influences bank funding and adds to nervousness among bankers, Aug. 6, 1985.

1-4017 *Business Week* article describes the problem of insider trading, which is running rampant despite a law enforcement crackdown and toughened penalties, April 29, 1985.

1-2995 *The Wall Street Journal* defines "repos" (repurchase agreements) within the government-securities market, April 22, 1985.

1-459 *Kansas City Business Journal* publishes series on shady business practices and stock trading by Billings Corp., a Missouri computer manufacturing and mineral development company, March 12-Dec. 30, 1984.

1-2046 *The Wall Street Journal* does article on newly active role of once timid limited partners; limited partners have begun charging general partners with securities fraud violations, August 1984.

1-2024 *The Kansas City Times* looks at bank vice president who sold millions of dollars in stock options, using his bank's name, in fraud scheme that flim-flammed Shearson/American Express; Shearson keeps quiet to avoid embarrassment, May 1984.

1-2468 *Common Cause* investigation of alleged securities trading violations by Thomas Reed, then a possible candidate for National Security Advisor, reveals forgeries and false information and an unusual settlement with the Securities and Exchange Commission allowing him to claim his innocence, January/February 1983.

1-2293 *Institutional Investor* runs exhaustive analysis on the collapse of Drysdale Government Securities; possible collapse for the market in U.S. government securities, September 1982.

1-3137 *WAND-TV* (Decatur, Ill.) examines possibly illegal stock sales by Dura-Plex Industries Inc.; report alleges the company misstated its financial picture and questions the stock sales activities of the company president; poor regulation of stock sales by the state, March 1981.

1-3263 *KREM-TV* (Spokane, Wa.) investigates two investment companies in Spokane; although customers and agencies do not detect abuses, the investigation reveals sloppy and deceptive business practices and possible mismanagement of large amounts of money, 1980.

SECURITIES AND EXCHANGE COMMISSION
See securities

SEGREGATION
See:
discrimination
minorities
redlining

SEWAGE
See:
public works
water pollution

SEXUAL HARASSMENT
See discrimination

SHERIFF

See also police

1-4051 *The Sacramento Bee* series examines violence in the Sacramento County Jail; allegations of brutality by sheriff's deputies, allegations that the sheriff refuses to look into complaints of brutality for fear of political retribution, Nov. 10-11, 1985.

1-2751 *St. Petersburg Times* examines a sheriff's department and uncovers various problems, from inept investigating to criminal action on the part of the sheriff and the deparment, December 1983-October 1984.

1-3302 *WZZM-TV* (Grand Rapids) airs two series on how Michigan sheriffs illegally profit from federally donated food; sheriffs use the food which is earmarked for non-profit programs in their for-profit jail kitchens, Feb. 6-9 and July 16-18, 1984.

1-207 *State Times* (Baton Rouge) reveals that sheriff's deputies collected thousands of dollars in witness fees not owed them by falsely claiming to be off-duty when subpoenaed, September 1984.

1-2629 *The Ledger and Enquirer* (Columbus, Ga.) runs series on how a rural Georgia sheriff fixed hundreds of traffic tickets over a period of years by arranging for them to be transferred out of Probate Court to him, for disposition in Superior Court, April 1983.

1-2442 *Milwaukee Sentinel* articles find irregularities in the Milwaukee County Sheriff's Department; deputies were using their positions to acquire goods, doing private work while on county's time-clock, 1983.

1-205 *The Tulsa Tribune* runs articles on corruption in a rural Oklahoma county; raise questions about quality of law enforcement — allegations of payoffs, jail brutality and possibility that police chief killed one of his officers; organized crime thought to be involved in other murders, February 1982.

1-3143 *KAIT-TV* (Jonesboro, Ariz.) investigates a county sheriff and finds a pattern of fraud in which the county was billed for unwarranted jail expenses, prisoner abuse was allowed and prominent residents were favored, 1980.

1-313 *Akron Beacon Journal* series, "The Untouchables," on the power and abuse of power by Ohio's sheriffs, March 1979.

1-339 *The News-Sun* (Waukegan, Ill.) runs articles on sheriff's deputies having sex with prostitutes while making prostitution arrests, June 1978.

SHIPPING

See also transportation

1-4052 *Chicago Tribune* article says while Port of Chicago maritime operations have languished, port district contracts have gone to allies and important politicians; the board that sets policy consists entirely of political appointees, none of whom have maritime expertise, Aug. 11, 1985.

1-2411 *News-American* (Baltimore) runs series on the unsafe conditions of America's aging merchant shipping fleet; the failure of the Coast Guard's inspections of ships, July 1983.

1-2336 *The Philadelphia Inquirer* reprint finds government aid programs have made it profitable to keep old, run-down merchant ships at sea, costing the lives of many merchant seamen, May 1983.

1-2330 *The Times-Picayune* (New Orleans) series, "The Troubled Port," reports on the failures of the Port of New Orleans' management and operations that have allowed the port's importance to slip to more aggressive competitors, June 1982.

1-590 *The Philadelphia Inquirer* issues reprint of investigation into United States Merchant Marine Academy, a private institution turned into a private preserve, August 1979.

SLUMLORDS
See also:
housing
real estate

1-235 *Los Angeles Times* series uses numerous documents to detail illegal practices of big time L.A. slumlord; series precipitated legal action, passage of reform legislation, April-December 1982.

1-2396 *The Orlando Sentinel* investigation of who owns city's slum housing finds many leaders in city business and government are owners and that they use their positions of power to ignore city housing laws, November 1982.

SMALL BUSINESS ADMINISTRATION
See also business

1-2997 *Newsday* (Long Island) investigates government loans to Long Island businessmen; uncovers conflicts of interests and sloppy lending practices by the Small Business Administration and the New York Job Development Authority, May 5-9, 1985.

1-2747 *The Kansas City Star* looks at the Small Business Administration's practice of making guaranteed bank loans to high-risk borrowers and finds loan failures on SBA guarantees are disproportionately higher than on conventional bank loans, Nov. 25-26, 1984.

1-3124 *KCNC-TV* (Denver) reports on how Small Business Administration approved phony loans in return for kickbacks from those loans, 1984.

1-625 *The Florida Times-Union* (Jacksonville) looks at documents that yield details of how Small Business Administration and credit union members got burned when credit union made illegal loan to unqualified borrower, February 1979.

SMOKING
See cigarettes

SMUGGLING
See also drug smuggling

1-148 *The Daily Report* (Torrance, Calif.) discusses rare bird-smugglers caught in Los Angeles by customs agents, Feb. 14, 1978.

SOCIAL SECURITY

1-2401 *Newsday* (Long Island) issues reprint on Reagan administration handling of Social Security, "The Disability Nightmare"; David Stockman conceived the plan that cut aid to thousands of the disabled in order to cut costs, March 1983.

1-480 *The Sacramento Union* series details how the disability insurance program of the Social Security system is bedeviled by delayed checks and overpayments; discourages beneficiaries from going back to work, February 1980.

1-689 *The Trentonian* (Trenton, N.J.) series examines how New Jersey prisoners are able to collect social security disability payments through an elaborate scam by faking mental illness, August 1979.

1-146 *The Kansas City Star* series gives excellent background on social security system; portrayal of system includes soaring costs, unequal distribution of benefits, internal management problems, etc., October 1978.

SOCIAL SERVICES
See:
day care centers
housing
nursing homes
social security
welfare

SPACE
See National Aeronautics and Space Administration

SPECIAL DISTRICTS
See also:
city government
conflicts of interests
county government
housing
state government

1-2172 *St. Paul Pioneer Press* examines the Metropolitan Waste Control Commission; finds pollution control equipment doesn't work, construction delays and overruns cost millions of dollars, consulting contracts go to friends, May 1983.

1-25 *The Desert Sun* (Palm Springs) runs investigation of Palm Desert, Calif., special water district, August 1981.

1-134 *Daily Herald* (Arlington Heights, Ill.) looks at sanitary district of Cook County, Ill., that is found to form million-dollar taxing agency with little accountability; it is fraught with conflicts of interests, violations of state law, and dubious money management policies, June 1978.

SPORTS
See also:
business
college athletics
gambling

1-512 *The Kansas City Star* says Jackson County Sports Complex Authority legally steered taxpayers' money to desired destinations, including friends, associates and people with favored political connections, May 12, 1985.

1-2750 *St. Petersburg Times* investigates violations of National Collegiate Athletic Association rules in the football program at the University of Florida; series found the university's classrooms and administration were implicated in the violations as well as athletic department, April 1983-December 1984.

1-3120 *KOIN-TV* (Portland) reports on problems with Oregon's boxing regulation; lack of statewide regulation allows medically banned fighters to fight outside Portland; man is illegally allowed to manage fighters, hire trainers and promote fights by local boxing commission, which operates without supervision, November 1984.

1-2009 *Los Angeles Times* says Olympic athletes continue to use drugs despite drug testing; use of steroids is widespread, January 1984.

1-2476 *St. Paul Pioneer Press* takes in-depth look at the Minnesota Twins' financial problems, October 1983.

1-2299 *Akron Beacon Journal* looks at Arthur Modell, controlling force behind the Cleveland Browns football team, who has his public image as general good guy altered by three lawsuits filed by a stockholder, January 1983.

1-256 *The Arizona Republic* (Phoenix) uses Internal Revenue Service and court records to document financial woes of Phoenix Inferno Soccer team; also article says the team was built on drug money, with the so-called owner serving as a front for five Miami businessmen connected to the Cuban underworld, 1983.

1-2505 *Fort Lauderdale News and Sun-Sentinal* runs series about links between drug smuggling and prominent sports figures, including National Football League players, offshore powerboat racers and car racers, June 1982.

1-2191 *The Hartford Courant* series profiles William Chipman, founder of a soccer team and a master manipulator of the limited partnership; Chipman gave investors false information, mismanaged and undercapitalized the venture and dipped into other investments in effort to save the team, August 1981.

1-2345 *The Philadelphia Inquirer* issues reprint on how a doctor prescribed and two other baseball fans delivered amphetamines to players on the Philadelphia Phillies; state prosecutes the fans, not the ballplayers, July 1981.

1-2257 *Los Angeles Herald Examiner* runs series on use of drugs by professional athletes, March 1981.

1-517 *Gannett News Service* issues reprint, "Money in Sports," on the business aspects of American sports, February 1981.

1-719 *Beaver County (Pa.) Times* reports on sweetheart deal for a public tennis program that handsomely rewarded the private operator of the sports facility; reporter searched through shoeboxes full of records in the basement of the county building to show that the private operator took 90 percent of the tennis program's $500,000 income, November 1980.

1-452 *Sports Illustrated* examines the death of middleweight Willie Classen and the shortcomings in the boxing system that led to his death, March 1980.

1-3351 *WAST-TV* (Albany, N.Y.) airs in-depth series on over-spending and mismanagement in construction for the 1980 Lake Placid Winter Olympics, January 1980.

1-3158 *KNXT-TV* (Los Angeles) examines the rise and fall of the Thunderbolts, a start-up professional football team, which defrauded ticket-holding fans with distorted claims about star players and coaches, 1980.

1-2361 *The Miami Herald* examines jai alai, a legalized betting sport for 44 years, as Florida law enforcement begins to look into possible arson, game fixing and state agency cover-up in connection with the sport, September 1979.

1-624 *Sports Illustrated* looks at spreading scandal of corruption, including game-rigging, in jai alai.

STATE GOVERNMENT
See also:
city government
conflicts of interests
county government
extradition
inspections
lawyers
liquor
politicians
regulation
special districts
toxic wastes
water

1-2999 *Syracuse Herald-American* makes use of financial disclosure forms to tell story of state legislators receiving money from medical and legal groups' political action committees while deciding on changes in the state's medical malpractice insurance system, August 11, 1985.

1-2998 *Syracuse Herald-American* looks at flight logs to evaluate the propriety of Gov. Mario Cuomo's use of state aircraft, May 12, 1985.

1-2740 *Miwaukee Sentinel* looks at a racing promotion contract awarded to a new firm by the board of the Wisconsin State Fair; reporter found the firm did not comply with the contract and subsequently lost $225,000, Nov. 6-9, 1984.

1-3242 *WTLC Radio* (Indianapolis) looks at past corruption in Indiana government and weaknesses in current laws that could lead to more corruption; makes recommendations, including establishing a "super watchdog" commission and expanding authority of State Ethics Commission and attorney general, Oct. 14, 21, 28 and Nov. 4, 1984.

1-2671 *The Advertiser* (Montgomery, Ala.) runs series on a friend and political associate of Alabama Governor George Wallace who was overpaid almost $500,000 for land on which the state built a river port, March-July 1984.

1-2779 *The Plain Dealer* (Cleveland) investigates abuses in the state agency that donates federal surplus equipment to towns, schools and charities in Ohio; reporter finds equipment was being diverted for personal use by officials, or otherwise misused and squandered, February-June 1984.

1-3059 *WTSP-TV* (Tampa) investigation of state Department of Transportation finds a head of maintenance purchased supplies from a company he owned; investigation also found poor management and inefficient vehicle repair system costs the state thousands of dollars, 1984.

1-2493 *Valley News Dispatch* (Tarentum, Pa.) article looks at how governor is using state monies in paying out large fees to law firms which have supported his bid for re-election, November 1983.

1-3043 *KTVI-TV* (St. Louis) finds Missouri state representative violated the law by failing to disclose he had introduced legislation to help his security firm and that he used a state paid trip to Florida to drum up business for his firm, September 1983.

1-2034 *The Boston Globe* reprint, "Power and Privilege," examines Massachusetts state legislature; it is controlled by two men, government practices lead to waste, etc., September 1983.

1-2425 *Rocky Mountain News* runs series, "The Legislature: In Whose Interest?", on inner workings of the Nevada Legislature; topics include special interest pressure, influence of campaign contributions, vote trading, backroom deals and drunkenness on duty, July 1983.

1-2482 *Newport News (Va.) Daily Press* and *Times-Herald* run articles on an obsecure bill introduced into the Virginia Legislature with the sole purpose of fianancially benefitting an ex-legislator, March 1983.

1-3246 *KMOX Radio* (St. Louis) looks at Missouri's expenditures on state services and finds the future of police protection, health care, higher education and welfare services jeopardized due to inadequate staffing and funding, Jan. 3-12, 1983.

1-2481 *Newport News (Va.) Daily Press* and *Times-Herald* run articles on the existence of a $100,000 slush fund held by the governor; because of a legal loophole, there was no requirement that the fund be disclosed or accounted for, January 1983.

1-2487 *The Birmingham News* publishes articles on the first year of George Wallace's fourth term as governor, 1983.

1-17 *Georgia Gazette* reports the Georgia Department of Labor commissioner using state employees for personal services and campaign contributions, 1981; later articles on his control of the state's largest political machine and use of extortion, prostitution, gambling, theft, obstruction of justice, fraud and perjury, 1983.

1-3042 *WBTV-TV* (Charlotte) finds North Carolina's attorney general failed to disclose a loan made to political supporters; the loan was part of deal that helped them get thousands of dollars worth of state business, 1983.

1-3037 *WIS-TV* (Columbia, S.C.) airs series on a state industrial commissioner charged with administering worker compensation claims who has filed seven claims, the last awarding himself $57,000, 1983.

1-3013 *WBRZ-TV* (Baton Rouge) documentary traces the business dealings of Louisiana governor Edwin Edwards and his involvement with an insurance company that he helped to get lucrative states contracts, 1983.

1-223 *The Evening Sun* (Baltimore) series, which led to resignation of state insurance commissoner, uncovers abuses of power, February-December 1982.

1-2561 *Nevada State Journal* studies the influence of special interests on both the legislative and executive branches of the Nevada government; special interests examined include the greyhound racing industry, optometrists, mobile home park owners, hospital associations and more, August 1982.

1-194 *St. Louis Post-Dispatch* publishes insider view of the network of special interests behind the state legislature, April 1982.

1-2228 *The Honolulu Advertiser* runs articles on the business relationship between the state of Hawaii and the governor's chief fund raiser; companies owned by the political insider get special treatment from the state and do a lot of business for it, 1982.

1-3352 *KGO-TV* (San Francisco) airs series on how California state legislators live in luxury using executive expense accounts, Nov. 3-5, 1981.

1-729 *The Denver Post* article uses state financial records to document how legislators abuse phone privileges by making personal calls and conducting private business with taxpayer funds, October 1981.

1-2277 *Charleston (W.Va.) Gazette* examines bureaucratic bog in West Virginia's Human Rights Commission; many cases are stalled, new biases have developed as a result of some Human Rights Commission regulations and staff competence is questioned, October 1981.

1-2576 *The Oregonian* (Portland) documents official misconduct in the state government; includes links between state senators and lobbyists, and conflicts of interests, January-August 1981.

1-2069 *The Daily News* (Virgin Islands) and *Gannett News Service* reprint shows mismanagement and corruption in government of the Virgin Islands, March 1981.

1-465 *Texas Monthly* article investigates misconduct by the Texas comptroller of public accounts; he used state employees for political purposes, awarded patronage to political allies, used office planes for pleasure trips, spent state funds without restraint, April 1980.

1-822 *New Jersey Monthly* investigation of gross abuse in the state's Urban Loan Authority program finds program designed to lend money to small businesses in decaying urban areas as a last resort instead lent money to well-financed companies in non-urban areas, many of them Mafia businesses, December 1979.

1-3227 *KGO-TV* (San Francisco) reveals that state legislators charge public for personal use of sports and recreation vehicles, September-November 1979.

1-775 *The Record* (Hackensack, N.J.) details factors behind the decay of a state beach-front park; management breakdown, improper use of funds, and pollution are cited, September 1979.

1-2524 *The Clarion-Ledger* (Jackson, Miss.) series on the Mississippi Governor's Highway Safety Program shows that federal bidding regulations have been breached, accounting and monitoring procedures have not been enforced, and services for which the agency paid were never delivered, March 1979.

1-338 *The Clarion-Ledger* (Jackson, Miss.) does articles on Mississippi Employment Security Commission's expensive "sweetheart" lease arrangement with a contributor to the governor's campaign, February 1979.

1-307 *The Record* (Hackensack, N.J.) does article on mismanagement in the handling of ticket sales in New Jersey's Garden State Arts Center, February 1979.

1-407 *Boston Herald American* runs series on Massachusetts Gov. Ed King's nomination of commissioner with ties to prominent organized crime families in the Boston area, February 1979.

1-386 *Courier-News* (Elgin, Ill.) reports a state representative doesn't care that someone voted in his name — which is forbidden by Illinois House rules — to override the governor's veto, December 1978.

1-2315 *The Clarion-Ledger* (Jackson, Miss.) finds the Mississippi Surplus Property Procurement Commission unable to account for thousands of dollars worth of equipment as a result of sloppy bookkeeping, mismanagement and apparent corruption, October 1978.

1-2126 *The Philadelphia Inquirer* issues reprint on systematic corruption in the Pennsylvania Assembly, September 1978.

1-123 *Charleston (W.Va.) Gazette-Mail* discovers state officials go convention-hopping with spouses at taxpayer expense, March 19, 1978.

1-21 *The Times-Picayune* (New Orleans) reporter discovers the state of Louisiana overbuying and underutilizing computers by $30 million annually, 1978.

1-391 *Elgin (Ill.) Courier-News* finds wallpaper in the office of a state representative costs more than 10 times the average in area stores, November 1977.

1-2313 *The Clarion-Ledger* (Jackson, Miss.) finds thousands of dollars designated to help Mississippi's poor were used to help then-Gov. Cliff Finch promote his monthly television show, expand his staff and pay his office expenses, March 1977.

1-401 *The Daily Oklahoman* (Oklahoma City) reports that private detectives hired by a House committee have evidence that Secretary of State John Rogers may have solicited a bribe, May 1975.

1-2197 *The Daily Oklahoman* (Oklahoma City) runs articles on the arrest of governor on bribery charges, 1975.

1-46 *The Charleston (W.Va.) Gazette* runs numerous stories on West Virginia governor's problems with the Internal Revenue Service, 1973.

1-43 *The Charleston (W.Va.) Gazette* runs numerous stories on West Virginia governor's administrative moves, May 1969.

1-409 *Boston Herald American* series details how insurance commissioner appointed by former Gov. Ed King filed false financial disclosure statements.

STATE POLICE
See police

STEALING
See theft

STOCKS
See securities

STREETS
See roads

SUBWAYS
See transportation

SUICIDE
1-2579 *Philadelphia Magazine* publishes in-depth article on the circumstances surrounding three teenage suicides in a quiet suburban community, October 1984.

1-2674 *The Journal* (Lorain, Ohio) does in-depth article regarding the suicide of a teen-age girl; reporter uses girl's diary and interviews with friends and family to piece together reasons why she took her life, 1984.

SURGERY
See:
doctors
hospitals
medicine

SYNTHETIC FUELS
See also energy

1-158 *The Wall Street Journal* examines poor management at the federal Synthetic Fuels Corp., August 9, 1984.

1-2402 *Newsday* (Long Island) reprint investigates U.S. synthetic fuels program; topics include connections of officials to corporations receiving billions of dollars in synfuels subsidies, politics of subsidies, methods used to select projects, December 1983.

TAXES
See also:
Internal Revenue Service
museums
property taxes

1-4019 *St. Louis Business Journal* article says downtown St. Louis buildings are routinely under-assessed, July 8, 1985.

1-4018 *Common Cause* runs article on how businesses write off luxury entertainment expenses to the U.S. taxpayer, May/June 1985.

1-166 *The Wall Street Journal* describes how phony "money management" firms lure many into making bad investments by promising tax shelters, which Internal Revenue Service rejects, June 1984.

1-2174 *The Indianapolis Star* articles find a convicted securities swindler's tax shelter scams perpetrated while working for a legitimate financial planning service; real estate investments money taken, 1982.

1-497 *San Diego Tribune* researches a tax shelter involving becoming ordained and chartering a church, May 1980.

1-350 *Call-Chronicle* (Allentown, Pa.) runs articles on an intricate tax shelter scheme based on phony coal mining operations, January 1979.

1-340 *KAET-TV* (Phoenix) reports on the Arizona Department of Revenue issuing "permanent extensions" to a small minority of companies, allowing them to pay their monthly sales tax 30 days after they are due, 1979.

TAXIS

1-1-825 *Daily Herald* (Arlington Heights, Ill.) runs series on a cab company breaking federal and state safety regulations by transporting radioactive pharmaceuticals to unauthorized locations, illegally using passenger cabs to transport them, and doing so in cabs with a host of mechanical and safety problems, February 1985.

1-3145 *KRON-TV* (San Francisco) investigates the taxi industry in that city and finds it is rife with payoffs to judges for favorable treatment, January 1980.

TEACHERS

See also:
education
schools
universities

1-2650 *The News Chief* (Winter Haven, Fla.) runs extensive series about lack of criminal background checks on applications for teaching jobs in Florida public schools; since running the checks is not a policy, potential child molesters get hired, March-December 1984.

1-2641 *The Anniston (Ala.) Star* series delves into the politics, finances and personalities of the Alabama Education Association — one of the nation's largest teacher lobbies; the powerful organization is more an advocate for its members' interests than for improvement in the educational system, April 8-11, 1984.

1-4020 *APF Reporter* article examines deficiencies in the National Teacher Examinations, standardized tests put out by the Educational Testing Service that are used to certify teachers, 1984.

TEAMSTERS

See labor unions

TELEPHONE COMPANIES

See also public utilities

1-4053 *Minneapolis Star and Tribune* and *St. Paul Pioneer Press Dispatch* articles report WCCO-TV investigation showed "GABTEEN," a Northwestern Bell service that offers party line conversations for teens, was being used for explicit sexual propositioning between teens and adults, Dec. 12, 1985.

1-708 *Atlanta Journal and Constitution* series describes how independent telephone companies in Georgia charge high rates for poor service and in turn use those funds for personal gain; series also examines the improprieties on the part of watchdog agencies that conducted shoddy, incomplete audits of the firms, July 1980.

TELEPHONE SALES, FRAUDULENT

1-180 *Fort Lauderdale News and Sun-Sentinel* does articles on proliferation of "boiler room" scams, in which phone sales bilk people for merchandise that buyer never receives, June 1984.

1-100 *The Christian Science Monitor* finds phone salesmen cheat public out of millions of dollars for overpriced products of dubious value, April 8, 1977.

TERRORISM

1-4021 *United Press International* reprints its coverage of the hijacking of TWA flight 847, 1985.

1-187 *The Wall Street Journal* says new terrorist groups are showing up in the United States; they may be off-shoots of old ones and they seem to be collaborative, July 26, 1984.

1-2789 *The Arizona Republic* (Phoenix) investigates terrorist activity in the United States, paticularly its ties to the Southwest; stories show how specific terrorist groups trained members, bought weapons and otherwise operated in the Southwest with little interference from U.S. law enforcement agencies, 1984.

1-2413 *The Miami Herald* runs investigation of anti-Castro terrorism, activities of pro-Castro Cuban spies and the response of American authorities, 1983.

1-119 *Newsletter on Terrorism* lists recent terrorist incidents and reviews books on terrorism; also some statistics, 1978.

1-139 *The Washington Post* describes Miami-based terrorist group that wants to liberate Cuba; is made up of seemingly peaceful members, Nov. 7, 1976.

THEFT

1-231 *The Kansas City Star* series gives overview of burglary in Kansas City area; find that it's becoming a crime without punishment, June 1981.

TOBACCO
See cigarettes

TOWING
See also automobiles

1-4022 *Press-Telegram* (Long Beach, Calif.) runs series on businesses, apartments, etc., signing carte blanche towing contracts that allow tow truck operators to tow cars without complaints and at all hours of the night, Oct. 21-25, 1984.

1-3016 *KBTV-TV* (Denver) series investigates illegal activities, police pay-offs and favors and harassment of drivers by the towing firm the City of Denver contracts with, 1983.

1-78 *Anaheim (Calif.) Bulletin* reports kickbacks by towing firms to tow cars at sports stadium, October 1978.

1-12 *Detroit Free Press* shows that firm with the city contract for towing vehicles was improperly impounding automobiles, June 1971.

TOXIC SHOCK SYNDROME
See medicine

TOXIC WASTES
See also:
carcinogens
chemicals
environment
hazardous substances
refuse collection
water pollution

1-591 *Worcester (Mass.) Magazine* publishes article on the toxic waste problem in Central Massachusetts, Nov. 20, 1985.

1-4023 *The Christian Science Monitor* reveals that high-tech industries are major contributors to toxic wastes in the nation's two oldest high-tech centers: Silicon Valley and Route 128 in Boston, Dec. 4, 1984.

1-750 *Daily Herald* (Arlington Heights, Ill.) runs article on leaking drums containing hazardous chemicals at Magee Industries, which is located near a vacant lot children play in, December 1984.

1-2777 *The Pittsburgh Press* follows state of Pennsylvania's drift toward a crisis over the disposal of domestic and industrial waste; finds inadequate state regulations and disposal facilities in Western Pennsylvania, Oct. 28-31, 1984.

1-2742 *The Sacramento Bee* publishes series on toxic chemicals leaking into underground water systems around the country from abandoned dump sites on U.S. military bases; reporters found the Defense Department program for dealing with the problem inadequate, Sept. 30-Oct. 5, 1984.

1-2244 *Jacksonville (Fla.) Times-Union/Jacksonville Journal* run series on storage of toxic wastes; officials in Florida and other states don't know where hazardous wastes are shipped; waste monitoring programs are wanting; Florida depends upon industry reports, many of which conflict or are inaccurate, October 1984.

1-2672 *The Advertiser* (Montgomery, Ala.) runs series on the illegal dumping of toxic waste by a company headed at the time by two Alabama state officials, July 31-August 4, 1984.

1-262 *Reader's Digest* article gives examples of how organized crime has found illegal dumping of toxic wastes can be profitable; shows how weak laws make it easy for the mob to move into the waste handling business, July 1984.

1-2770 *Burlington County (N.J.) Times* looks at the waste oil industry in New Jersey, which turns waste oil into commercial heating fuel; reporter finds company systematically mixed chemical wastes into the heating oil that was later sold to schools, hospitals, factories and other large institutions, June 24-27, 1984.

1-2772 *New York Tribune* publishes series on the disposal of toxic wastes in and around the New York City area; series looks into how the proximity of the wastes to the city affects the quality of life of residents, January-March 1984.

1-3104 *CBS News* reports on the business of getting rid of toxic wastes — sneaking toxic chemicals into oil, involvement of organized crime and legitimate oil businesses, 1984.

1-2767 *Delaware County (Pa.) Daily Times* looks into the improper disposal of toxic wastes at a Philadelphia area landfill; series also goes into record of a New Jersey waste hauler under indictment for dumping hazardous wastes, 1984.

1-2555 *Bucks County Courier Times* (Levittown, Pa.) discloses the existence of a 60-acre chemical landfill on the Delaware River banks and determines that although some of the chemicals threatened local drinking water, state and federal agencies had taken no action, October 1983.

1-3021 *WHA-TV* (Madison) documentary probes toxic waste problem in Wisconsin and the state's delay in applying for Superfund status, October 1983.

1-2420 *Asbury Park (N.J.) Press* describes illegal "bootleg" clamming — the practice of taking clams from polluted waters — that is a profitable business in New Jersey, October 1983.

1-2422 *The Press-Enterprise* (Riverside, Calif.) continues coverage of the Stringfellow Acid Pits toxic waste dump, focusing on government inaction in cleaning up the dump; also, analysis of birth defects in the area, March-June 1983.

1-2477 *The Indianapolis Star* series examines the inner workings of the Enviro-Chem hazardous waste recycling facility that was ordered closed, leaving behind 24,000 drums of toxic chemicals at one of the most dangerous waste sites in the country, May 1983.

1-3049 *WFAA-TV* (Dallas) airs series on some illegal practices of waste disposal companies; draining restaurant grease into city sewers, dumping it on private property, mixing in hazardous chemicals; also the failure of the city to regulate disposal of hazardous waste, 1983.

1-3041 *WTHR-TV* (Indianapolis) documentary is a wide-ranging study of the hazardous waste problem nationally, with a focus on certain Indiana waste sites, 1983.

1-3036 *WOWT-TV* (Omaha) finds Nebraska Department of Environmental Control's hazardous waste monitoring program lacking in many ways; poorly organized, understaffed, too easy on those it regulates, 1983.

1-3007 *WSMV-TV* (Nashville) airs series on all aspects of hazardous waste problem in Tennessee — illegal dumping, culprits responsible for it, government failure to control the problem, water pollution, dioxin problem, 1983.

1-2591 *The New York Times* stories look at dioxin contamination in United States; failure of chemical companies to disclose known dangers; failures of Environmental Protection Agency to take action; dioxin in the food chain and in farmland, 1983.

1-2488 *The Orlando Sentinel* runs articles on the toxic waste disposal practices of eight companies owned by Arthur Greer, 1983.

1-3276 *WJAR-TV* (Providence) shows how men with ties to the Mafia commandeered illegal dumping of deadly toxic wastes from New Jersey into Rhode Island, September 1982.

1-3184 *KOY Radio* (Phoenix) investigates chemical dumping in the Scottsdale area and how Motorola failed to stop dumping even after potential health effects were made known, 1981-1982.

1-2077 *The Courier-Journal* (Louisville) does series on the failure of the city's Metropolitan Sewer District to prevent industry from pouring waste water containing toxic metals into city sewer system at levels far greater than its regulations allow, August 1981.

1-3353 *KTVY-TV* (Oklahoma City) airs series on the toxic waste problem in Oklahoma, 1981.

1-834 *Several publications* from many states examine the organized crime ties of SCA Services Inc., the third largest waste disposal company in the country and its attempts to move into hazardous waste disposal, 1981.

1-500 *The Daily Review* (Towanda, Pa.) reports area men were illegally dumping toxic wastes in several area townships and on privately owned property, December 1980.

1-526 *New Castle (Pa.) News* reveals that "pickle liquor," a highly toxic waste, was flowing from a steel plant onto a slag dump in violation of pollution laws and was possibly running into a river, February 1980.

1-444 *The Associated Press* series uncovers organized rings that illegally dump hazardous wastes in the Northeast, 1980.

1-3170 *WSOC-TV* (Charlotte) airs five-part series on a Boston-based waste treatment and disposal firm moving into the region; ties with organized crime and improper waste management raised concern among politicians and residents of Charlotte, September 1980.

1-513 *The Courier-Journal* (Louisville) issues reprint of investigation into problem of toxic wastes and toxic waste dumping, December 1979.

1-760 *The Morning Tribune* (Lewiston, Idaho) finds that federal agencies were dumping large volumes of low-level radioactive liquid waste into the Snake River Aquifer, Idaho's major water table, and in a subsequent probe exposes major accidental spills, November-December 1979.

1-648 *The Bristol (Conn.) Press* uses local and state files, interviews and stake-outs to find that city officials were allowing illegal dumping of carcinogenic industrial waste at municipal landfill, July-December 1979.

1-195 *The Philadelphia Inquirer* series gives overview of chemical dumping across country and cites failure of government to take action, September 1979.

1-229 *Newsday* (Long Island) series on disposal of hazardous wastes in the nation, state and region looks into possible solutions, April 1979.

TRADE SCHOOLS
1-4024 *The Milwaukee Journal* article describes the lack of proper regulation of for-profit cosmetology schools in Wisconsin; how the schools make money from government loans, July 21, 1985.

TRAINS
See railroads

TRANSPORTATION
See also:
air-traffic controllers
airlines
automobiles
buses
hazadous substances
railroads
taxis
trucks

1-4057 *The Herald* (Arlington Heights, Ill.) series finds NORTRAN, a suburban Chicago transit system, operating a fleet of structurally defective buses, made even more hazardous because of a lack of regular preventive maintenance, Nov. 10-12, 1985.

1-2928 *Arkansas Democrat* (Little Rock) special section on the safety danger of used buses; acquired from school districts by churches and other private groups, the buses become accidents waiting to happen because of poor maintenance and a regulatory void, Oct. 20, 1985.

1-2797 *Los Angeles Times* looks critically at a proposed subway system for the city of Los Angeles; reporters find claims that the project would reduce pollution and congestion and help to reshape the city were unfounded, July-December 1984.

1-2737 *Sun-Times* (Chicago) investigates the Chicago Transit Authority and finds a massive breakdown in transit maintenance due to mismanagement has led to numerous cancellations of rush-hour bus runs as well as a long history of inferior transit service, Dec. 2-7, 1984.

1-3118 *WCAU-TV* (Philadelphia) investigation of that city's mass transit system finds it is wasting thousands of dollars and polluting by idling buses for hours, exposing workers and passengers to asbestos through subway station ventilation system; also looks at rapid, dangerous deterioration of an elevated rail line, May 1984.

1-2220 *The San Francisco Bay Guardian* finds Bay Area Rapid Transit's Berkeley Hills Tunnel a disaster waiting to happen; BART has made dangerously inadequate preparations to deal with fires in underground and underwater sections; officials deny any problem exists, September 1982.

1-3270 *WJLA-TV* (Washington) airs series on safety lapses in the planning of Washington's subway system, November 1981.

1-165 *The Philadelphia Inquirer* documents unsafe conditions of Philadelphia's transit system, the nation's third largest; system was quietly collapsing as board took operating money from maintenance fund for years, April 1981.

1-478 *Sacramento Union* series finds chronic maintenance deficiencies and other operating problems were concealed by Sacramento Regional Transit District, February 1981.

1-445 *Philadelphia Magazine* runs article on crime in that city's subway system, June 1980.

1-634 *The Boston Globe* examines all aspects of the Massachusetts Bay Transportation Authority — from bus service to employee hiring and pensions — and finds that an alliance between unions and politicians is responsible for making it the most expensive, least productive major transit system in the country, February 1980.

1-90 *The Boston Globe* series identifies management failures in city's transit system, 1979.

TRASH HAULERS
See refuse collection

TRUCKS
See also transportation

1-238 *The Hartford Courant* finds car-truck accidents are on the increase; this article explores causes, including inadequate safety inspection and lax maintenance, October 1984.

1-3121 *KPRC-TV* (Houston) series finds Texas truck safety laws inadequate and enforcement of laws virtually nonexistent, allowing unsafe trucks to stay on the road, 1984.

1-3274 *WZZM-TV* (Grand Rapids) examines the problem of unfit trucks and drivers on the highways; shows many firms falsify safety records, May 10-15 and 17-19, 1982.

1-3159 *KNXT-TV* (Los Angeles) looks at the safety record of the trucking industry and finds widespread problems with drug abuse and lack of inspection of trucks, 1980.

1-2181 *New Jersey Nightly News* airs investigation into mob infiltration of trucking industry, May 1979.

UNEMPLOYMENT
See:
business
employment
job training

UNIONS
See labor unions

UNIVERSITIES
See also:
colleges
diploma mills
education
nonprofit organizations

1-2822 *The Plain Dealer* (Cleveland) series examines the dramatic academic decline of Case Western Reserve University, where the administration's approach to problem solving has been to cut out programs, March 10-12, 1985.

1-2821 *The Plain Dealer* (Cleveland) series finds a glaring lack of fiscal controls, department chairmen using their public positions for private gain and a power struggle for control of the millions of dollars generated at the Ohio State University medical college, Sept. 30-Oct. 3, 1984.

1-2673 *Temple University News* (Philadelphia) article investigates a city councilman's being paid $3,000 for teaching a class at Temple University law school even though he owed $2,000 on a defaulted student loan at the same university; reporter uses student loan and state common pleas court records, March-April 1984.

1-193 *The Washington Monthly* looks at rising tuition costs and says a reverence for academia is allowing public to be ripped-off, August 1983.

1-3038 *WJLA-TV* (Washington, D.C.) investigates improprieties at Southeastern University; among them: the awarding of sweetheart contracts by the business manager who pays exorbitant prices for goods and services supplied by friends and business partners; conflicts of interests on the board of trustees; and the awarding of degrees to a number of people who hadn't earned them, including a member of the board, 1983.

1-2359 *Minneapolis Star and Tribune* says in a period of budget cuts and hard times, University of Minnesota professors are teaching significantly fewer classroom hours than they once did, yet were given one of their largest pay increases in a decade, 1981.

1-2157 *Minneapolis Star and Tribune* series looks at the finances and politics of the University of Minnesota as it faces severe fiscal crisic, 1981.

1-748 *The Anniston (Ala.) Star* series examines illegal use of university reserve funds to pay for cars and entertainment for university officials and the lobbying efforts of the university alumni, December 1980.

1-2569 *The Daily Oklahoman* (Oklahoma City) questions the financial practices of the University of Oklahoma and its principal fund-raising arm, saying that some fund-raising activities are improper and possibly illegal, January 1980.

1-2190 *The Milwaukee Journal* articles on University of Wisconsin administrators find corporation they set up to benefit the university could reap them substantial benefits also; investigation finds dean who was president of the corporation left last university job under fire for other business dealings, August 1979.

1-271 *WUMB Radio* (Boston) report examines mishandling of money collected from student activities fee at the University of Massachusetts-Boston, April 1978.

URBAN RENEWAL
See also city government

1-1-1006 *The Columbus Dispatch* special section evaluates Columbus' future in terms of growth, planning and redevelopment of the city's downtown, Sept. 8, 1985.

1-2092 *Chicago Tribune* series says fraud, government bungling and political favoritism have turned a government program to curb urban blight into a system that rewards real estate speculators with big profits and often actually contributes to neighborhood deterioration, May 1981.

UTILITIES
See public utilities

VETERANS
See also carcinogens

1-3113 *WRTV-TV* (Indianapolis) airs series on poor medical care at the state-run Indiana Veterans Home; patients in need of hospitalization, receiving outdated drugs, prescription of mind altering drugs to patients who were not mentally ill, October 1984.

1-2595 *The Plain Dealer* (Cleveland) runs series on Post Traumatic Stress Disorder, which may affect one million combat veterans of Vietnam; the failure of the federal agency charged with treating these veterans, July 1983.

1-294 *Canadian Broadcasting Corporation* surveys Canadians who took part in U.S. atomic tests and cleanups in Nevada in the 1950s and finds their cancer rate is six times that of the rest of the population; also investigates the lack of government compensation for these veterans, February 1982.

VETERANS ADMINISTRATION
See also hospitals
1-2823 *Fort Lauderdale News and Sun-Sentinel* series finds excessive patient deaths, inept disciplining of doctors and dangerously unrestrained growth have plagued the Veterans Administation heart surgery network for more than a decade, Nov. 25-28, 1984.
1-18 *The Kansas City Times* finds doctor at Veterans Administration Hospital in Leavenworth, Kan., deceives some veterans participating in study and violates VA guidelines, 1982.
1-2135 *Minneapolis Star and Tribune* series examines need for and economics of a proposed Veterans Administration hospital in that city; looks at VA hospitals in other cities, 1981.
1-569 *The Peninsula Times-Tribune* (Palo Alto, Calif.) series examines crimes ranging from drug abuse by patients and staff to medical negligence and the lack of judicial action taken in the Menlo Park Veterans Administration mental hospital; the three-month investigation used internal memos, crime records and more than 40 interviews with patients, staff and local authorities, October 1979-January 1980.

VETERINARY MEDICINE
1-2635 *Veterinary Economics* publishes article on the practices and collapse of the country's largest franchised veterinary hospital, and how its business practices affected franchises, June 1984.

VICE
See prostitution

VIDEO PIRACY
1-2636 *The Rebel* does article on how movies are illegally copied and distributed to U.S. companies and military bases on video cassettes, January 1984.

VIETNAM
See military

VIRGIN ISLANDS
1-2069 *The Daily News* (Virgin Islands) and *Gannett News Service* reprint shows broad-scale mismanagement and corruption in government in the Virgin Islands, March 1981.

VOTING
See elections

WASTE TREATMENT SYSTEMS
See water pollution

WATER
See also:
agriculture
chemicals
environment
special districts
water pollution

1-2281 *The Register* (Orange County, Calif.) series examines future of Southern California's water supply and the politics that affect it, December 1984.

1-2824 *The Dallas Morning News* runs special section on the future of water resources in Texas; topics include cities' water supplies and treatment systems, environmentalist/developer conflict over water policy and water recovery in the Texas plains, August 19, 1984.

1-2068 *National Journal* says despite mounting water management problems, waste and population shifts, a policy vacuum continues at the federal and state levels, January 1984.

1-2110 *The Kansas City Times* series, "The Next American Crisis," looks at chaotic management of water in the United States, May 1981.

1-696 *Savannah Morning News* does series of articles on the threat posed to the city water supply by uncontrolled industrial and agricultural expansion, October 1980.

1-488 *The Kansas City Star* looks at the Missouri River: its impact on the region's development, man's development of the river, life on the river and bid-rigging tied to the river's development, August 1980.

1-525 *Willamette Week* (Portland) details a controversy between houseboat owners and some harbor developers who were planning riverfront condominiums; article also deals with state policy on moorages, August 1980.

1-568 *News-American* (Baltimore) examines poor safety monitoring and lack of communication on the part of officials in the city's water department that resulted in the death of a kidney patient, December 1979.

1-342 *Tucson Citizen* runs series on the failure of the Arizona Land Department to enforce groundwater laws; among the findings: investigations into illegal irrigation have been ordered dropped, the department sells huge quantities of water to mining companies for a pittance, February 1979.

1-2460 *The Denver Post* series examines irrigation in the area of the Ogallala aquifer (High Plains region) and changes it is undergoing due to potential scarcity and the high cost of energy to pump it; water in the aquifer is dropping at an alarming rate, 1979.

W

WATER POLLUTION
See also:
agriculture
cancer
environment
water

1-3000 *The Sacramento Bee* finds that high levels of selenium near federal water projects in the West have poisoned wildlife, livestock and people in 15 western states while the federal Bureau of Reclamation is ignoring the problem, Sept. 8-10, 1985.

1-2676 *The Free Press* (Quakertown, Pa.) runs series on how state and federal programs designed to protect waterways from pollution are not working; series focuses on a Quakertown sewage treatment plant, Dec. 17-21, 1984.

1-1007 *The Times Leader* (Wilkes-Barre, Penn.) special section on water pollution problems in northeast Pennsylvania follows leakage of sewage into the area's water supply that led to 400 cases of giardiasis; coverage includes state regulatory inadequacies, poor planning by water and sewage officials, December 1984.

1-2781 *United Press International* runs series on how a large federal water project has resulted in the pollution of farmland and wildlife refuges in San Joaquin Valley, Aug. 13-17, 1984.

1-2718 *The Capital* (Annapolis, Md.) uncovers incidents of sewage being spilled into a creek from a state-run sewage treatment plant; reporter went through reams of state documents after getting tip from a state employee, June 22, 1984.

1-167 *Asbury Park (N.J.) Press* runs comprehensive overview of New Jersey's polluted or endangered water, including tap and bottled water, aquifers, wells, rivers, May 1984.

1-2005 *Fort Lauderdale News and Sun-Sentinel* looks at pollution of South Florida's drinking water, September 1983.

1-2521 *The Free Lance-Star* (Fredericksburg, Va.) investigation reveals two nuclear reactors heating up a lake in violation of state standards, with two counties putting partially treated sewage in a river and three local governments failing to responsibly protect state waters, February-August 1983.

1-2484 *San Jose Mercury-News* reprint, "Clean Industry, Dirty Water," says toxic chemicals, primarily from high-technology industries, are endangering the water supply in Silicon Valley, July 1983.

1-2117 *California Journal* runs article on political battles over agricultural pesticides and their effect on California drinking water, May 1983.

1-2210 *The Times* (Hammond, Ind.) series, "Cancer Cluster," looks into a cluster around Lake Dale with a cancer rate 2.5 times the national norm, and a Hodgkin's Disease rate 25 times the norm; inefficient septic systems and government neglect blamed, May 1982.

1-14 *Tampa Tribune* looks at gypsum piles leaking pollutants into Tampa Bay, 1982.

1-3264 *KYTV-TV* (Springfield, Mo.) series exposes plans by Arkansas' Department of Pollution Control and Economy to lower what environmentalists call one of the state's most critical water pollution standards, Nov. 25-27, 1981.

1-3356 *KPIX-TV* (San Francisco) airs series on dangerous levels of lead in San

183

Francisco water and the water department's failure to test for a dangerous parasite despite having reason to believe it might have contaminated the water supply, Nov. 2-4, 1981.

1-2153 *Mother Jones* article looks at radioactive waste in the sea; leaking drums containing radioactive waste found near San Francisco, July 1981.

1-2108 *Springfield (Mass.) Valley Advocate* runs article on continuing contamination of groundwater and the Connecticut River as a result of Monsanto's dumping of chemical wastes, October 1981.

1-3174 *KGBT-TV* (Harlingen, Texas) finds that community's water system has high levels of DDT and other pesticides; officials knew of health hazards but kept information from the public, 1981.

1-3156 *WABC-TV* (New York) program, "The Poison Water," discovers that unsuspected chemical dumping in a New Jersey community's water supply accounts for increased respiratory ailments and rare cancers, November 1980.

1-3221 *WCBS-TV* (New York) reports that chemical dumpers, many of whom have previously been sentenced to jail and fined for illegal activities, continue to pollute New Jersey's water supply, 1979.

1-3213 *WBRZ-TV* (Baton Rouge) investigates the deliberate polluting of the Mississippi by companies that clean out liquid carrier barges in violation of environmental regulations, 1979.

1-201 *Fort Worth Star-Telegram* shows that Dallas restaurants illegally dump grease trap waste into that city's sewers, knowing that city officials do not enforce the city ordinance prohibiting the practice, November 1977.

1-734 *The Philadelphia Inquirer* series, "The Assault on the Seas," delves into the problem of ocean dumping of waste: who does it, what problems it creates, and how the government fails to deal with the problem, August 1977.

WEAPONS
See also:
Army
handguns
military
nuclear weapons

1-1008 *The New York Times* publishes article on the theft and black market trafficking of tens of millions of dollars worth of advanced, American-made military weapons, Sept. 29, 1985.

1-121 *The New York Times* reprint, "Weapons in Space," includes implications of new weapons era, the origins of "Star Wars," American technology and Soviet technology and tactics, March 3-8, 1985.

1-3111 *ABC News* investigation of the effctiveness of the Pershing II missile raises serious doubts about the military's claim that the weapon is effective; military rushed through testing of the missile, August 1984.

1-2771 *The Leesburg (Fla.) Commercial* runs a series on an army air base that was used for testing and storing chemical weapons during World War II; after a local well-digger was burned when working at the site, reporter investigated the possibility that chemical weapons might still be buried there, July 13-16, 1984.

1-2796 *The Wall Street Journal* uncovers a secret Soviet program to use genetic engineering techniques to create new biological weapons; reporter made use of secret U.S. and Soviet military documents, April-May 1984.

1-685 *National Journal* questions the feasibility of the highly touted Assault Breaker weapons system, a high-tech, long-range conventional weapons system, October 1983.

1-2319 *The Dallas Morning News* finds illegal trafficking of small weapons is flourishing at such a pace that U.S. law enforcement authorities are almost powerless to stop it; the black market is major outlet, November 1982.

1-57 *Atlantic* article about Divad weapons system boondoggle says in development of an "ultra" weapon for the Army, whether it worked became a side issue; more effective weapons were rejected because they were simpler and cheaper; also, two articles that indicate Department of Defense's new efforts against fraud are ineffective and aimed at small contractors because larger ones are too essential, October 1982.

1-3256 *WFAA-TV* (Dallas) examines the investigation of an international arms dealer charged with conspiracy to sell tanks, artillery and missiles to Iran and Iraq, Sept. 26, 1982.

1-205 *The New Republic* article examines the massive lobbying campaign to approve sale of AWACs planes to Saudi Arabia; documents how Saudi government pressured American corporations doing business there to push for approval, February 1982.

1-3357 *ABC News Closeup* reports on the Soviet-backed Vietnamese use of biological weapons against Hmong villagers in Laos, Dec. 21, 1981.

1-48 *Newsday* (Long Island) finds New York organized crime families trading guns for drugs in Latin America, October 1979.

1-427 *Rutland (Vt.) Herald* does series on illegal arms shipments from Vermont to South Africa, including details on how customs laws were violated, December 1978.

WELFARE
See also housing

1-2542 *The Journal-Times* (Racine, Wis.) does investigation in which reporter applies for welfare using false financial data and gets it; reporter found case workers often don't check application information, case workers are overworked, local government has no access to a person's basic financial information such as Social Security data, October 1983.

1-2396 *The Sacramento Union* runs series, "Odd Partners in Crime," on how government confidentiality and secrecy laws about welfare and public aid recipients prevent the capture of thousands of criminals, November 1982.

1-3135 *KSL-TV* (Salt Lake City) reporter goes undercover to expose fraud and waste in the administration of unemployment compensation and food stamp programs; programs have lax standards for verifying identities of applicants, May 1982.

1-2241 *Los Angeles Times* series says leaders of a federally funded community organization, East Los Angeles Community Union, founded to fight poverty in East Los Angeles, have misused federal funds by setting up a $50 million corporate conglomerate, March 1982.

1-547 *Times-Union* (Albany) series on New York State's welfare program looks at the costs to taxpayers, the level of benefits received and problems encountered in the system of aid to the poor, August 1980.

1-3148 *WJZ-TV* (Baltimore) investigates heating oil rip-offs in a federally funded program for the poor, March 1980.

1-653 *The Cincinnati Enquirer* looks at the spending irregularities and waste of federal tax funds in that city's anti-poverty program; abuses include administering funds to those not eligible for assistance as well as profitmaking from funds held in bank account, April-July 1979.

WILLS
See probate

WIRETAPS
See organized crime

WITNESS PROTECTION PROGRAM
See also organized crime

1-771 *Richmond Times-Dispatch* runs articles on a Mafia hitman who testified under the witness protection program, March 1985.

1-200 *The Wall Street Journal* does article on poorly supervised federal witness security program, which gives new identities to criminals — often to start all over commiting crimes with impunity, February 1984.

1-3112 *WSB-TV* (Atlanta) reports on a woman accused of stealing thousands of dollars from people while protected under the federal witness program, 1984.

1-3122 *WSOC-TV* (Charlotte) series centers on one bad apple in discussing the federal witness protection program, 1984.

1-632 *The Denver Post* runs investigation of the federal witness protection program; findings show how witnesses return to crime, lack of supervision, failure of federal agencies to cooperate with local law enforcement, overexpenditures, December 1981.

1-4025 *Newsday* (Long Island) articles describe problems of federal narcotics trafficking by the U.S. Marshals Service, which is agency charged with protecting witnesses; questions of proper use and protection of witnesses in the program, 1974-1980.

1-387 *The Honolulu Advertiser* runs article on the government's practice of giving new identities to people deeply involved in serious crime — expecially organized crime — for testifying in major criminal cases, November 1978.

WORKER SAFETY
See:
agriculture
asbestos
chemicals
Occupational Safety And Health Administration

YOUTH
See juveniles

ZONING
See also:
city government
county government
land fraud
real estate

1-1-430 *The Miami Herald* article investigates zoning in Hialeah; among the findings: city officials rezone for personal profit; members of the City Council solicit and offer bribes for zoning changes, January 1985.

1-2028 *Columbia (Mo.) Daily Tribune* shows that city's planning and zoning commission said to favor developers; possible conflicts of interests on commission, June 1984.

1-2290 *The Miami Herald* series,"Miami Zoning: Growing Without a Plan," examines city's zoning and planning system; among findings: planning has broken down, many exceptions to zoning restrictions are granted, land-development industry is biggest campaign contributor to city commissioners, May 1983.

1-28 *The Towson Times* (Baltimore) shows Baltimore County planning and zoning officials accept bribes, August 1982.

1-2213 *The Miami Herald* issues reprint on illegal activities by developers who sought to make North Key Largo a resort community; avoidance of zoning laws, conflicts of interests, illegally approved developments, July 1982.

1-2082 *New West* does article on politics of zoning and building codes that have allowed builders to erect structures, including schools and sports stadiums, posing a deadly threat to the public, August 1981.

ZOOS
See also animal abuse

1-1-2763 *The Atlanta Journal and Constitution* uncovers suspicious transfers and deaths of animals belonging to the Atlanta Zoo, reflecting poor management of the zoo by city officials, May-August 1984.

1-3063 *Channel 11* (Atlanta) reports on inadequacies — including lack of a veterinary clinic — that caused deaths of animals at Atlanta Zoo, 1984.

1-35 *Federal Times* series shows animals in Washington, D.C.'s National Zoo get poor care, March/April 1977.